Advance Reviews of *THE FUTURE OF HUMANKIND Why We Should Be Optimistic*

"The title of this book says it all: the future of humankind is indeed at stake. Whatever your ideas may be on how we can face and resolve the serious and urgent challenges to our very existence, John Hands' book really brings all the relevant facts and problems together in a magnificently coherent way. It is at one and the same time a treasure trove of research and careful arguments, and a clarion call to action."
    —Professor Denis Noble CBE, FRS, FMedSci, MAE, author of *The Music of Life: Biology Beyond Genes*

"*The Future of Humankind* isn't just exhaustively researched and relevant to every human being; it's majestic. Impossible to not finish."
    —Perry Marshall, author of *Evolution 2.0*

"Predicting the future is ever a daunting and a hazardous task. John Hands critically examines current predictions of our extinction, survival, and trans-formation before, with polish and verve, he projects into the future the pattern of our evolution from the origin of the universe to produce a unique and astonishing forecast."
    —Michael Fossel, author of *The Telomerase Revolution*

"With verve and insight, John Hands tackles that most pressing of all questions—the future prospects for our planet and our species. His balanced interrogation of the threats posed by pandemics and climate change and science's promises of salvation could not be more timely."
    —Dr James Le Fanu, author of *Why Us?*

"What is the future of mankind? John Hands uses a scientific perspective, extraordinary insight and solid materials to give a very valuable answer. I believe his book can inspire more people to think about the destiny of mankind."
    —Dr Feng Liu, author of *Rise from Superintelligence*, member of the Chinese Academy of Sciences Research Group

Praise for *COSMOSAPIENS Human Evolution from the Origin of the Universe*

"A 700-page description of the state of current scientific knowledge about the origin of matter, life and humanity, plus a bold attempt to assess its limits. It is lucid and intelligible to the non-specialists—Hands was originally trained as a chemist, but has also published three novels. This is a book of astonishing ambition and scope, more like the work of a great Victorian polymath than most popular science books."
—Tim Crane, *The Times Literary Supplement* Book of the Year

"Argues that mind and matter evolved in unison and, one day, human consciousness and the star-filled universe will be revealed as part of the same cosmic whole. Such ideas were lapped up by the 19th-century followers of Hegel and it is both shocking and invigorating to hear them stated again…in the context of a quantum universe."
—Nicholas Blincoe, *The Telegraph* Best Science Books of 2015

"A substantial, sceptical survey of the current state of scientific knowledge of about the most basic questions… [Hands] is always fair, and he writes from what must be the best point of view for a scientist—he is a dispassionate agnostic about everything, except those few things which can fulfil Popper's falsification principle… An invaluable, encyclopedic achievement."
—A N Wilson, *The Times Literary Supplement* Book of the Year

"It would scarcely be possible, without Hands's own overarching perspective, to grasp the central reality of contemporary science…an irresoluble tension between the awesome achievement of science in the recent past and the compelling signs that for all that we might learn there is, after all, more than we can know. . . *COSMOSAPIENS* is dispassionate, even-handed, authoritative and immensely persuasive."
—James Le Fanu, *The Tablet*

"This groundbreaking book will surely become a classic of scientific thinking.

It should be on the shelf of anyone who has ever asked 'What are we?' and 'Why are we here?'"
—*Huffington Post* (USA)

"*COSMOSAPIENS* is an audacious tour by a single author of all that science can teach us about the origin and evolution of humanity in the universe, start to finish. Its encyclopedic sweep can be read straight through or browsed in parts of special interest."
—Edward O Wilson, University Professor Emeritus, Harvard University

"In this audacious, ambitious, and philosophically completist study, Hands leads an interdisciplinary search through all the current human knowledge that may help answer two burning questions: What are we, and where do we come from?... The result is a pearl of dialectical reasoning between Hands and the most celebrated experts he can find. In today's age of specialization, readers will welcome this throwback to the days of the well-informed layperson, conversant and opinionated in a variety of topics... Hands grounds his musings in logic and scientific fact to produce a thoughtful treatise for the eternally curious."
—Starred review, *Publishers Weekly*

"From dark energy to the selfish gene, Hands looks at how we know what we know—and what we don't. An overview of thought on this ever-fascinating subject."
—*The Observer* (UK)

"A triumph of detailed conceptual analysis covering the fields of fundamental cosmology, physics, biology and the evolution of philosophical and religious ideas...a truly exceptional piece of work."
—David Lorimer, *The Science and Medical Network Review*

"A thought-provoking, super interesting read, guaranteed to get the grey matter working."
—Natasha Harding, *The Sun*

"This book packs a punch and will not let the reader down."
—*San Francisco Book Review*

"An exhaustive, fascinating look at humankind's role in the story of the universe."
—Adam Morgan, *Chicago Review of Books*

"A thoughtful, well-written volume."
—*Library Journal*

"A compendious work that will intrigue serious readers."
—Kirkus Reviews

"John Hands has attempted a remarkable thing: nothing less than an exhaustive account of the current state of scientific knowledge about the origins and evolution of the cosmos, life and humanity. His driving questions are those that have inspired all of science, religion and philosophy: What are we? Where do we come from? What is the source of consciousness, value and meaning? Hands painstakingly summarises the current state of knowledge in a huge variety of fields, from cosmology to evolutionary psychology, in enviably lucid prose. His conclusions are measured and sceptical, and his conception of the limits of science is well-argued: he gives an extremely clear view of what science has established, what it has not established, and what it never will. This is a truly exceptional piece of work."

—Tim Crane, Knightbridge Professor of Philosophy, University of Cambridge

"John Hands is an astute observer of recent trends in scientific ideas bold enough to point out what he sees as sense and nonsense and intelligently explain why. Even in cases where one might disagree, the arguments are thought-provoking."

—Paul Steinhardt, Albert Einstein Professor in Science, Princeton University

"Hands's book is a game-changer. In the tradition of Thomas Kuhn's *The Structure of Scientific Revolutions*, this lucidly written, penetrating analysis challenges us to rethink many things we take for granted about ourselves, our society, and our universe. It will become a classic."

—Peter Dreier, E P Clapp Distinguished Professor of Politics, Occidental College

"*COSMOSAPIENS* is a stunningly ambitious book that aims to draw together the best of modern scientific knowledge to answer fundamental philosophical questions: How did the universe begin? How did life start? And how did our species evolve from simple organisms? Hands spent more than a decade researching the book, and while the resulting work has won widespread praise and multiple awards, it has also met with hostility from some parts of the scientific establishment for daring to challenge some orthodoxies. In particular

Hands concludes that the dominant explanations in cosmology—the Big Bang Theory—and evolution by natural selection driven by 'selfish' genes no longer fit the evidence and need revising or replacing altogether."
—Craig Kenny, *Camden New Journal*

"There have been numerous books seeking to tell a tale that opens with the beginning of our universe and…concludes with 'the ultimate' event: the emergence of our species, *Homo sapiens*. None has done this better, more clearly, and with greater thought and documentation than John Hands. But he goes on to conclude that, uniquely as far as we know, we are the unfinished product of an accelerating cosmic evolutionary process and the self-reflective agents of our future evolution. A work as bold, broad, and challenging as this will no doubt tweak the bias any one of us may have regarding a particular event, but, then, so did Darwin's *On the Origin of Species*."
—Jeffrey Schwartz, Professor of Physical Anthropology and of The History & Philosophy of Science,at the University of Pittsburgh

"An encyclopaedic account of the evolution of humans, from the origin of the universe onwards… Any conventional Darwinist (and I am one of them) will find a lot to take exception to: but disagreement is the fuel of progress and if you enjoy an argument this is the book for you."
—Professor Steve Jones, author of *The Language of the Genes*

"A fine book…brave, very wide ranging, synoptic. It will interest many readers because of its comprehensive set of interwoven topics, life, consciousness, evolution of the biosphere including a cogent critique of the NeoDarwinian Synthesis, of the human, and beyond."
—Professor Stuart Kauffman, author of *At Home in the Universe*

"A magisterial, persuasive and thought provoking survey of the horizons of modern science."
—Dr James Le Fanu, author of *The Rise and Fall of Modern Medicine*

"An intellectual tour-de-force: a review of about all the major scientific theories that purport to explain origins of the universe, matter, life and mind. The approach is refreshingly agnostic, as the author systematically points out how much we still don't know and perhaps never will know. He critically dissects the relevant observations, theories and hypotheses, both mainstream and alternative, pointing our both their strengths, and—alas much more numerous—weaknesses. As such, he provides a welcome counterpoint to the sensationalism that typically accompanies the latest 'discoveries'...that are most often outdated within a couple of years as new data or interpretations come in. Yet, in spite of this skeptical stance, he genuinely attempts to synthesize the cumulative results, following the emergence of humanity from the Big Bang (which may never have happened) via the formation of matter in stars and the origin of life on Earth to the development of consciousness and culture. Moreover, he manages to explain all these intrinsically very difficult concepts and theories in a clear and readable language, without falling into the common style of popularization that substitutes anecdotes and human interest for scientific reasoning. The book is highly recommended for anyone wishing to get a deeper insight into the fundamental but typically arcane theories that purport to explain where we and the universe that surrounds us are coming from."

—Professor Francis Heylighen, Evolution, Complexity and Cognition Group, Free University of Brussels

"It often takes an outsider to see the limitations of conventional science. As far as biological evolution is concerned, John Hands has done a remarkable job of disentangling the many topics that are long overdue for reinterpretation. The enormous effort he has made to cover so many evolutionary questions is heroic. That is the first step to making progress. A major accomplishment."

—Professor James Shapiro, author of *Evolution: A View from the 21st Century*

"An audacious and admirable book. John Hands tackles the major questions of science ranging from the origin of the universe to the evolution of humans. The book is written with engaging style, and the strongest scientific ideas across a swathe of fields in physics and biology are presented lucidly."

—Larry Steinman, Professor of Neurological Sciences, Stanford University

"With depth and virtuosity, John Hands explores the Big Questions of human existence: Who are we? Why are we here? Where are we headed? This is a vital work of science fact...Hands's voyage of inquiry will not only educate you, it will also surprise."

—Derek Shearer, Director, McKinnon Center for Global Affairs, Los Angeles

"John Hands came looking to science for the big picture: what can it tell us about who we are?...and emerged as what we might call a scientific critic in the tradition of Victorian sages like William Whewell...His clear, careful and critical exposition of cosmological speculations reveals the gulf between them and the ideal of scientific theories developed mathematically, tested, and confirmed by observation and experiment. All interesting theories have to have loose ends and gaps, but…Hands finds in them and their proponents evidence of the tunnel vision that comes with narrow specialisation, intense competition for patronage and limited funds, and a dogmatism that recalls the Inquisition… Hands came to realise, and makes us realise, how much we don't know. Nevertheless, he is optimistic, and when he comes to human evolution and a schematic view of our history, he is hopeful and sees progress in understanding and co-operation. From his book we get that big picture he sought."

—Professor David Knight, author of *The Making of Modern Science*

THE FUTURE OF HUMANKIND

Also By John Hands

Non-fiction
Housing Co-operatives
COSMOSAPIENS Human Evolution from the Origin of the Universe

Novels
Perestroika Christi
Darkness at Dawn
Brutal Fantasies

THE FUTURE OF HUMANKIND

Why We Should Be Optimistic

JOHN HANDS

First published in the UK in 2023 by Castleton Publishers
67 Battledean Road
London N5 1UX
T: Int + 44 (0) 20 7226 8226
E: info@castletonpublishers.co.uk

A CIP catalogue record for this book is available from the British Library.

Hardback ISBN-13 978 0 9933719 4 3   ISBN-10 0993371949
eBook ISBN-13 978 0 9933719 6 7   ISBN-10 0993371965

This book is typeset using Atomik ePublisher from Easypress Technologies.

To all those with an open mind

Acknowledgments

It is impossible to name everyone who helped bring this book to fruition. Of the very many specialists who generously shared their expertise with me, I'm particularly indebted to those who responded to my request to check draft sections for errors of fact or omission or unreasonable conclusions and to make any other comments. I list them here within broad areas of study, each of which encompasses fields relevant to the book. Their descriptions represent the posts they held when consulted.

Human extinction by natural disasters: Emeritus Professor Vincent Courtillot, former Director of the Institut de Physique du Globe, Paris; Martin Beech, Professor Emeritus, Department of Astronomy, University of Regina, Canada; David Archibald, Professor Emeritus of Biology and Curator of Mammals, San Diego State University, USA; Peter Veres, astronomer, Minor Planet Center, Smithsonian Astrophysical Observatory, Cambridge, Massachusetts; Qicheng Zhang, graduate student researching comets and asteroids at Caltech; Paul Wignall, Professor of Palaeoenvironments at the University of Leeds; Professor Gerta Keller, Department of Geosciences, Princeton University; Mike Poland, Scientist-in-Charge, Yellowstone Volcano Observatory, USA; Professor Stephan Sobolev, Institute of Geosciences, University of Potsdam, Germany; David Pyle, Professor of Earth Sciences, University of Oxford; Jessica Whiteside, Associate Professor of Geochemistry, National Oceanography Centre, University of Southampton; Niall Johnson, Australian Commission on Safety and Quality in Health Care; Anton Erkoreka, the Basque Museum of the History of Medicine; David Morens MD, Senior Advisor to the Director, National Institute of Allergy and Infectious Diseases, National Institutes of Health, USA; Nita Madhav, Chief Executive Officer, Metabiota, San Francisco; Professor Alex Greenwood, Head of Department of Wildlife Diseases, Leibniz Institute for Zoo and Wildlife Research, Freie Universität Berlin.

Human extinction by warfare and accidents: Bruce Kent, President of the Movement for the Abolition of War and Vice-President of the Campaign for Nuclear Disarmament; Carey Sublette, author of *Handbook of Nuclear Weapons* (to be published); Chris Griffith, producer of the website http://www.atomicarchive.com; Kerry Emanuel, Professor of Atmospheric Science, Massachusetts Institute of Technology; Russell Seitz, Senior Research Fellow, The Climate Institute, Harvard University; Steven Starr, Clinical Laboratory Science Program Director, University of Missouri Hospital and Clinics; Alexandra Levy, Vice President, Atomic Heritage Foundation, Washington, DC; Dr Jonathan Cobb, Senior Communication Manager, World Nuclear Association; Dr. Marilee Shelton-Davenport, Senior Program Officer on the Board on Chemical Sciences and Technology (BCST) at the National Academies of Sciences, Engineering and Medicine, USA; David Leigh, Royal Society Research Professor & Sir Samuel Hall Chair of Chemistry, University of Manchester, UK; Eric Drexler, Senior Research Fellow, Future of Humanity Institute, University of Oxford.

Human extinction by population explosion and climate change: Dennis Meadows, coauthor of *The Limits to Growth* and *Limits to Growth: The 30-Year Update*; Sam Cole, coauthor of *Models of Doom: A Critique of The Limits to Growth*; John Boardman, Professor Emeritus, Environmental Change Institute, Oxford University Centre for the Environment; Dr. Benny Peiser, Director of the Global Warming Policy Foundation, London, UK; Professor Sami Solanki, Director of the Max Planck Institute for Solar System Research, Göttingen, Germany; Clare Nullis, Media Officer, World Meteorological Organization; Professor Ross McKitrick, University of Guelph, Canada; John Rafferty, editor of Earth and life sciences, *Encyclopedia Britannica*; Jeremy Shakun, Assistant Professor, Department of Earth & Environmental Sciences, Boston College, USA; Anders Carlson, Associate Professor, College of Earth, Ocean, and Atmospheric Sciences, Oregon State University, USA; Professor Albert Klein Tank, Director of Met Office Hadley Centre, UK; John Christy, Distinguished Professor of Atmospheric Science and Director of the Earth System Science Center at The University of Alabama, USA; Professor Judith Curry, former Chair of the School of Earth and Atmospheric Sciences, Georgia Institute of Technology, USA; Richard Black, Director of Energy & Climate Intelligence Unit, UK; Simon Robertson, University of New South Wales, Australia; Professor Lee Kump, Dean in the College of Earth and Mineral Sciences, Penn State University, USA; Katharine Mach, Associate Professor, Rosenstiel School of Marine and Atmospheric Science, University of Miami, USA.

Human extinction by artificial intelligence: Professor Yong Shi and Dr. Feng Liu, Chinese Academy of Sciences, Beijing; Johnny Luu, Head of Communications, Waymo (formerly the Google self-driving car project),

Mountain View, California; Eric Enge, Digital Marketing Practice Leader at Perficient Digital, Boston, Massachusetts.

Human survival by space colonization: Iain Nicolson, writer and lecturer in astronomy and space science; Jim Pawelczyk, Associate Professor of Physiology and Kinesiology, Penn State University, USA; Al Globus, space settlement engineer and advocate; Stephen Ashworth, Fellow of the British Interplanetary Society and writer on space-related topics.

Human survival by extending healthspan: Professor Hiroshi Ishiguro, Director of the Intelligent Robotics Laboratory, Osaka University, Japan; Jacob George, National Science Foundation Graduate Research Fellow at the University of Utah Biomedical Engineering Department, USA; Michael Blaese, former Chief of the Cellular Immunology Section of the National Institutes of Health's National Cancer Institute; Ken Culver, former Fellow and Senior Clinical Investigator at NIH's National Cancer Institute; Jennifer Doudna, Chair in Biomedical and Health Sciences and Professor of Molecular and Cell Biology and of Chemistry at the University of California, Berkeley; George Church, Professor of Genetics at Harvard Medical School; Paul Knoepfler, Professor of Cell Biology and Human Anatomy, University of California Davis School of Medicine; Lee McGuire, Chief Communications Officer, Broad Institute of MIT and Harvard; Edward McCabe, Distinguished Professor Emeritus, David Geffen School of Medicine, University of California, Los Angeles; Professor Jinsong Li, Shanghai Institute of Biochemistry and Cell Biology, China; Barbara Sibbald, Deputy Editor of the *Canadian Medical Association Journal*; Dr. Emma Haapaniemi, Group Leader, Gene Editing, Centre for Molecular Medicine, University of Oslo, Norway.

Human survival by achieving immortality: Aubrey de Grey, Chief Science Officer and Cofounder, SENS Research Foundation, Mountain View, California; Preston Estep, Cofounder and Chief Scientific Officer of Veritas Genetics; Michael Fossel, Founder and President of Telocyte, a company focused on curing Alzheimer's disease; Calvin Harley, President, Founder, and Chief Scientific Officer of Telomere Diagnostics, Menlo Park, California; Jan Vijg, Professor and Chair, Department of Genetics, Albert Einstein College of Medicine, New York; Gordon Lithgow, Professor and Vice President, Academic Affairs, Buck Institute for Research on Aging, Novato, California; Judith Campisi, Professor at the Buck Institute for Research on Aging; Tom Kirkwood, Emeritus Professor, Institute for Ageing, Newcastle University, UK; Éric Le Bourg, CNRS (National Centre for Scientific Research) researcher at Paul-Sabatier University, Toulouse, France; Dennis Kowalski, President, Cryonics Institute, Clinton Township, Michigan, USA.

The transformation of humans: Natasha Vita-More, Executive Director of Humanity+ (formerly known as the World Transhumanist Association), Los Angeles, California; Gopal Sarma, physician-scientist serving as scientific advisor to the Models, Inference, and Algorithms Initiative at the Broad Institute of MIT and Harvard.

Any remaining errors are entirely my responsibility. Not all those listed above agreed with my evaluation of the predictions covered in Parts 1, 2, and 3. Several disagreed with others in their field.

JH
London, 2023

Table of Contents

1

Introduction

It was never easy to look into the future, but it is possible and we should not miss our chance.

Andrei Linde

In *COSMOSAPIENS Human Evolution from the Origin of the Universe*[*] I examined all the available scientific evidence and, where such evidence was absent, the most reasonable scientific conjectures about how we evolved from the origin of the universe to the present day.

I shall now attempt to see what the future holds for the human species. To do so, I evaluate in Part 1 the current major predictions that we shall become extinct, in Part 2 the predictions that we shall survive, in Part 3 that we shall be transformed, and in Part 4 I set out my own, very different forecast based on projecting into the future the distinct pattern revealed in *COSMOSAPIENS*.

I have tried to make the book accessible to readers with no scientific background. Where a technical term occurs I give the definition in the text, and I've compiled these definitions in the Glossary towards the end of the book.

My conclusions are summarized at the end of each chapter and of each Part.

---

[*] Hands (2017).

Part 1

EXTINCTION

2

Natural disasters

Even with all our technology and the inventions that make modern
life so much easier than it once was, it takes just one big natural
disaster to wipe all that away and remind us that, here on Earth, we're
still at the mercy of nature.

Neil deGrasse Tyson

The human species could be made extinct in two ways. All humans could
be killed either immediately or else more gradually if the human population
is reduced to below a minimum viable size or if our habitat, which includes
our food chain, is irreparably damaged. Unlike that for any other species, the
human habitat covers the globe. And also unlike any other species we humans
attempt to identify, and estimate the probability of, potential causes of our
extinction and take measures to try and counter them.

These potential causes are either natural or anthropogenic (human-made).
In this chapter I shall consider the probabilities and predictions of natural
disasters that pose an existential threat to humans, while the following chapters
of Part 1 I will do the same for anthropogenic existential threats.

Such natural disasters may be categorized as astronomical, geophysical, or
pandemic.

Astronomical

I shall divide astronomical disasters into two types: supernovae and gamma
ray bursts; and asteroid and cometary impacts.

Supernovae and gamma ray bursts

supernova	The collapse of a massive star into a neutron star or black hole when its nuclear fuel runs out (Type I) or else a white dwarf star is triggered into runaway nuclear fusion by acquiring matter, usually from a binary companion through accretion or merger (Type II). Either event generates a huge amount of electromagnetic radiation. Supernova remnants may be a source of cosmic rays.
gamma ray burst	A brief, intense explosion of high-frequency electromagnetic radiation. Gamma ray bursts have been observed in distant galaxies and can last from 10 milliseconds to several hours. A typical burst releases as much energy in a few seconds as the Sun will in its entire 10-billion-year lifetime.

Supernovae and gamma ray bursts (GRBs) release enormous amounts of energy that could conceivably damage Earth's biosphere from great distances. Radiation from these sources could penetrate the atmosphere, produce a flash of ultraviolet (UV) energy, and possibly result in cosmic ray showers and the formation of nitrous oxides that could destroy the ozone layer protecting Earth from the Sun's UVB radiation and thereby cause DNA damage to species on Earth's surface.

Because of uncertainty as to how the biosphere would respond to such radiation and ozone depletion, we do not know how far away such events would need to be in order to pose no extinction threat. Supernovae radiate in all directions, making their effects decline with the square of the distance. GRBs are directional, beaming much of their energy in two narrow cones, and hence they have a longer reach in some directions but not others.

Current estimates for a safe distance that would prevent a supernova from causing ozone depletion are some tens of parsecs.[*] A UV flash may damage the biosphere up to 150 kiloparsecs from a GRB, but this would affect only one of Earth's hemispheres. A safe distance to prevent GRB ozone destruction may be 12–14 kiloparsecs.

There are no supernova or GRB candidates at unsafe distances from the Sun that will explode in the current epoch.[†] The estimated rate of Earth-affecting

[*] A unit of distance used in astronomy, equal to about 3.26 light years or 3.086×10^{13} kilometers.

[†] An epoch is a geologic unit of time. The current epoch is called the Holocene, which began 11,700

events is likely to be of the order of 1 in 100 million years, assuming random locations in the galactic disk and current observed rates.[1]

Asteroid and cometary impacts

asteroid	A rocky object smaller than a planet that orbits the Sun or another star; also known as a minor planet. The orbits of most of the asteroids in the solar system are between the orbits of Mars and Jupiter, while some are beyond Neptune.
comet	A small body, usually a few kilometers across, consisting of water ice and frozen gases embedded with rock and dust that orbits the Sun and also other stars. Comets usually have eccentric orbits, typically with a much greater inclination to the plane of Earth's orbit around the Sun. When they pass close to the Sun they develop diffuse gaseous envelopes and sometimes long dust and ion tails.

Asteroids with orbits that pass close to Earth are known as Near Earth Asteroids (NEAs). In 1980 physicist Luis Alvarez, his geologist son Walter, and nuclear chemists Frank Asaro and Helen Michel proposed that one such asteroid hit the Earth 65 million years ago and caused the Cretaceous–Tertiary extinction of dinosaurs and half of all Earth's species then considered to have occurred at this time.[*]

They hypothesized that the impact of an asteroid with a diameter of 10 ± 4 kilometers would send about 60 times the asteroid's mass into the atmosphere as pulverized rock. A fraction of this dust would spread worldwide and stay in the atmosphere for several years. The resulting decrease of sunlight on the surface would suppress photosynthesis, destroying plants and species that depend on plants to survive.

They didn't propose where this impact had occurred. Their main evidence was significantly higher levels of iridium consistent with those of extraterrestrial origin in exposed levels of deep-sea limestone in Italy, Denmark, and New Zealand dating from 65 million years ago.[2]

According to Walter Alvarez this mass extinction occurred in as brief a period as one to 10 years.[3]

years ago after the last major ice age.
[*] Now referred to as the Cretaceous–Palaeogene extinction event of 66 million years ago with a claimed disappearance of up to 75% of marine genera and up to 50% of all plants and animals.

Scientists later discovered a massive crater at Chicxulub on Mexico's Yucatán Peninsula, which they concluded was the site of the asteroid impact. The view developed that this impact had indeed caused the Cretaceous–Tertiary* mass extinction by generating global wildfires, earthquakes, and a global dust cloud rich in sulfuric acid that blocked out the Sun for many months, resulting in global cooling, acid rain, and the destruction of food chains.

Although many scientists questioned this account, in 2010 an interdisciplinary group of scientists announced that they had reviewed 20 years' research and concluded that the Chicxulub impact was the sole cause of the mass extinction and that the Alvarez hypothesis was correct.[4] This became the accepted theory and was portrayed in subsequent popular science books and in museums. Hence the possibility exists that another sufficiently large impact could cause a mass extinction, including human extinction.

Set against this, however, is the persuasive challenge by geophysicists, biologists, and other scientists to the group's findings. Geophysicists Vincent Courtillot and Frédéric Fluteau accused the group of committing "a substantial error and a fundamental misrepresentation of our paper."[5] Princeton geoscientist Gerta Keller and others charged the group of using

> a selective review of data and interpretations by proponents of this viewpoint. They ignored the vast body of evidence inconsistent with their conclusion— evidence accumulated by scientists across disciplines (paleontology, stratigraphy, sedimentology, geochemistry, geophysics, and volcanology) that documents a complex long-term scenario involving a combination of impacts, volcanism, and climate change.

They identified some of the key evidence that the group overlooked and concluded that, when this evidence is taken into account, it is clear that there is

> a long-term multicausal scenario [that] is inconsistent with the model proposed by [the group].[6]

Evolutionary biologist J David Archibald and 22 other scientists pointed out that the group

> conspicuously lacked the names of researchers in the fields of terrestrial vertebrates, including dinosaurs as well as freshwater vertebrates and invertebrates

and that

the simplistic extinction scenario presented in the Review has not stood up to the countless studies of how vertebrates and other terrestrial and marine organisms fared at the end of the Cretaceous. Patterns of extinction and survival were varied, pointing to multiple causes at this time.[7]

A large asteroid certainly impacted at Chicxulub about 66 million years ago. However, the evidence that it was the cause of a mass extinction at the Cretaceous-Paleocene (K–Pg) boundary is contentious, and that such a mass extinction occurred within a timespan of years is without foundation.

The fossil evidence supports a much more gradual extinction of most of the claimed species. The fossil record is richest for marine organisms, but a detailed picture across the K–Pg boundary is known only for planktonic foraminifera and calcareous nanoplankton, and their extinctions occurred over an extended period, starting well before and finishing well after the boundary. Brachiopods suffered badly across the boundary but, although claims are similarly made for ammonites, there are too few ammonite-bearing sections to show whether their extinction was gradual or abrupt. Cretaceous species of calcareous nanoplankton survived across the boundary and became extinct some tens of thousands of years later.

Among the vertebrates, mammals underwent a gradual change, with drastic reductions occurring only in the marsupials. The boundary also does not seem to have posed many problems for turtles, crocodiles, lizards, and snakes, all of which came through virtually unscathed.

There are very few fossil specimens of the thousand or so species of dinosaur believed to have existed at that time, and there is only one area where a dinosaur-bearing sedimentary transition across the K–Pg boundary has been examined, and this extends from Alberta in Canada to the northwestern USA. Records of dinosaurs in this area during the later part of the Cretaceous show a gradual decline in diversity, with a drop from 30 to 7 genera over the last 8 million years of the Cretaceous, which suggests a more gradual extinction, while some dinosaurs evolved into birds.[8*]

Evidence that previous mass extinctions have been associated with supervolcanic eruptions has been growing (see page 12). This led to a 2019 claim that four eruptions of the Deccan Traps large igneous province in India played a significant role in the K–Pg extinctions.[9] A supervolcanic eruption belches large volumes of sulfur dioxide and carbon dioxide (CO_2)

---

[*] For a more detailed consideration of mass species extinctions and their causes, see Hands (2017, pp. 293–295).

into the atmosphere. This sulfur dioxide then converts to sulfuric acid, which condenses rapidly in the stratosphere to form fine sulfate aerosols. These increase the reflection of radiation from the Sun back into space, thereby cooling the Earth's lower atmosphere, but the effects last only a few years. CO_2, on the other hand, is a greenhouse gas that warms the atmosphere, and it remains in the atmosphere very much longer. Hence there could have been climate swings between cold and warm periods that affected the survival of various species.

The balance of evidence strongly suggests that an asteroid impact was not the main cause of a mass species extinction 66 million years ago, and certainly not within less than 10 years as claimed by Walter Alvarez. Moreover, from observations and analyses conducted by NASA's Spaceguard program, we now know that there are no comparably large asteroids (diameter greater than 5km) in orbits that could potentially hit Earth.[10]

A cometary impact could prove devastating. A typical comet would encounter Earth at a much higher relative velocity than a NEA because of its highly elliptical orbit, and such a long-period comet would be discovered only if it was on a direct impact course.[11] These long-period comets are the most numerous type, originating from the Oort cloud far beyond the orbit of Pluto, and they are unobservable until they reach the inner solar system (i.e. closer to the Sun than Jupiter) because they have very dark surfaces.[12] Furthermore, comets are subject to forces other than gravity because sublimation of their nucleus volatiles and ices pushes them slightly off their gravitational orbit. Although such forces are many orders of magnitude weaker than gravity, they make long-term predictions of cometary paths difficult.[13] This reduces the time for a countermeasure to be implemented, such as launching an interceptor spacecraft to explode a nuclear bomb and deflect the comet's path.[14]

However, in 2019, Qicheng Zhang and colleagues modeled an Earth- and space-based high-powered laser system that was capable of deflecting away a 500m-diameter comet on an Earth collision approach. The development of such a system, or, more practically, the temporary repurposing of a laser system constructed for another use, could prevent any Earth impact.[15]

Moreover, comets of all groups are estimated to be responsible for less than 1 percent of all impact events in Earth's recent geological record. No comets of any size have been confirmed to have impacted Earth in historical times, nor is one expected to impact in the foreseeable future.[16]

Hence it is safe to conclude that impacts from asteroids or comets pose no existential threat to humans.

Geophysical

Because the human habitat is global, a geophysical existential threat to humans must be global. This rules out local disasters such as landslides, hurricanes, earthquakes, flooding, and normal volcanism. Anders Sandberg, research fellow at Oxford University's Future of Humanity Institute, says that the most plausible geophysical threat is supervolcanism.[17]

Supervolcanism

supervolcano	A volcano that has had an eruption with a Volcanic Explosivity Index (VEI) of 8, the largest value on the index, producing at least 1,000 cubic kilometers of deposits. These are often referred to as supereruptions.
supereruption	An eruption that produces at least 1,000 cubic kilometers of deposits.

The Yellowstone Caldera in Wyoming, USA, is an example of the result of supervolcanism. It was formed by a supereruption of 1,000 cubic kilometers that occurred 630,000 years ago[18] and generated a huge basin-like depression known as a caldera.

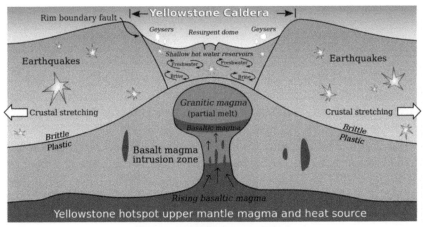

Figure 2.1 Yellowstone Caldera

Such supereruptions take place when magma (hot molten rock in the mantle) rises into the Earth's crust but is unable to break through it. Pressure builds in a large and growing magma pool until the crust is unable to contain the pressure and it bursts out, leaving a basin-like depression.

| mantle | The mostly solid bulk of the Earth's interior that lies between the Earth's dense, superheated core and its thin outer layer, the crust. The mantle is about 2,900 kilometers thick and makes up 84 percent of Earth's total volume. |

Mass species extinctions are now being linked to large igneous provinces (LIPs).

| large igneous province (LIP) | An area of millions of square kilometers of lava formed by a series of eruptions over hundreds of thousands to millions of years of vast volumes of molten rock from deep cracks in the Earth's surface that spread out from the cracks, cool, and solidify. |

LIPs are thus distinct from calderas, such as the Yellowstone Caldera, that are formed by a single explosive supereruption lasting days to weeks.

Although the eruptions that create a LIP occur over some million years or so, the eruptions pulse in much shorter—and hence more concentrated—bursts.

Brown University paleobiologist Jessica Whiteside and colleagues claimed evidence of a CO_2 super-greenhouse effect about 200 million years ago, supporting the hypothesis that the Triassic–Jurassic mass extinction—in which 75 percent of all species are thought to have perished—was caused by a series of eruptions that produced the giant Central Atlantic Magmatic Province (CAMP), the Earth's largest igneous province, covering an area of more than 9 million square kilometers.[19]* Probably five big pulses, each lasting 10,000–20,000 years, produced the CAMP, and each of these pulses comprised 2 to 10 gigantic eruptions that far exceeded any supereruptions in the last few million years.[20]

These LIP-creating eruptions pump out ash and a mixture of gases. The ash blocks sunlight, while one of the emitted gases, sulfur dioxide, is converted to sulfuric acid in the atmosphere; this rapidly condenses to form fine sulfate aerosols that reflect back radiation from the Sun. Both cause cooling, even freezing, to produce what is called a volcanic winter. While this cooling lasts only five or so years after the eruption ceases, if the eruption lasted a decade or a hundred years, the cooling would last this long plus the subsequent five years, resulting in a mass species extinction on land.

The CO_2 released would cause ocean acidification and a lack of oxygen that,

---

* Now estimated at more than 11 million square kilometers, larger than the continental USA (Jessica Whiteside, personal communication, October 17, 2019).

combined with the released hydrogen sulfide, would—it is claimed—produce marine species extinction.[21] CO_2 is a greenhouse gas that, when released into the atmosphere, causes warming over a period of decades to centuries, followed by cooling over tens of thousands of years as CO_2 is gradually removed from the atmosphere and locked away for decades or centuries in such things as plants, soils, oceans, and rocks.

Leeds University Professor of Palaeoenvironments Paul Wignall says a problem arises here because, although the calculated volumes of environmentally damaging gases released during LIP-creating eruptions are large, they are spread over the lifetime of these eruptions, which may be a million years. Gases do not linger in the atmosphere over such long periods, leaving ample time for recovery between eruptions. Hence environmental damage must be done either by an individual eruption or by a series of closely spaced ones. He concludes that, although studies suggest extinction events coincide with the onset of LIP eruptions, the volume of gases emitted by an individual eruption is relatively small, and so the environmental impact should be minor.[22]

Potsdam University geodynamic modeler Stephan Sobolev and colleagues examined the Siberian Traps LIP, the emergence of which coincides with the Permian Triassic extinction event 252 million years ago, the largest mass extinction in the Earth's history, which is thought to have resulted in the loss of 95 percent of marine species and 70 percent of land species. Sobolev and colleagues present geochemical and petrological evidence that ascending mantle plumes incorporate oceanic crust that has been recycled into the mantle via ocean trenches to the point where up to 20 percent of the plume may consist of this material. This changes the way magma reaches the Earth's surface and greatly increases the volume of gases released. If this finding is supported by other studies, this could solve the problem claimed by Wignall.[23]

Oxford University volcanologist Professor David Pyle argues that, while we still don't have a mechanistic understanding of how emissions from LIPs affect the global environment, emissions from LIPs could be considerably enhanced by the release of gases from the rocks through which the magmas have passed.[24]

Moreover, Jessica Whiteside maintains that in several cases we know that individual LIP eruptions were very large and concentrated, with volumes exceeding historical eruptions by orders of magnitude. These mega-eruptions tended to be clustered, with only short periods of time between them, and, as has been observed in several cases, CO_2 would have built up quickly, potentially with catastrophic consequences.[25]

Overall, however, the geological record suggests that such series of gigantic eruptions producing LIPs of millions of square kilometers associated with mass species extinctions are rare, occurring once every 10 to 100 million years.

Supervolcanic eruptions producing more than 1,000 square kilometers of ejected matter occur more frequently, approximately every 100,000 years.[26] The most recent supervolcanic eruption occurred 22,600 years ago at Taupo in New Zealand and produced about 1,130 cubic kilometers of volcanic ash.[27] I can find no report that it had a global effect that reduced—still less posed an existential threat to—the human population.

We may conclude that supervolcanism poses no existential threat to humans, while LIP-creating series of gigantic eruptions claimed to be associated with mass species extinctions are so rare that the future of the human species will be determined by other factors considered in subsequent chapters of this book.

Pandemic

pandemic   A disease that spreads across several continents.

Influenza poses one of the most serious threats to humans because its cause, influenza viruses, are easily transmitted by one person coughing or sneezing and others inhaling, it takes time for symptoms to develop, and the symptoms can easily be mistaken for other illnesses, thus allowing the infected person to travel and spread the particular virus.

Influenza pandemics have recurred many times since the 16th Century. The deadliest influenza pandemic on record is the "Spanish flu" of 1918–1920. It was given this name because, during the First World War, Spain was a neutral country with a free media that reported on the outbreak in Madrid in late May 1918. The Allies and the Central Powers had wartime censors who suppressed news of outbreaks in their countries in order to keep morale high.

The first case very probably occurred at a US army base, Camp Funston in Fort Riley, Kansas in early March 1918. Infected soldiers most likely spread the disease to other military camps across the country. Later that month 84,000 American soldiers headed across the Atlantic to the European battlefields, followed by 118,000 more in April. The overcrowded troopships provided ideal conditions for the transmission of the disease, as did the army camps and trenches of the battlefields.[28]

Anton Erkoreka of the Basque Museum of the History of Medicine concludes that the deadliness of the Spanish flu was inextricably linked to the conditions suffered by soldiers in the First World War, which made them vulnerable to the virus, followed by their return to their home countries across five continents.[29] David Morens, senior scientific advisor to the director of the USA's National

Institute of Allergy and Infectious Diseases, disagrees. He maintains that this does not explain higher death rates among soldiers in US and UK camps than in the trenches, nor the high mortality in such countries as India.[30]

However, some 1.3 million Indians fought in the First World War. Moreover, the other 30 combatant countries used troops from their colonies across the globe. Morens counters by maintaining that, of the global population at that time, only a very small percentage were directly involved in combat, and a larger but still small percentage lived in countries where war took place, and yet the vast majority of deaths, and the highest death rates by far, occurred in places completely untouched by the war, e.g., Alaska and remote parts of India.[31]

Erkoreka argues that the peak of the pandemic occurred in the fall of 1918 and coincided with the end of the war. The return of troops to their countries of origin at the beginning of 1919 favored the pandemic's expansion in the countries and islands of the Southern Hemisphere, with higher mortality rates occurring in some native populations of Oceania, America, and Asia.[32]

Pandemics usually have a higher death rate among the very young and the very old. This particular influenza pandemic caused a very high death rate in people aged between 20 and 40, which has never been seen before or since.[33] This favors the First World War soldiers/returnees argument.

Crucially, this particular virus hadn't been identified at the time, and no antiviral drugs to treat the infection or antiviral vaccines to prevent it spreading were used. This influenza pandemic killed an estimated 40–50 million people globally, representing some 2.5 percent of the world's population.[34]

Since then there have been three influenza pandemics: in 1957, 1968, and 2009. This last one resulted in between 100,000 and 400,000 deaths in its first year,[35] when the world's population was 6.872 billion.[36] The most vulnerable people were in the less developed countries of Central and West Africa, Southeast Asia, and Latin America that have poor public health systems.[37]

If not new viruses, then new strains of an influenza virus will emerge, as it did in the 2009 pandemic. However, considerable progress has been made since 1920 in the diagnosis, prevention, control, and treatment of influenza. Continuing research will enable us to reduce still further the death toll of influenza pandemics by developing improved antiviral vaccines together with campaigns and support from bodies such as the World Health Organization (WHO).[38]

Another pandemic viral infection is the human immunodeficiency virus (HIV). This retrovirus—an RNA virus—attacks the body's immune system and leaves the individual increasingly susceptible to a wide range of other infections, including the HHV8 virus that causes a type of cancer called Kaposi's sarcoma, which a healthy immune system can fight off. The most advanced stage of HIV infection is Acquired Immunodeficiency Syndrome (AIDS), which can take from 2 to 15 years to develop and can result in death from a wide range of diseases.

The HIV retrovirus is transmitted from infected individuals through the exchange of body fluids such as semen and vaginal secretions, breast milk, and blood. The transmission occurs through having unprotected anal or vaginal sex, breastfeeding, sharing contaminated needles when injecting drugs, and receiving infected blood transfusions. [39]

The HIV/AIDS pandemic has killed more than 35 million people since 1981. [40] Today we have effective antiretroviral drugs. These drugs do not cure the retrovirus but suppress its replication within a person's body, allowing the individual's immune system to strengthen and regain the capacity to fight off other infections. [41] Increasing access to such a therapy and awareness of how the retrovirus is transmitted have led to a steep fall globally in HIV/AIDS deaths. There were 770,000 HIV/AIDS deaths in 2018, 56 percent fewer than the peak of 2004 and 33 percent fewer than in 2010 despite a period of substantial population growth in many severely affected countries in Africa. [42]

A more likely existential threat to humans comes from an infectious agent that exists in a nonhuman host, technically called a pathogen reservoir. If the pathogen—the infectious agent—is easily transmitted to humans and causes a high death rate, then it could repeatedly infect the human population over many years, not only killing large numbers but also causing the collapse of human organizations vital for survival, such as those for food production and distribution and medical care, until the human population succumbs and dies off. [43]

This appears to have been the infection pattern for the worst pandemic in human history in terms of death rate. Between 1340 and 1400CE the Black Death reduced the human population from an estimated 443 million to 350–375 million. It took 100 years for the global human population to recover to its previous level. [44]

It was called the Black Death because its victims became covered in black boils that oozed blood and pus. We now know that the infectious agent was the bacterium *Yersinia pestis*, which was hosted by small mammals and transmitted by their fleas. Humans can be infected by the bite of infected vector fleas, through unprotected contact with infectious bodily fluids or contaminated materials, or by inhaling droplets produced by the coughing or sneezing of a victim of pneumonic plague. [45]

The bacterium *Yersinia pestis* causes three kinds of plague: bubonic, the most common, that produces swelling in lymph nodes situated in the groin, armpit, or neck; septicemic, when the bacterium multiplies in the bloodstream, producing fevers and chills, extreme weakness, abdominal pain, diarrhea, vomiting, and the blackening and death of tissues in fingers, toes, and nose; and pneumonic that affects the lungs and is the least common but the most deadly because it can spread from person to person via cough droplets and progress rapidly when it can produce respiratory failure.[46]

At the time of the Black Death pandemic no one knew what caused plague or how to treat it and stop it spreading. Yet even so it killed an estimated maximum of 20 percent of the human population.

Plague currently poses no threat to the survival of the human species because we now know what causes it, we can detect it through such measures as a rapid dipstick test that is now widely used in Africa and South America, and we can cure it with antibiotics and supporting therapies. From 2010 to 2015 there were 3,248 cases of plague reported worldwide, accounting for 584 deaths.[47]

The most recent disease to be officially declared a pandemic by the WHO, on March 11, 2020, was Covid-19. A pneumonia of unknown cause was detected in Wuhan, China, and first reported to the WHO Country Office in China on December 31, 2019. It was later identified as a new coronavirus labeled severe acute respiratory syndrome coronavirus 2 (SARS-CoV-2).[48]

People catch Covid-19 from the coughing or exhalation of an infected person that produces airborne droplets. This can occur directly, when someone breathes in those droplets, or indirectly, when someone touches a surface on which those droplets have fallen and then goes on to touch his or her own face. Some infected people don't have any symptoms, but they can still pass on the disease to those who are more vulnerable to acute symptoms. The latter include those over 70 years of age and those with underlying health problems such as high blood pressure, heart problems, or diabetes. Prompted by the WHO, most countries adopted measures such as lockdowns and social distancing in order to reduce transmission of the virus. Some introduced travel restrictions for people from other countries.

Illness due to Covid-19 infection is generally mild, especially for children and young adults. About 80 percent of people recover from the disease without needing special treatment. However, it can cause serious illness: about one in every five people (20 percent) who catch it needs hospital care, and around one in six (17 percent) develops severe pneumonia, acute respiratory distress syndrome, septic shock, and/or multiorgan failure.[49]

The rapid spread of the virus induced alarm, if not panic. On March 31, 2020, UN Secretary-General António Guterres declared that "Covid-19 is the greatest test that we have faced together since the formation of the United Nations."[50] According to Yale University economist Robert Shiller, the Covid-19 health pandemic generated an anxiety pandemic about its economic consequences, and both pandemics fed into each other.[51] Stock markets around the world plummeted, with some partial bounce backs, producing in March 2020 the two largest one-day drops in the Dow Jones industrial average since the stock market crash of October 1987.[52]

Some speculated that Covid-19 would prove as fatal as the deadly "Spanish flu" of 1918-1920. As noted previously, however (see page 14), that particular virus hadn't been identified at the time and there were no drugs or antiviral vaccines available. Medical technology has developed significantly in the last 100 years. By April 8, 2020, four weeks after the WHO declared Covid-19 a pandemic, 115 vaccine candidates had been identified, of which five moved into clinical development.[53] On June 24, 2020, China approved experimental vaccines for emergency use to protect people in high-risk occupations such as frontline health workers, border officials, and overseas workers, even though the vaccines hadn't yet completed Phase 3 clinical trials. China also approved the CanSino vaccine for limited use in the Chinese military for one year.[54] On August 11, 2020, Russia became the first country in the world to approve a vaccine for Covid-19, named Sputnik V.[55]

In the West, collaboration between multinational pharmaceutical organizations, university research groups, and governments produced a raft of vaccine candidates. The failure rate of candidate vaccines in general is high. On December 2, 2020, the partnership between Pfizer and BioNTech gained the approval of the UK's Medicines and Healthcare products Regulatory Agency (MHRA) for its messenger RNA (mRNA) vaccine BNT162b2.[56] The UK became the first country to approve this vaccine and the first country in the West to approve the use of any Covid-19 vaccine.[57]

Developments continued apace. By May 21, 2021, 15 vaccines had received approval from different governments around the world.[58]

What is significant is how effective most of these vaccines have been. Two injections of the Pfizer–BioNTech vaccine spaced 21 days apart proved 95 percent effective at preventing Covid-19 in those without prior infection and 100 percent effective at preventing severe disease. In early May 2021 this vaccine was found to be more than 95 percent effective against Covid-19 variants first detected in the UK and South Africa. The Moderna vaccine, using the same technology as the Pfizer–BioNTech vaccine, has a similarly high efficacy at preventing symptomatic disease.

Johnson & Johnson uses a different technique called a carrier vaccine. Scientists engineer a harmless adenovirus as a shell to carry genetic code on the spike proteins of the adenovirus to the vaccine recipient's cells (akin to a Trojan Horse). Once the code is inside the recipient's cells, the cells produce a spike protein to train the body's immune system, which creates antibodies and memory cells that protect against an actual SARS-CoV-2 infection. Clinical trials produced very rare but serious blood clotting problems among women aged 18–48. One dose proved 72 percent effective overall and 86 percent effective against severe disease, with marginally less effectiveness against the UK and South African variants. Johnson & Johnson planned a second Phase 3 clinical trial to see if two doses at two months apart would provide better protection.

The Oxford–AstraZeneca vaccine employs a similar technique to the Johnson & Johnson vaccine and produced similar rare problems. Two doses 4–12 weeks apart showed 76 percent effectiveness at reducing the risk of symptomatic disease 15 days or more after the second dose and 100 percent effectiveness against severe disease. Oxford–AstraZeneca also said that the vaccine was 85 percent effective at preventing Covid-19 in people over 65 years old.

The Novavax vaccine is a third type, called a protein adjuvant. It contains the spike protein of the coronavirus itself, but formulated as a nanoparticle that cannot cause disease. When the vaccine is injected, this stimulates the immune system to produce antibodies and T-cell immune responses. Trials of two doses of this vaccine three weeks apart have so far shown 96.4 percent efficacy in reducing mild and moderate disease and 100 percent efficacy against severe disease from the original strain of Covid-19.[59]

The Russian Sputnik V vaccine employs a similar technique to the Johnson & Johnson vaccine except that it uses two adenovirus vectors. These are given 21 days apart. The team responsible claimed 91.6 percent efficacy from 21 days after the first dose.[60]

The Phase 3 trials of China's existing vaccines remained unpublished at the end of May 2021. The director general of China's Center for Disease Prevention and Control was quoted at a Chengdu conference on Covid-19 vaccines on April 11, 2021 as saying "We will solve the problem that current vaccines don't have very high protection rates." His words spread rapidly on Chinese social media before being censored. China's leading vaccines are largely based on inactivated virus technology of long standing, a technology different from the other vaccines described above. It is thought that China's pharmaceutical firms are now pursuing the mRNA technology used by Pfizer–BioNTech and Moderna.[61]

It is not enough to design effective vaccines. If they are to combat a pandemic, doses must be produced in very large numbers and be effectively administered. Western governments bought huge volumes of vaccine doses manufactured by large Western pharmaceutical companies, and they planned vaccine rollouts prioritizing the most vulnerable. This process was led initially by the UK, which provided one dose to 57.6 percent and two doses to 35.4 percent of its population by May 25, 2021, with the USA rapidly catching up.

Over the next five months, however, the picture rapidly changed, as shown by Table 2.1, which lists the vaccination records of countries with medium-sized or larger populations.

Table 2.1 Vaccinations as a percentage of population at October 20, 2021

Country	At least 1 dose	2 doses
Chile	84%	75%
Spain	81%	79%
Cambodia	80%	76%
South Korea	79%	67%
Canada	78%	73%
Italy	77%	70%
Japan	76%	69%
France	75%	67%
United Kingdom	73%	67%
Brazil	73%	50%
Australia	71%	67%
Germany	68%	65%
United States	65%	56%
Turkey	65%	56%
India	50%	21%
Russia	34%	31%
Global	36%	11%

Source: Our World in Data

The data in Table 2.1 uses official numbers from governments and health ministries and should be treated with caution. For example, on October 20, 2021 Brazilian senators voted to recommend charging President Bolsonaro with crimes against humanity after Brazil's death toll from Covid-19 reached 600,000, the world's second highest. Other charges include falsification of documents and misusing public funds to spread false news about the pandemic. Bolsonaro had stated on Facebook that vaccines do not reduce the risk of contracting the disease and that they cause other infections.[62]

China, with the largest population in the world, has been erratic in reporting vaccinations and is not included as an individual entry in Table 2.1. Consequently, the percentage of the global population vaccinated is questionable because this figure includes China's population.

Many of the countries with high vaccination rates are among the richest countries in the world, while poorer countries are greatly disadvantaged in securing vaccines. By October 20, 2021 only 7 percent of Africa's population had received one dose and 5 percent had received two doses.

To help redress the balance, four international organizations set up COVAX in order to accelerate the development and manufacture of Covid-19 vaccines and guarantee fair and equitable access for every country in the world. COVAX aims to provide doses for at least 20 percent of every country's population.[63]

However, Health Policy Watch reported on October 20, 2021 that "COVAX was so underfunded that it couldn't buy enough vaccines, and its paralysis fuelled bilateral deals between pharmaceutical companies and the high-income countries (HIC) that were also COVAX members."[64] The latter were motivated in part by the desire to give booster vaccinations after it became clear that the effectiveness of the double vaccination decreased after six months or so.[65]

It is impossible to give exact figures of Covid-19 casualties because many countries lack the necessary analytical tools, and many untested patients who die from Covid-19 will not be recorded as such. The best estimates available are from the WHO's record of reported laboratory-confirmed Covid-19 cases and deaths. On October 20, 2021 this showed 241,411,380 cases and 4,912,112 deaths.[66]

The global population at that time was 7,868,764,000.[67] Hence the number of recorded deaths at October 20, 2021 accounted for 0.06 percent of the global population. Even if the number of deaths increases 100-fold before vaccinations have contained the infection globally, this would still be only 6 percent of the human race, which doesn't constitute an existential threat to humankind.

Conclusions

1. The first type of astronomical disaster—supernovae or gamma ray bursts—poses no existential threat to humans on Earth because no potential candidates are sufficiently close for their energy releases to fatally damage Earth's atmosphere. Moreover, the probability of new such events occurring sufficiently close is negligible.

2. Of the second type—asteroid and cometary impacts—the hypothesis that an asteroid was responsible for an end-Cretaceous sudden mass extinction 66 million years ago has been disproven: the fossil evidence supports a much more gradual extinction of most of the claimed species, including many species of dinosaur, while some dinosaur species evolved into birds. Furthermore, there are no sufficiently large asteroids in orbits that could potentially hit Earth. Cometary

paths are more difficult to predict and track, and they leave less time in which to launch a nuclear bomb to deflect a threatening comet. However, laser systems could be developed or repurposed to deflect such an approaching comet. Moreover, comets of all groups are estimated to be responsible for less than 1 percent of all impact events in Earth's recent geological record. No comets of any size have been confirmed to have impacted Earth in historical times, nor is one expected to impact in the foreseeable future. Hence it is safe to conclude that impacts from asteroids or comets pose no existential threat to humans.

3. The most dangerous geophysical threat is a series of pulsed eruptions over hundreds of thousands to millions of years of vast volumes of molten rock from deep cracks in the Earth that spread out from these cracks, cool, and solidify to form a large igneous province. These are claimed to be associated with mass extinctions in the past. However, they are so rare—occurring approximately every 10–100 million years—that the future of the human species will be determined by other factors within this time frame. Supervolcanic eruptions producing more than 1,000 square kilometers of ejected magma occur more frequently, roughly every 100,000 years. The most recent occurred 22,600 years ago, with no evidence of a global effect that reduced—still less posed an existential threat to—the human population. Consequently, geophysical events do not threaten the extinction of the human species.

4. The pandemic that caused the biggest death rate in human history, the 14th Century Black Death, was caused by an infectious agent that existed in a nonhuman host, enabling it to repeatedly infect the human population over some 60 years. Yet even at a time when no one knew what caused the Black Death or how to treat it and stop it spreading, it killed a maximum of 20 percent of the human population. Now that we have this information and the means to combat plague, this death rate is minute. In 1918–1920, in the unusual conditions following the First World War and, crucially, with no antiviral drugs to treat the infection, nor antiviral vaccines to prevent it, the deadliest influenza pandemic killed some 2.5 percent of the global population, while the last influenza pandemic, in 2009, killed a maximum of 0.006 percent of the global population. The HIV/AIDS pandemic has caused the deaths of a maximum of 0.5 percent of humans on the planet, and this death rate has plummeted in recent years. The Covid-19 pandemic seems likely to account for the deaths of less than 6 percent of the

human population. Although new pandemics may arise in the future, the continuing development of medical technology means it is safe to conclude that pandemics pose no existential threat to the human species.

I conclude with a high degree of confidence that natural disasters pose no threat to extinguish the human species.

3

Warfare and accident

Every inhabitant of this planet must contemplate the day when this planet may no longer be habitable. Every man, woman and child lives under a nuclear sword of Damocles, hanging by the slenderest of threads, capable of being cut at any moment by accident or miscalculation or by madness. The weapons of war must be abolished before they abolish us.
President John F Kennedy, 1961

Although some forecast that the human species could be ended by a natural disaster, most forecast that scientific and technological developments have given us humans the means to destroy our species. In this chapter I will consider the predictions that warfare and accidents pose existential threats to humankind. In the following chapters I will examine such predictions about a population explosion, climate change, and artificial intelligence.

Warfare

Nuclear

In a 2017 poll conducted by *Times Higher Education* and the Lindau Nobel Laureate Foundation of 50 Nobel Prize winners in science, medicine, and economics, almost a quarter (23 percent) identified nuclear war as the biggest threat to humankind.[1]

The specter of a nuclear holocaust began to haunt the public imagination in August 1945 when the USA dropped an atomic bomb on the Japanese city of Hiroshima, followed three days later by one on Nagasaki. Each bomb was made using nuclear fission technology.

The Hiroshima bomb had an explosive power of 15 kilotons of TNT. Calculating the casualties of this bomb is immensely difficult because of extensive population shifts in the months prior to the bombing and the destruction of record-keeping facilities due to the bombing.

The most reliable highest estimate of the number of Japanese citizens killed directly by the Hiroshima bomb is 67,076 out of a total population of 255,200. Adding in workers from outside the city, captive foreign laborers, and the military (the Second General Army HQ occupied a large district in the city center near where the bomb exploded, while 20,000 other troops were also camped in the city) produces a fatality estimate of 88,000 from a maximum population of 298,000. Survivors who died subsequently from radiation-induced cancers were estimated at some 400 by 1997.

Although the Nagasaki bomb was more powerful, due to its target and the city's geography the immediate fatalities of this bomb were fewer. The most reliable highest estimate of the number of Japanese citizens killed directly by the Nagasaki bomb is 39,970 out of a population of 173,783 within a 15km radius of the explosion's epicenter. Adding in non-Japanese citizens and the much fewer military personnel than in Hiroshima produces an estimated death toll of 46,100.

Nearly all the deaths from these bombings occurred within three months of the attack. Longitudinal studies of a large group of survivors contradict claims that there was a higher mortality rate after that time.[2]

The specter of a nuclear holocaust took an even more frightening dimension in 1961 when the Soviet Union tested a bomb they called Big Ivan (Western governments used the code name Tsar Bomba) based on nuclear fusion technology. It had an explosive power of 50 megatons of TNT, some 1,400 times the combined power of the Hiroshima and Nagasaki bombs and 10 times the combined power of all the bombs used in the Second World War. It remains the most powerful nuclear weapon tested to date.[3]

After the detonation of the Hiroshima and Nagasaki atomic bombs in 1945, the world's stockpile of nuclear weapons increased dramatically during the Cold War between the USA and the USSR. Each side aimed to develop the capability to launch a nuclear strike that would obliterate the other side even after suffering a devastating attack itself. According to the doctrine of mutual assured destruction, appropriately abbreviated to MAD, this would restrain the other side from launching a first strike. It is difficult to give precise numbers of nuclear weapons because of the secrecy that shrouds such weapons programs.

Figure 3.1 Global nuclear weapons stockpiles, 1945–2020
Sources: Kristensen Hans M and Robert S Norris (2014); Stockholm, International Peace Research Institute (2018); Gordon, Michael, *The New York Times* "U.S. Nuclear Plan Sees New Weapons and New Targets", (9 March 2001) accessed 9 September 2018; https://www.nti.org/learn/countries/kazakhstan/nuclear/ accessed 9 September 2019; https://www.nti.org/learn/countries/ukraine/ accessed 9 September 2019; https://www.nti.org/analysis/articles/belarus-nuclear-disarmament/ accessed 9 September 2019; *SIPRI Yearbook 2020* (2020) Table 10.1, p. 326

Figure 3.1, compiled from the best estimates available, shows this dramatic rise in the world's nuclear weapons stockpile, peaking at some 61,660 in 1985 followed by a steep decline to approximately 13,400 in 2020, of which the USA and Russia account for 91 percent. The estimates include the weapons of India, Pakistan, and North Korea—countries that have announced they possess them. It also includes Israel, which has never admitted to possessing nuclear weapons despite overwhelming evidence that it has the largest and most sophisticated nuclear arsenal outside of the five states recognized by the 1968 Treaty on the Non-Proliferation of Nuclear Weapons: the USA, Russia (formerly the Soviet Union), the UK, France, and China.[4]

The primary reason for the steep decline after 1985 was the crippling effect on the Soviet economy of their cost. This prompted Soviet President Mikhail Gorbachev to propose to US President Ronald Reagan at their October 1986 summit meeting in Reykjavik, Iceland that both sides reduce their nuclear weapons by 50 percent. Reagan declined, but he did agree to the Intermediate-Range Nuclear Forces (INF) Treaty, which was signed in December 1987 and entered into force on June 1, 1988. It banned nuclear-capable missiles with a range between 500km and 5,500km, and it led to the destruction of 846 US and 1,846 Soviet missile systems.[5]

This was followed by the Strategic Arms Reduction Treaty (START I), first proposed in the 1980s by President Reagan, that required the USA and the Soviet Union to reduce their deployed strategic arsenals to 1,600 delivery vehicles carrying no more than 6,000 warheads. Its implementation was delayed for several years because of the collapse of the Soviet Union and the ultimately successful efforts to denuclearize Ukraine, Kazakhstan, and Belarus by transporting their nuclear weapons to Russia. The treaty was finally signed in July 1991. The START I reductions were completed in December 2001 and the treaty expired in December 2009. Attempts to implement a follow-on treaty, START II, foundered, as did START III.

On May 24, 2002 Presidents George W Bush and Vladimir Putin signed the Strategic Offensive Reductions Treaty (SORT) under which the USA and Russia agreed to reduce their strategic nuclear arsenals to 1,700–2,200 warheads each. The warhead limit took effect and expired on the same day, December 31, 2012. SORT was replaced by New START, a legally binding, verifiable agreement that limits each side to 1,550 strategic nuclear warheads deployed on 700 strategic delivery systems. The warhead limit is 30 percent lower than the 2,200 upper limit of SORT, and the delivery vehicle limit is 50 percent lower than the 1,600 allowed by START 1.

New START was signed by US President Barack Obama and Russian President Dmitry Medvedev in April 2010, and ratified by a three-quarter majority of the US Senate in December 2010 and by the Russian parliament in January 2011. It entered into force on February 5, 2011 and was due to expire in February 2021. On January 26, 2021 the new US President Joe Biden agreed with President Putin to extend the treaty to 2026; the extension was ratified by Russia's Duma and confirmed by US Secretary of State Antony Blinken.[6]

The overall decline in nuclear weapons shown in Figure 3.1 continued—despite some tweets calling for their increase by Obama's successor, President Donald Trump—to a global level of approximately 13,400 by 2020. Many of these are retired and awaiting dismantlement, while others are in central storage and would require transport and loading onto launchers before they could become fully operational. Some 3,750 are deployed with operational forces, of which nearly 2,000 are kept in a state of high operational alert.[7]

While these reductions were taking place, governments were modernizing their nuclear armory and testing new delivery systems.[8]

Since the beginning of the Obama Administration, the USA has repeatedly accused Russia of failing to return to full and verified compliance with the INF Treaty by developing mobile intermediate-range missile systems. As a result the USA announced on August 2, 2019 that it was withdrawing from the INF Treaty.[9] While this will increase tensions between the USA and Russia, it will not result in an increase in nuclear warheads under the New START Treaty.

As far as long-range missiles are concerned, it is worth noting that a test firing of a Trident II D5 missile in 2016—the first for four years—by the UK's HMS *Vengeance* submarine had to be aborted and the missile destroyed when it veered off target and headed towards the Florida coast. Although the submarine was British and part of the UK's so-called "independent nuclear deterrent", Trident missiles are manufactured and maintained in the USA. Reportedly there had been a failed Trident II test firing by the USA in 2011 and the problem had been the missile's guidance system.[10] In 2017 the US navy started replacing the Trident II D5 missile with an enhanced version, D5LE, with an improved guidance system.[11]

I think it highly improbable that North Korea will launch a nuclear attack on the USA or one of its allies because a retaliatory strike would be fatal for the North Korean regime. I also think it improbable that India and Pakistan will engage in nuclear warfare in one of their periodic border disputes, or that Israel will use its nuclear weapons against a Middle Eastern neighbor. Even if any of these things did occur, the consequences would be appalling for the populations targeted, but it would not extinguish the human species.

However determined the Putin regime may be to take control of the territory of the former Soviet Empire, it is highly improbable that this will lead to a deliberate nuclear exchange between Russia and the USA acting on behalf of NATO. More possible is that a nuclear war could be triggered by accident. Eric Schlosser, author of *Command and Control: Nuclear Weapons, the Damascus Accident, and the Illusion of Safety* (2013), documents incidents from the Cold War era, including the Cuban Missile Crisis of 1962, when false alarms nearly triggered nuclear exchanges.

Hundreds of land-based Minuteman III missiles formed part of launch-on-warning, an essential part of the Single Integrated Operational Plan (SIOP), America's nuclear war plan that aimed to destroy 12,000 targets within the Soviet Union. Despite leading scientists, generals, US politicians, and officials like former Defense Secretary Robert McNamara calling the policy crazy and demanding its abandonment, Schlosser maintained in 2016 that Minuteman III missiles still sat in their silos armed with warheads and ready to go.

Schlosser argues that the systems devised to govern the use of nuclear weapons, like all complex technological systems, are inherently flawed. Many of the nuclear weapon systems on both sides are aging and obsolete. The personnel who operate these systems often suffer from poor morale and poor training. Moreover, today's command-and-control systems must contend with threats that barely existed during the Cold War: malware, spyware, worms, bugs, viruses, corrupted firmware, logic bombs, Trojan horses, and all the other modern tools of cyber warfare.

Schlosser concluded in 2016 that "today, the odds of a nuclear war being started by mistake are low—and yet the risk is growing, as the United States and Russia drift toward a new cold war."[12]

If such an event were ever to happen, human civilization would suffer a horrendous setback (assuming the missile guidance systems are accurate), but it would not destroy the human species. Apart from the large and continuing reduction in the number of nuclear missiles (see page 27), the bombs of the 1980s were much, much larger—commonly exceeding 500 kilotons and even reaching 20 megatons in the Russian armory—than those on deployment today, which, for the USA, are mainly 100 kilotons. Russia probably retains some larger warheads on some of its early intercontinental ballistic missiles but around 100 kilotons on its later ones.[13]

Some, however, hold a different opinion. In 2015 Steven Starr, medical technologist and a member of the Physicians for Social Responsibility, predicted that, after a US and/or Russian nuclear weapons launch, a nuclear winter would follow that "would cause most humans and large animals to die from nuclear famine in a mass extinction event similar to the one that wiped out the dinosaurs."[14]

The prediction of a nuclear winter that threatens human extinction following a nuclear war was first made in a December 1983 *Science* article "Nuclear Winter: Global Consequences of Multiple Nuclear Explosions" by R P Turco, O B Toon, T P Ackerman, J B Pollack, and Carl Sagan,[15] and publicized the following year in a book *The Cold and the Dark: The World after Nuclear War* by Paul Ehrlich, Carl Sagan, Donald Kennedy, and Walter Orr Roberts.[16] These publications warn that nuclear war would send a giant cloud of black dust into the atmosphere that would cover the globe, blocking out the sunlight and producing a climate change like that which caused the sudden mass extinction of the dinosaurs and half of Earth's species.

I considered the claim about this particular mass extinction in Chapter 2 and concluded it was extremely doubtful (see pages 7–9).

Skeptical atmospheric scientists argued that model ignored a variety of factors. It was one-dimensional: it did not take into account north-south and east-west directions, but instead treated the Earth as a homogeneous all-land sphere having a temperature that depended only on the up-down direction (i.e. atmospheric altitude). The model had no geography, no winds, no seasons, an instantaneous spread of smoke to the hemispheric scale, and no feedback of atmospheric circulation changes on the rate of smoke washout by rainfall.

In 2006 Russell Seitz, Senior Research Fellow at the Climate Institute since 2013, made a particularly withering critique. He alleged that astronomer and science popularizer Carl Sagan had developed the computer model with fellow disarmament activists for political reasons. The model was based on a string of flawed assumptions and used worst-case guestimates for its data. "This is not physics, but a crude exercise in 'garbage in, gospel out'." He claimed the *Science* article was not peer reviewed, and that when other scientists developed more authentic models, the postulated effects of the Sagan model were disproven.[17]

In a summer 1986 *Foreign Affairs article* entitled "'Nuclear Winter' Reappraised," National Center for Atmospheric Research scientists Starley Thompson and Stephen Schneider concluded that "on scientific grounds the global apocalyptic conclusions of the initial nuclear winter hypothesis can now be relegated to a vanishingly low level of probability."[18]

Seitz quotes other scientists who criticized the nuclear winter model. MIT nuclear physicist and nuclear disarmament advocate Professor Victor Weisskopf: "Ah! Nuclear Winter! The science is terrible, but perhaps the psychology is good." Nobel laureate physicist Richard Feynman: "You know, I really don't think these guys know what they're talking about." Harvard atmospheric scientist Professor Michael McElroy: "They stacked the deck." Physicist Freeman Dyson of the Institute for Advanced Studies at Princeton: "It's an absolutely atrocious piece of science, but I quite despair of setting the public record straight… Who wants to be accused of being in favor of nuclear war?" Professor George Rathjens of MIT, chairman of the Council for a Livable World, which promotes policies to reduce and eventually eliminate nuclear weapons: "Nuclear Winter is the worst example of the misrepresentation of science to the public in my memory."[19]

In January 1986 MIT climatologist Professor Kerry Emanuel commented in the journal *Nature* on the political erosion of the objectivity vital to scientific endeavor: "Nowhere is this more evident than in the recent literature on 'Nuclear Winter,' research which has become notorious for its lack of scientific integrity."[20]

In 2009, however, Starr, writing in the *Bulletin of International Commission on Nuclear Non-proliferation and Disarmament*, declared "A series of peer-reviewed studies, performed at several US universities, predict the detonation of even a tiny fraction of the global nuclear arsenal within large urban centers will cause catastrophic disruptions of the global climate and massive destruction of the protective stratospheric ozone layer. A nuclear war fought with several thousand weapons would leave the Earth uninhabitable." [21]

He mentions the widespread criticism of the nuclear winter publications, calling them a smear campaign that for almost two decades prevented further studies of a nuclear winter. He went on to say

> Yet the basic findings of the nuclear winter research, that extreme climatic changes would result from nuclear war, were never scientifically disproved and have been strengthened by the latest studies. *Most importantly, the new studies show that the original research actually underestimated by an order of magnitude the amount of time the soot from nuclear firestorms would remain above cloud level to block sunlight* [my italics]. This greatly magnifies the impact such a global smoke layer would have on weather and climate. The new studies clearly demonstrate that massive changes in climate created via nuclear conflict…would certainly have catastrophic and devastating impacts on human populations. [22]

The new studies he refers to are written principally by climatologist Alan Robock, then at the University of Maryland, and the authors of the original 1983 *Science* article using, he claims, the latest NASA Goddard Institute for Space Studies climate model.

They are in sharp contrast to the studies and analyses carried out by other scientists (most of whom advocate total nuclear disarmament) referred to above that *do* disprove the nuclear winter hypothesis. Yet, as we saw above, Starr was still making this claim in 2015, despite the massive reduction in both the number of operational nuclear weapons and their explosive power since the 1980s (see page 29).

In November 2018 climatologist Kerry Emanuel said his 1986 letter to *Nature*, which complained about the integrity of the original nuclear winter paper, outlined some of the main problems with that paper, "and I have not seen anything that would change my mind about it. Unlike the initial detonations themselves, the energy density of subsequent fires is not enough to enable the smoke plumes to reach the stratosphere, where they could persist long enough to affect climate." [23]

In the unlikely event of a full-scale US–Russia nuclear exchange, millions would perish in the initial blasts in Russia, Europe, and North America. The human species, however, would survive because of its resilience. As noted above, the highest estimate states that the bomb dropped on Hiroshima wiped out 29 percent of its 298,000 population in 1945, and yet by 2016 the city's population had recovered and grown to 1.196 million.[24] Most Southern Hemisphere populations would be largely unscathed by the direct effects of a US–Russia nuclear exchange, although the indirect effects such as large disruptions of trade and aid—but not any claimed "nuclear winter"—would be severe.[25]

Hence predictions that nuclear warfare will cause human extinction are almost certainly wrong.

The 50 Nobel Laureates polled in 2017 are the latest group of leading thinkers to have raised humanity's awareness of the evils of nuclear warfare, a process that began when philosopher Bertrand Russell, Albert Einstein and other distinguished scientists published in 1955 what became known as the Russell-Einstein Manifesto. They posed the stark question: "Shall we put an end to the human race; or shall mankind renounce war?"[26]

Governments ignored these warnings. During the huge increase in nuclear weapons in the 1980s, organizations like the Campaign for Nuclear Disarmament (CND) achieved massive public support. They were, however, attacked as communist dupes or worse. It is a mark of our evolution as a self-reflective species that CND's aims are now enshrined in the Treaty on the Prohibition of Nuclear Weapons, which was negotiated as a legally binding instrument at the United Nations and completed on July 7, 2017. The treaty prohibits the use, threat of use, development, production, manufacturing, acquisition, possession, stockpiling, transfer, stationing, and installment of nuclear weapons or assistance with any prohibited activities. By December 2020 it had been signed by 86 member states of the United Nations.[27]

Advocates of the nuclear status quo criticize the treaty.[28]

Like most treaties it is open to differing interpretations. Verification and compliance measures are to be determined by a designated "competent international authority." The treaty does not solve the perennial problems of facilities enriching or reprocessing uranium for nuclear energy supply that can be switched to making nuclear bombs, or rockets used for peaceful purposes like placing satellites in orbit that can be used to deliver nuclear bombs, or bombers for delivering conventional weapons that can be used for delivering nuclear explosives. Moreover, no state already possessing nuclear weapons has signed—or is likely in the foreseeable future to sign—the treaty.

However, the treaty does reinforce the Nuclear Taboo hypothesis developed by international relations expert Nina Tannenwald from 1999. This says that nuclear weapons have become stigmatized as unacceptable and illegitimate weapons of mass destruction: states are not free to use them without incurring moral opprobrium, political costs, and exclusion from the bounds of civilized international society.[29]

Steven Pinker traces the gradual acceptance of this hypothesis, arguing that nuclear weapons' destructive capacity violates any conception of proportionality in the waging of war and that plans for civil defense are a travesty. "The fact that wars both large (Vietnam) and small (Falklands) were not deterred by the increasingly ineffectual nuclear threat was a small price to pay for the indefinite postponement of Armageddon."[30]

In 2008 former senior US officials George Schultz, Secretary of State in the Reagan administration, William Perry, Secretary of Defense under Clinton, Henry Kissinger, National Security Advisor and Secretary of State under Nixon and Ford, and Sam Nunn, a Chairman of the Senate Armed Services Committee published a manifesto "A World Free of Nuclear Weapons". This proposed a series of steps to rid the word of nuclear weapons.[31]

Senior US Republican and Democratic statesmen supported the manifesto's authors. In 2008 Bruce Blair cofounded the organization Global Zero to work with political leaders, senior military commanders, and national security experts from across the political spectrum and in every nuclear-armed region of the world to achieve the permanent removal of all nuclear weapons by 2030. By December 2020 its aims had been backed by an impressive international list of 283 current and former leaders in the field, including former Presidents Mikhail Gorbachev and Jimmy Carter.[32]

In accepting the 2017 Nobel Peace Prize on behalf of the International Campaign to Abolish Nuclear Weapons for its work on the Treaty on the Prohibition of Nuclear Weapons, Executive Director Beatrice Fihn said

> No nation today boasts of being a chemical weapon state. No nation argues that it is acceptable, in extreme circumstances, to use sarin nerve agent. No nation proclaims the right to unleash on its enemy the plague or polio. That is because international norms have been set, perceptions have been changed. And now, at last, we have an unequivocal norm against nuclear weapons. Monumental strides forward never begin with universal agreement. With every new signatory and every passing year, this new reality will take hold.[33]

Of course, such progress will encounter setbacks, evidenced by Syrian President Bashar al-Assad's use of chemical and biological weapons—a war crime under international law—from 2013 to 2018.[34] However, the Treaty on the Prohibition of Nuclear Weapons combined with the growing international support for their abolition reinforces the trend in Figure 3.1 and counters even further the prediction that the human species will be made extinct through nuclear warfare.

Biological

One of the reasons Martin Rees gave in his 2003 book *Our Final Hour* for humans having only a 50 percent chance of surviving the 21ˢᵗ Century was that we could be extinguished by biological warfare.

Biological warfare is the deliberate use of infectious viruses, bacteria, or any other biological toxins in order to kill large numbers of people. As an indication of its potential, the influenza pandemic of January 1918–December 1920, the so-called Spanish flu virus (see pages 14 to 15), infected an estimated one third of the world's population and caused an estimated 50 million, and possibly 100 million, deaths.[35]

The Biological and Toxin Weapons Convention drawn up in April 1972 prohibits the development, stockpiling, production, or transfer of biological agents and toxins of "types and quantities" that have no justification for protective or peaceful use. Furthermore, it bans the development of weapons, equipment, or delivery systems to disseminate such agents or toxins. As of December 2020, 109 states had signed this treaty, which doesn't, however, provide for any external checks.[36]

Of these states, 16—Canada, China, Cuba, France, Germany, Iran, Iraq, Israel, Japan, Libya, North Korea, Russia, South Africa, Syria, the UK, and the USA—plus Taiwan have had, or are currently suspected of having, biological weapons programs.[37] In the case of the USA its biological weapons arsenal was destroyed by February 1973, but the US Army Medical Research Institute of Infectious Diseases (USAMRIID) continued research to develop defenses against a biological weapons attack.[38]

In 2017 Bill Gates warned world leaders at the Munich Security Conference that bioterrorists unleashing a pandemic could kill more people than those killed by a nuclear war.[39]

Although the threat of bioterrorism has been raised before, very few actual examples have been recorded since the Second World War. In 1993 the Japanese cult Aum Shinrikyo failed in its attempt to cause an anthrax epidemic in Tokyo (though it was more successful two years later by releasing the chemical sarin on the Tokyo subway system at rush hour, killing 13 and seriously injuring more than 50).[40]

In the days following the al-Qaeda attack on New York's World Trade Center and the Pentagon on September 11, 2001, a series of anthrax-laced letters containing al-Qaeda slogans were posted to two US senators and several news agencies. 25 people became ill, five of whom died in the worst case of bioterrorism in US history. In 2008 a federal prosecutor formally declared Bruce Ivins, a microbiologist at the USAMRIID where he had been trying to develop a vaccine against anthrax, as the sole person responsible for creating and mailing the letters. Ivins, who had a history of mental illness, committed suicide before he could be brought to trial. Some biologists and chemists doubted that the federal investigators had got the right man, but the FBI confirmed their conclusions. [41]

The rapid developments in synthetic biological technology have raised the risk of a new generation of bioweapons according to a report published in 2018 by the National Academies of Science, Engineering, and Medicine commissioned by the US Department of Defense. In the future scientists may be able to recreate dangerous viruses from scratch, make harmful bacteria more deadly, and modify common microbes so that they churn out lethal toxins once they enter the body. Moreover, many such weapons may be able to be made relatively easily and cheaply. [42]

As far as an existential threat to humankind is concerned, however, a terrorist group is unable to manufacture sufficient quantities of biological agents to inflict more than a small number of deaths. Even a large, technologically sophisticated nation would not unleash such a weapon on an enemy without ensuring it could protect key sectors of its own population from its effects or from a retaliatory strike. There is a negligible probability of human extinction through biological warfare.

Accident

Nuclear
In 1979 a partial nuclear meltdown occurred in one of the two Three Mile Island nuclear reactors in the USA, releasing radioactive gases and radioactive iodine into the environment. More than half of the 663,500 people within the 20-mile radius evacuation zone remained. Most of these evacuees returned to their homes within three weeks. Epidemiological studies concluded that the accident had no long-term cancer effects. [43]

In 1986 an explosion and fires at the Chernobyl nuclear power plant in the Ukrainian Soviet Socialist Republic flung large quantities of radioactive particles into the atmosphere. Most were deposited nearby, but lighter particles were blown by winds over much of the western USSR and parts of Europe. 134 of the 600 workers at the plant suffered acute radiation sickness, and 28 died within three months. Recovery for the survivors took several years. In addition, increased incidents of leukemia and cataract damage occurred among these survivors. This was classified as a Level 7 event (the maximum) on the International Nuclear Event Scale.

By 2005 more than 6,000 thyroid cancers had been diagnosed in children and adolescents living in Ukraine, Belarus, and the most affected regions of Russia, a large fraction of which was most likely due to the Chernobyl accident.[44] Some estimates predict that cancer deaths might eventually reach 4,000 among the cleanup workers.[45]

In 2011, a second Level 7 event was registered when a tsunami following an earthquake caused nuclear meltdowns at the Fukushima Daiichi Nuclear Power Plant in Japan. Radiation leaked from the plant, and the government established a 30km-radius evacuation zone. By March 2017 all evacuation orders in the areas outside the difficult-to-return zone had been lifted.[46]

Unlike Chernobyl there were no acute radiation injuries or deaths among the workers or the public as a result of these meltdowns. The UN Scientific Committee on the Effects of Atomic Radiation concluded that the rates of cancer or hereditary diseases were unlikely to show any discernible rise in affected areas because the radiation doses people received were too low; the evacuations reduced their radiation exposure by a factor of 10.[47]

Any deaths and casualties that occurred were due to the trauma of the evacuations, especially among the elderly, in the wake of the earthquake and tsunami as well as the nuclear power plant meltdowns. According to the Japanese government's Reconstruction Agency, there were 2,202 disaster-related deaths in Fukushima due to evacuation stress, interruption to medical care, and suicide. As of March 2018 there had not been a single case of cancer linked to radiation from the plant.[48]

It is safe to conclude that nuclear power plant accidents carry no threat of making the human race extinct.

Nanotech

nanotechnology	The invention, manufacturing, and use of tools or machines constructed from single atoms or molecules. Compared with structures consisting of the same substances at a normal scale, nano-structures typically exhibit different properties such as chemical reactivity, mechanical strength, and optical, electrical, and mechanical behavior due to their larger surface-to-mass ratio and to quantum mechanical effects.

Eric Drexler, an MIT engineer who became one of the leading advocates of nanotechnology in the 1980s, predicted in his 1986 book *Engines of Creation* that in future we will be able to build whatever we need—chairs, computers, rocket engines, and so forth—much more cheaply and efficiently by assembling them from atoms and molecules. Assemblers the size of cells would be programmed to collect atoms and molecules as raw materials and convert them into the building blocks of the desired product.

To manufacture items on a human scale, enormous numbers of assemblers would be needed. This would be achieved by the assemblers replicating themselves by the same process.

He warned, however, that if an accident resulted in such self-replication not being stopped, the assemblers would consume all available atoms and molecules, including those of human beings and the entire biosphere, until nothing remained but an immense, sludge-like robotic mass that he referred to as "gray goo."[49] This was widely quoted as a means by which the human species could become extinct.

In 2000 nanomedical scientist Robert A Freitas Jr considered the "gray goo" problem. He estimated that the minimum replication time for the smallest nanomachine feeding on biomass is approximately 100 seconds, in theory leading to Earth's biomass being consumed in less than three hours. After examining a range of scenarios, he concluded that they all appeared to permit vigilant monitoring, thus enabling the rapid deployment of effective defenses.[50]

In 2005 inventor and futurist Ray Kurzweil used Freitas's minimum replication time, but estimated that 130 replications would be needed for out-of-control replicators to destroy the Earth's biomass, theoretically achievable in about 3½ hours. However, the rate of destruction would be much slower because biomass is not efficiently laid out. He envisaged a two-phased attack by self-replicating nanobots (the name given to nanorobots or nanomachines). In phase 1 the nanobots would take several weeks to spread throughout the biomass, but they would use up an undetectable portion of carbon atoms. Then phase 2 would begin with the seed nanobots expanding rapidly in place to destroy the biomass in about 90 minutes. "The point is that without defenses the available biomass could be destroyed by gray goo very rapidly."[51]

In response to this, Drexler said in 2004 that nanotechnology-based manufacturing systems could be restricted to using inorganic atoms and molecules and that self-replication is unnecessary. He called for a ban on anything resembling a self-replicating nanomachine.[52]

In the same year the Royal Society and the Royal Academy of Engineering published a report entitled *Nanoscience and Nanotechnologies: Opportunities and Uncertainties*, which said that "we have heard no evidence to suggest that mechanical self-replicating nanomachines will be developed in the foreseeable future."[53]

It wasn't until 2017 that the first claim was made for the construction of a synthetic nanobot that could build other molecules. A team led by David Leigh of the University of Manchester's School of Chemistry in the UK constructed a robot from 150 atoms of carbon, hydrogen, oxygen, and nitrogen that is capable of manipulating a single molecule. The team can program this molecular nanobot in a special solution to reversibly switch between right-handed and left-handed assembly modes by adding or subtracting protons (hydrogen ions, H^+) in a seven-step process that produces an excess of any one of four possible diastereoisomers.[54]

diastereoisomer	A molecule that has the same formula and structure as another but is arranged differently in space and is therefore not a mirror image of the other.

This elementary molecular robot in a flask that requires human programmers in order to function in a very limited way is a far cry from Kurzweil's two-phase attack by uncontrolled self-replicating nanomachines. The latter's speculation is not a viable threat to the human species.

Conclusions

1. Predictions that nuclear warfare, biological warfare, or bioterrorism will cause the extinction of the human species are contradicted by the scientific and sociological evidence.
2. Nuclear power plant accidents carry no threat of making humans extinct.
3. Predictions that self-replicating nanomachines, or nanorobots, could destroy all the Earth's biomass, including humans, are speculations lacking any scientific foundation.
4. Warfare and terrorism will continue to inflict devastation on some communities and a few countries in the foreseeable future, but the evidence strongly suggests this will continue to show an overall continuing decrease in deaths as a percentage of the human population.

4

Population explosion and climate change

The battle to feed all of humanity is over.
Paul Ehrlich, 1968

Right now, we are facing a man-made disaster of global scale. Our greatest threat in thousands of years. Climate change. If we don't take action, the collapse of our civilizations and the extinction of much of the natural world is on the horizon.
Sir David Attenborough, 2018

We're going to become extinct. Whatever we do now [about global warming] is too late.
Frank Fenner, 2010

Humans will be extinct within ten years.
Guy McPherson, 2017

In the 2017 poll of Nobel Laureates quoted in the previous chapter the largest percentage of respondents (34 percent) identified not nuclear warfare but population explosion and environmental degradation as the greatest threats to humankind.

Population explosion
Fears about a population explosion were raised in the 1950s and 1960s. They were fuelled by the 1968 publication of Paul Ehrlich's *The Population Bomb*, which begins with the prediction

> The battle to feed all of humanity is over. In the 1970s hundreds of millions of people will starve to death in spite of any crash programs embarked upon now. At this late date nothing can prevent a substantial increase in the world death rate.[1]

39

Ehrlich, a Stanford University professor of biology who specialized in butterflies, argued that population growth was outstripping food production and that massive famines would occur soon, possibly in the 1970s and certainly by the 1980s.[2]

The charismatic Ehrlich accepted invitations to repeat his message at numerous conferences during the following years. Addressing the British Institute for Biology in 1972 he predicted that

> By the year 2000 the United Kingdom will be simply a small group of impoverished islands, inhabited by some 70 million hungry people of little or no concern to the other 5–7 billion inhabitants of a sick world.

Before leaving he commented "If I were a gambler, I would take even money that England will not exist in the year 2000."[3]

The momentum grew with the 1972 publication of *The Limits to Growth*, heralded as the report of the first computerized model of variables in five categories: population increase, agricultural production, consumption of non-renewable resources, industrial output, and pollution. Commissioned by the Club of Rome—a group of concerned high-level politicians, economists, scientists, and business leaders from across the globe—its four authors predicted that unless world trends in population growth and industrialization were checked and pollution severely curbed, the most probable result would be a "sudden and uncontrollable decline in both population and industrial capacity" before 2072.[4]

The report was not submitted for peer review before publication. Several academics who later examined its analyses criticized its methodology. In 1973 researchers at the Science Policy Research Unit of the University of Sussex published *Models of Doom: A Critique of The Limits to Growth* in which they concluded that the authors' methods, data, and predictions were deeply flawed. For example, only about 0.1 percent of the data on the required variables was available, and they criticized the *Limits* authors for drawing sweeping conclusions from so precarious a database. Moreover, their computer model of the world was sensitive to a few key assumptions that are difficult to justify. They concluded the *Limits* model had a built-in Malthusian bias arising from the authors' beliefs and that it did not accurately reflect reality.[5]

Nonetheless a skillful and highly effective publicity campaign resulted in *The Limits to Growth* book launch being attended by leading politicians and opinion-formers. The book's conclusions featured on the front page of *The New York Times* and appeared prominently in most major media outlets. The book went on to sell more than 30 million copies in over 30 countries.[6]

Its computer model assumed that the five variables analyzed would grow exponentially while the ability of technology to increase resources would grow only linearly.

In reality, the opposite occurred.

According to the US Census Bureau's International Database, the global population growth rate decreased significantly from 1963 to 2020 and is forecast to continue decreasing until 2060 (see Figure 4.1).

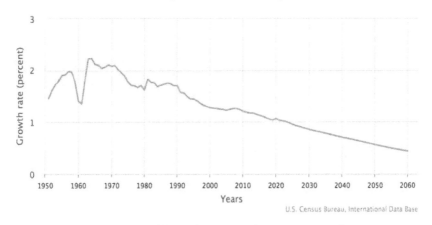

Figure 4.1 World population growth rates: 1950–2060
Source: US Census Bureau, International Database, October 8, 2021 Update

In 2004 three of the report's original four authors published *Limits to Growth: The 30-Year Update*, in which they argued that updates to their computer model of 1992 had shown that humankind had already overshot the limits of the Earth's resources to provide for its population. They declared

> we are much more pessimistic about the global future than we were in 1972…
> Much will have to change if the ongoing overshoot is not to be followed by
> collapse during the twenty-first century.[7]

The Limits to Growth had a positive effect in raising public awareness of key global social and economic issues. The authors' advocacy for a more equitable distribution of the world's resources, more responsible policies on pollution and the environment, and a more enlightened attitude towards birth control is laudable. However, they hand ammunition to opponents of such measures by persisting with a computer model that is fundamentally flawed and whose assumptions and predictions are demonstrably wrong.

Ehrlich's predictions were also wrong. Despite his wager, England still exists today. The UK's population in 2000 was 58,886,100,[8] the vast majority of whom were not hungry. Perhaps Ehrlich failed to distinguish between butter-flies and humans. Unlike the former, and any other known species, humans possess self-reflective consciousness. This enables us uniquely to reflect on the evidence and take appropriate action. There are no butterfly, or indeed chim-panzee, groups that devise, develop, and globally publicize artificial methods of birth control. There are no worldwide butterfly or chimpanzee businesses that invent new methods of food production and distribution. There are no global butterfly or chimpanzee organizations that campaign to protect the environment from other butterflies or chimpanzees who pollute and damage it.

There were no such human organizations 150 years ago. We have begun to take measures, however gropingly, to ensure that we, as a species, do not face extinction due to uncontrolled growth in our population that we lack the means to feed.

Climate change

The existential threat

The quote from the iconic British broadcaster Sir David Attenborough below the chapter heading is taken from his address to the UN-sponsored climate talks for the 165 signatory states of the United Nations Framework Convention on Climate Change (UNFCCC) held in December 2018 at Katowice in Poland.[9]

The even more pessimistic prediction by Frank Fenner, an Australian professor of virology with an interest in the environment, was given in an interview in June 2010. He said the population explosion, unbridled consumption, and climate change would mean "*Homo sapiens* will become extinct, perhaps within 100 years…It's an irreversible situation."[10]

Back in November 2006 the independent scientist and environmentalist James Lovelock, who pioneered the idea of the Earth as a living organism, declared that billions of people could be wiped out over the next century because of climate change. As the planet heats up humans will find it increas-ingly difficult to survive. In a lecture given at the Institution of Chemical Engineers in London he urged people to drop the phrase "global warming," which has cozy connotations, and instead start to think of it as "global heating."[11]

The claim that climate change will result in the extinction of the human species has grown significantly in recent years. It has been fed by scientists like Guy McPherson, professor emeritus of natural resources and ecology and evolutionary biology at the University of Arizona, who coined the phrase "near-term human extinction" (NTHE).[12]

In 2002 McPherson concluded that climate change would most likely result in human extinction by 2030. By 2017 he had given up hope of us surviving climate change. "Humans will be extinct within ten years."[13] He has built a following through his website *Nature Bats Last*[14] and a heavy schedule of workshops and media interviews. McPherson is extremely critical of mainstream climate scientists, scientific societies, and governments whom he accuses of aggressively muzzling scientists.

While McPherson's views are extreme, many others claim that if we don't take drastic measures to reduce if not eliminate human-made emissions of greenhouse gases, most especially CO_2, then climate change will result in human extinction. David Wallace-Wells is a deputy editor of *New York* magazine. The title of his 2019 book, *The Uninhabitable Earth: A Story of the Future*[15], conveys his message. He begins

> It is worse, much worse than you think. The slowness of climate change is a fairy tale… The earth has experienced five mass extinctions before the one we are living through now…all but the one that killed the dinosaurs involved climate change produced by greenhouse gas. The most notorious was 250 million years ago; it began when carbon dioxide warmed the planet by five degrees Celsius, accelerated when that warming triggered the release of methane, another greenhouse gas, and ended up with all but a sliver of life on Earth dead. We are currently adding carbon to the atmosphere at a considerably faster rate; by most estimates at least ten times faster.[16]

To assert that the Permian–Triassic extinction event of 250 million years ago began when CO_2 warmed the planet by 5°C is somewhat misleading. His own note, 231 pages later, referencing that statement says "There is some considerable debate about the precise mix of environmental factors (volcanic eruptions, microbial activity, Arctic methane) that brought about the end-Permian extinction."

Claims have been made that there were from one to three distinct pulses, or phases, of that extinction.[17] Professed causes for of the extinction include one or more of large meteor impacts, massive volcanic eruptions such as the Siberian Traps,[18] and climate change brought on by large releases of underwater methane or methane-producing microbes.[19]

However, reliable data for any cause are lacking. The evidence has been destroyed by plate tectonics and seafloor spreading or is buried deep under many layers of rock, and the proposed causes have almost invariably been contested.[*]

Even if the current rate of increasing CO_2 in the atmosphere is 10 times

---

[*] See Hands (2017, pp. 293–295) for a more detailed discussion of mass extinction events and their possible causes.

that it was during the Permian–Triassic extinction, the time frames are very different. Many geologists and paleontologists contend that the Permian extinction occurred over the course of 15 million years during the latter part of the Permian, while others claim that the extinction interval was much more rapid, lasting only about 200,000 years, with the bulk of the species losses occurring over a 20,000-year span near the end of the period.[20] The current time frame that Wallace-Wells is considering is from now to the end of the century, some 80 years. If our current rate of increasing CO_2 in the atmosphere is 10 times greater than during the Permian extinction, then this 10-fold greater rate multiplied by 80 years gives an equivalent of 800 years of increasing CO_2 during the Permian extinction. Yet even the shortest claimed time span for the Permian extinction is 20,000 years, meaning that there was 25 times more CO_2 in the Permian atmosphere to cause an increase in temperature of 5°C.

Wallace-Wells scatters his book with predictions from a range of sources, only some of which are peer-reviewed scientific papers, of the consequences of not meeting the goal of the Paris Agreement, which was signed in 2016 as part of the UNFCCC. This goal is to keep the increase in global average temperature to well below 2°C above preindustrial levels, and specifically to limit the increase to 1.5°C, which would substantially reduce the risks and effects of climate change. The strategy includes a reduction of greenhouse gas emissions, an increase in the energy (on the basis of consumption) coming from renewables, and an increase in energy efficiency. Each country determines, plans, and reports on its own contributions to this goal.[21]

Wallace-Wells vividly depicts a devastating cascade of interlinked disasters if the global temperature exceeds the Paris target when, he says, we are speeding along to more than 4°C warming by 2100. Whole regions of Africa, Australia, and the USA, parts of South America north of Patagonia, and Asia south of Siberia will be rendered uninhabitable due to direct heat, desertification, and flooding. This will lead to huge numbers of climate refugees, with worst-case estimates predicting a billion or more, as well as leading to numerous deaths through warfare. Even if we implement immediately all the commitments made in the Paris Agreement, we are likely to reach about 3.2°C of warming, which will bring about the collapse of the planet's ice sheets, flooding not just Miami and Dhaka, but Shanghai, Hong Kong, and hundreds of other cities around the world.

Moreover, "we will be left with an atmosphere that contains 500 parts per million of carbon—perhaps more. The last time that was the case, sixteen million years ago, the planet was not two degrees warmer; it was somewhere between five and eight."[22]

The cascade Wallace-Wells depicts is that melting of the planet's Arctic ice means less sunlight being reflected back to the Sun and more being absorbed by a planet warming faster still, leading to an ocean that is less able to absorb atmospheric carbon and so the planet warms even faster. A warming planet also melts the Arctic permafrost, which contains 1.8 trillion tons of carbon—more than twice as much as is suspended in the Earth's atmosphere—and some of which, when it thaws and is released, may evaporate as methane that, when judged on the timescale of two decades, is 86 times more powerful than carbon as a greenhouse gas.

Moreover, a hotter planet causes forest dieback, which results in a dramatic stripping back of the planet's natural ability to absorb carbon and turn it into oxygen, which means still hotter temperatures, which means more dieback, and so on. Higher temperatures mean more forest fires, resulting in fewer trees, thus producing less carbon absorption, leading to more carbon in the atmosphere, all causing an increasingly hotter planet. A hotter planet generates more water vapor in the atmosphere and, since water vapor is a greenhouse gas, this produces higher temperatures still, and so on. Warmer oceans absorb less heat, which means more heat stays in the air, and warmer oceans also contain less oxygen. This spells doom for phytoplankton—which do for the oceans what plants do on land, digesting carbon and producing oxygen—which heats the planet still further. And so on.

Climate-driven water shortages or crop failures drive climate refugees into nearby regions already struggling with resource scarcity. Sea-level rises inundate cropland with more and more saltwater flooding, transforming agricultural areas into brackish sponges no longer able to adequately feed those living off them. Such flooding also cripples chemical and nuclear plants, causing the release of toxic plumes.

Although he concedes uncertainty about when these results will happen, Wallace-Wells' message is unremitting. We have provoked a climate system "that will now go to war with us for many centuries, perhaps until it destroys us."[23] Climate change is an existential crisis and "the worst-case outcome puts us on the brink of extinction."[24]

Seventeen scientists reviewed Wallace-Wells' work and concluded that it contains several claims that are factually wrong, claims that are contradicted by other claims, and claims that go beyond the evidence in their descriptions of such worst-case scenarios.[25]

Extinction Rebellion, an international non-violent* civil disobedience

* Not all of its leaders speak with the same voice. Extinction Rebellion's cofounder and leading strategist Roger Hallam has said: "We are going to force the governments to act. And if they don't, we will bring them down and create a democracy fit for purpose...and yes, some may die in the process"; https://policy-exchange.org.uk/wp-content/uploads/2019/07/Extremism-Rebellion.pdf, p. 9.

movement launched in October 2018 in the UK, warned in 2019 of the existential crisis confronting humankind and other species if no drastic action on climate change is taken, specifically for the world to go to net zero emissions by 2025, a goal that no government or climate scientist deems achievable. "We are living through the sixth mass extinction... There is no planet B. This is where we will live, or go extinct as a species, with the millions that have been driven to extinction."[26]

A similar warning was given by Swedish schoolgirl Greta Thunberg. In May 2018 Swedish climate activist Bo Thoren, whose strategy was to gain attention by involving young people, approached the competition winners of an environmental writing competition with a plan for a school strike. Greta, who had come second, was the only one to respond.

Ingmar Rentzhog, founder of an investment relations company and the social media platform We Don't Have Time, learned of 15-year-old Greta's planned strike a week before it was due to take place (August 20, 2018) via a mailing list that Thoren sent out. Rentzhog went to the school, took a photograph of Greta and her banner, and posted it on his social media website and mailing list.[27]

The photograph and the story of the small, charismatic Greta, a self-proclaimed sufferer from Asperger's syndrome, obsessive-compulsive disorder, and selective mutism who says she suffered from depression as a child, went viral on social media. By December 2018 more than 20,000 students in some 270 towns and cities in countries across the world had opted for a Friday school strike. By this time the striking Greta had become an international celebrity, and that month she was invited to address delegates at the United Nations Climate Change Conference at Katowice in Poland where she castigated them for their inaction.[28]

In February 2019 she told the European Economic and Social Committee that the European Union must reduce its CO_2 emissions by double its 40 percent goal by 2030, and in April at the European Parliament in Strasbourg she criticized members for failing to hold an emergency summit on climate change, for which she received a standing ovation.[29]

She was nominated by three Norwegian Members of Parliament for the 2019 Nobel Peace Prize[30] and named by *Time* magazine as one of the 100 most influential people of 2019.[31]

Inspired by her, networks of school students organized school strikes for Friday September 20, 2019, to demand action on climate change prior to the UN Climate Action Summit of September 23. They invited adults to join them, and many did. Millions of demonstrators protested in some 185 countries across the globe, culminating in Greta Thunberg speaking at a rally outside the UN headquarters in New York.[32]

In April 2019 she declared "We are in the midst of the sixth mass extinction and the extinction rate is up to 10,000 times faster than what is considered normal" and "Around the year 2030… we will be in a position where we will set off an irreversible chain reaction beyond human control that will most likely lead to the end of our civilization as we know it."[33]

In order to evaluate these predictions of existential threats to the human species, I will begin by considering the meaning of key words.

Definitions

Among those predicting extinction, "climate change" tends to be equated with global warming, more especially that caused by human activities. The scientific definitions are different, and may be summarized as:

weather	The current state of the atmosphere measured by temperature, pressure, humidity, precipitation (such as rain, hail, or snow), sunshine, cloudiness, and the direction of winds.
climate	The average over several decades of regular variations during the year of surface and air temperatures, air pressure, humidity, precipitation (such as rain, hail, or snow), sunshine, cloudiness, and winds for a specified region of the Earth.
climate change	A change in the climate measured over several decades.

Weather is current, usually described over a period of days or weeks at the most, while climate and climate change are usually defined over a period of several decades.

global warming	A gradual increase in the overall temperature of the Earth's atmosphere and oceans, usually attributed to an increase in the greenhouse effect.

While global warming is often assumed to be due to human activities, this is not necessarily the case.

greenhouse effect	A natural process by which radiation from a planet's atmosphere warms the planet to a temperature above what it would be without its atmosphere.

The Earth's dry atmosphere comprises approximately 78.1 percent nitrogen (N_2), 20.9 percent oxygen (O_2), 0.9 percent argon (Ar), and 0.1 percent other gases, referred to as trace gases. The amount of atmospheric water vapor varies between 0 and 4 percent of the total atmosphere and averages between 2 and 3 percent. Included in the trace gases are naturally generated CO_2 at 0.04 percent and even smaller amounts of methane (CH_4), sulfur dioxide (SO_2), ozone (O_3), and nitrous oxide (N_2O).[34]

Although water vapor and the trace gases listed above comprise a very small portion of the atmosphere, they play an important role as greenhouse gases.

Solar energy at a range of wavelengths reaches the Earth's atmosphere. Part is reflected back into space, part absorbed by the atmosphere and clouds, and part is absorbed by the Earth's surface. Because the Earth's surface is colder than the Sun, it radiates heat away at longer, infrared wavelengths. The small amounts of greenhouse gases in the atmosphere absorb some of this infrared radiation and re-radiate it, warming the atmosphere and the Earth's oceans and landmasses.

This process has been occurring for millions of years and maintains the Earth's temperature at around 33°C warmer than it would otherwise be. Without greenhouse gases warming the Earth, non-microbial life could not have existed and evolved.[35]

Since the Industrial Revolution began over 200 years ago, human activities have been increasing the amounts of greenhouse gases in the atmosphere and more recently adding artificial ones.

I think it important to differentiate between processes that are natural and those that are caused by human actions (anthropogenic), and so I will use where appropriate an additional definition, anthropogenic climate change.

anthropogenic climate change	Climate change caused by human activities.

Human activities that increase the greenhouse effect include the following: the burning of fossil fuels like coal, oil, and natural gases in manufacturing processes, diesel and petrol in vehicle engines, and aviation kerosene in airplanes that all increase the level of CO_2 in the atmosphere; deforestation that reduces vegetation's absorption of carbon dioxide from the atmosphere; the breeding for food of cattle, who discharge methane into the atmosphere; and more recently a variety of industrial processes that emit fluorinated gases like chlorofluorocarbons which, although produced only in small quantities, are more potent greenhouse gases than CO_2 and methane.

Causes of climate change

Climate change is caused by a multiplicity of interacting factors, each operating over different timescales. The principal ones are as follows.

Solar radiation

Almost all the energy that affects the climate on Earth originates from the Sun. Electromagnetic energy emitted by the Sun passes through space until it hits the Earth's atmosphere. Only about 40 percent of the solar energy intercepted at the top of the atmosphere passes through to the Earth's surface. The rest is reflected or absorbed by the atmosphere.[36]

Solar activity

The Sun doesn't radiate uniformly, but has episodes of more intense solar flares, usually observed near its surface and in close proximity to a group of sunspots.

A 2003 analysis of ice cores in Greenland by scientists at the Max Planck Institute for Solar System Research shows that the Sun has been more active in radiating energy during the second half of the 20th Century than at any time in the previous 1,150 years. Over the last century the number of sunspots rose at roughly the same time that the Earth's climate became steadily warmer. According to the research team's leader, Sami Solanki, their data suggest that changing solar activity has contributed to climate change in the past.

In Solanki's opinion, the indirect impact of more intense sunshine on the ozone layer may be affecting the climate more than sunlight itself. The change in solar brightness over the preceding 20 years is not enough to cause the observed changes in the climate, but these indirect effects may play a larger role[37] (see *Ozone layer*, page 51).

Orbital shape

The shape of the Earth's orbit round the Sun, referred to as its eccentricity, varies every 100,000 years between mildly elliptical, as at present, and nearly circular. These changes in distance from the Sun affect the amount of solar radiation reaching the Earth's surface.[38]

Earth's axial tilt

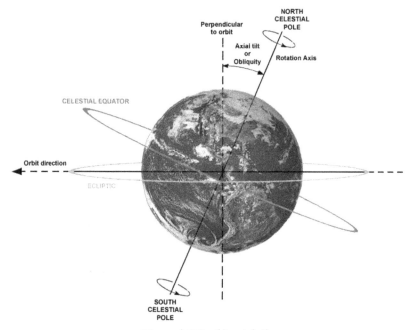

Figure 4.2 Earth's axial tilt

The Earth's axis of rotation is tilted with respect to its orbital direction (see Figure 4.2). This axial tilt, currently 23.44°, generates seasonal variations in temperature that are different at different latitudes.

Variation of axial tilt

The axial tilt varies between 22.1° and 24.5° over a cycle of about 41,000 years. When the angle increases the summers become warmer and the winters become colder. However, these effects are not uniform everywhere on the Earth's surface. Increased tilt increases the total annual solar radiation at higher latitudes and decreases the total closer to the equator.

The current axial tilt is roughly halfway between its extreme values. The tilt last reached its maximum in 8,700 BCE. It is now in the decreasing phase of its cycle and will reach its minimum around the year 11,800 CE. This decreasing tilt, by itself, promotes an overall cooling trend. Because most of the planet's snow and ice lies at high latitudes, a decreasing tilt not only means less overall heating from the Sun in summer but also less heating at higher latitudes, resulting in melting less of the previous winter's snow and ice. This has contributed to the Earth's periodic ice ages as proposed in the Milankovitch hypothesis (see page 53).[39]

Earth's precession

As it spins on its axis the Earth slowly wobbles like a top that is slowing down. This results in the North Pole changing from pointing at the star Polaris (the North Star), as it does now, to pointing at the star Vega. This wobble, called precession, changes over 23,000 years and affects the severity of the seasons in one hemisphere of the Earth compared with the other.

Quantity of greenhouse gases in the atmosphere

Water vapor makes the greatest contribution to the greenhouse effect (see page 47). As noted above, the average amount of water vapor in the atmosphere is between 2 and 3 percent, while CO_2 levels are near 0.04 percent. This means that, under average conditions, there is more than 60 times as much water vapor in the atmosphere than CO_2.[40]

Carbon dioxide content of the oceans

The oceans contain more CO_2 than the atmosphere and they can also absorb CO_2 from the atmosphere. When the CO_2 is in the oceans it does not trap heat as it does when it is in the atmosphere. If CO_2 leaves the oceans and moves back into the atmosphere this causes a warming effect.[41]

Ozone layer

Atmospheric ozone has two effects on the temperature balance of the Earth. It absorbs solar ultraviolet radiation, which heats the stratosphere, and it also absorbs infrared radiation emitted from the Earth's surface, effectively trapping heat in the troposphere. Thus the climate impact of changes in ozone concentrations varies with the altitude at which these ozone changes occur.

The major ozone losses that have been observed in the lower stratosphere due to human-produced chlorine- and bromine-containing gases have a cooling effect on the Earth's surface. On the other hand, the ozone increases that are estimated to have occurred in the troposphere because of surface-pollution gases have a warming effect on the Earth's surface, thereby contributing to the greenhouse effect.[42]

Volcanic activity

Major volcanic eruptions spew gases, aerosol droplets, and ash into the stratosphere.

Ash falls from the stratosphere within a few days to a few weeks and has no impact on climate change.

The most significant impact arises from the conversion of sulfur dioxide to sulfuric acid, which condenses rapidly in the stratosphere to form fine sulfate aerosols. These increase the reflection of radiation from the Sun back into space, thereby cooling the Earth's lower atmosphere. Several eruptions during the past century have caused a decline in the average temperature at the Earths surface of up to 0.2°C for periods of one to three years. The CO_2 released in contemporary volcanic eruptions has never caused a detectable global warming of the atmosphere.[43]

Changes in ocean currents

Ocean currents redistribute heat around the world and have a major impact on climate.

The Gulf Stream and the North Atlantic Current transport huge volumes of warm salty tropical water north to the Greenland coast and to the Nordic Seas. Heat radiating off this water helps warm the countries of northwest Europe, which are at the same latitude as Labrador and Greenland. Further north, frigid Arctic winds cool this salty water, increasing its density and causing it to sink, feeding deepwater currents that push cold water south, all the way down to Antarctica. Eventually, the cold bottom waters return to the surface through mixing and wind-driven upwelling, forming a conveyor belt that encircles the globe (see Figure 4.3).

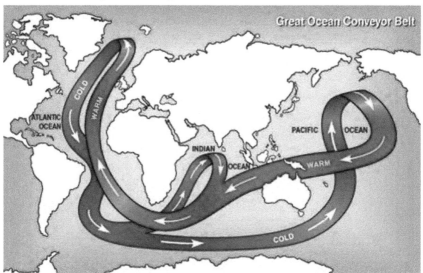

Figure 4.3 Global (or Great) Ocean Conveyor Belt

Current climate computer models that predict global warming show that such warming will melt the Greenland ice sheet. This has two consequences. First, this melted freshwater flows into the North Atlantic. Second, retreating ice

52

cover exposes more of the ocean surface, allowing more moisture to evaporate into the atmosphere to produce more snow and rain in the North Atlantic. Because salt water is denser and heavier than freshwater, this influx of freshwater would make the surface layer more buoyant. It would no longer sink, thus slowing, if not stopping, the global ocean conveyor belt and preventing the flow of warm tropical water north into the polar seas. Temperatures in northwest Europe could drop by as much as 5°C.

Ice-core records from Greenland and other proxy records suggest that abrupt changes in ocean currents triggered dramatic temperature fluctuations in the past. The example usually cited is the Younger Dryas of about 12,900–11,700 years BP, which temporarily reversed the gradual climatic warming after the Last Glacial Maximum started receding around 20,000 BP (see Figure 4.4). These change took place over decades and resulted in a temperature drop of 2–6°C and advances of glaciers over much of the Northern Hemisphere. Although its cause is still debated intensively, many climate scientists attribute this to warming that melted an immense glacial lake called Lake Agassiz in central Canada. Its natural dams collapsed and the contents of the entire lake flowed into the North Atlantic via the Saint Lawrence River. This massive infusion of fresh water diluted the polar seas to the point where the water was no longer dense enough to sink and so reduced or halted the global ocean conveyor belt.[44]

Vegetation coverage
On a global scale, patterns of vegetation and climate are closely correlated. Vegetation absorbs CO_2, and this can buffer some of the effects of global warming.[45] Conversely, removing vegetation, such as by deforestation, reduces the absorption of atmospheric CO_2.

Human activity
I will consider this in more detail in a later section of this chapter.

Climate changes in the past

Quaternary Period
The Quaternary Period is the geological term for the time from 2.588 million years ago to the present. It is divided into two epochs: the Pleistocene, from 2.588 million years ago to 11,700 BP, and the Holocene, from 11,700 BP to the present.

The Quaternary is characterized by the growth and decay of ice sheets associated with Milankovitch cycles.

Milankovitch cycles	The collective effect of variations in eccentricity of the Earth's orbit (over 100,000 years), the Earth's axial tilt (over 41,000 years), and the Earth's axial precession (over 23,000 years), resulting in cyclical variations of solar radiation reaching the Earth and strongly affecting climate patterns according to the hypothesis of Milutin Milankovitch.

Large ice sheets at least 4km thick at their maximum covered parts of Europe, North America, and Siberia. During and between these glacial periods, rapid changes in climate and sea level occurred.[46]

Many anthropologists maintain that these changes drove the emergence of the human species. However, the evidence is too scarce to establish humankind's evolutionary pathways from our hominid predecessors.[47]

Since humans emerged

An interglacial—a warmer period between glaciations—began approximately 130,000 BP and ended approximately 116,000 BP.[48] Temperatures were 1–2°C warmer than the present. The global sea level peaked at 5.5–9.0 meters above the present level, leaving smaller ice sheets than today in both Greenland and Antarctica.[49]

Figure 4.4 shows temperature changes in the last 20,000 years. It begins with the peak of the most recent glacial period when global mean temperatures were more than 3°C cooler,[50] and the sea level some 120 meters lower, than now.[51] Continental ice sheets extended well into the middle latitude regions of Europe and North America, reaching as far south as present-day London and New York City.[52]

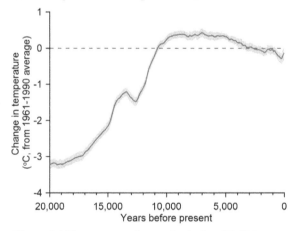

Figure 4.4 Temperature changes in the last 20,000 years
Sources: Shakun et al. (2012, *Nature*) and Marcott et al. (2013, *Science*)

Between about 19,000 and 10,000 years ago the whole globe warmed, ice sheets retreated from the Northern Hemisphere continents, and CO_2 concentrations rose, probably owing to degassing from the deep Southern Ocean.

The Northern and Southern Hemispheres show different patterns of temperature change. The Holocene Epoch—from 11,650 BP to the present—is usually referred to as an interglacial. At its height, between 9,500 BP to 5,500 BP—referred to as the Climatic Optimum or Holocene Maximum—temperatures were more than 0.5°C warmer than current temperatures.[53] These are global mean temperatures, and it is probable that temperatures were significantly higher than 0.5°C compared with today in higher latitudes and lower in the far Southern Hemisphere.*

The effects on sea levels and precipitation resulted, for example, in the Nile having three times its present volume,[54] while much of the Sahara was a fertile savannah supporting large herds of animals including water-dependent species like the hippopotamus, as evidenced by the Tassili N'Ajjer frescoes of Algeria.[55]

The Holocene Maximum saw the beginning and flourishing of great civilizations such as the Mesopotamian, Ancient Egyptian, and Indus Valley civilizations.[56]

The conventional predictions

The conventional predictions of climate change are given by the Intergovernmental Panel on Climate Change (IPCC). This body was established in 1988 by the United Nations Environment Programme (UNEP) and the World Meteorological Organization (WMO). It is administered by a staff of 12 in Geneva who support a 34-member Bureau that invites many scientists in relevant disciplines to assess the current state of knowledge about climate change and produce assessments of the published scientific literature that governments can consider as a basis for action.

The IPCC's First Assessment Report (FAR) was published in 1990 and played a decisive role in the creation of the United Nations Framework Convention on Climate Change (UNFCCC), the key international treaty to reduce global warming and cope with the consequences of climate change.[57] Article 1(2) of the UNFCCC says

"Climate change" means a change of climate which is attributed directly or

---

* Temperatures before about 150 years ago are estimated on indirect evidence—referred to as proxy data—such as ice cores, isotopic ratios, and pollen data. The models used to estimate these temperatures necessarily require many assumptions.

indirectly to human activity that alters the composition of the global atmosphere and which is in addition to natural climate variability observed over comparable time periods. [58]

The 2007 Fourth Assessment Report (AR4) encountered difficulties ascertaining accurate estimates, and so it gave six possible future climate outcomes by the end of the 21st Century if governments took no steps to reduce the increase in greenhouse gases caused by human activities. The highest predicted global temperature increase was 4.0°C (uncertainty range 2.4–6.4°C) while the lowest was 1.8°C (1.1–2.9°C). The predicted corresponding sea level rises were between 26–59cm and 18–38cm respectively. [59]

The 2013/14 Fifth Assessment Report (AR5) reduced these projected global temperature increases. Its model simulations indicate global surface temperatures relative to 1850 are likely to exceed 1.5°C by the end of the 21st Century. On the other hand it increased the predicted sea level rise to 26–82cm. The findings of its Report for Policy Makers on the physical science basis of climate change since AR4[60] may be summarized as follows

(a) Warming of the climate system is unequivocal, and many of the observed changes since the 1950s are unprecedented over decades to millennia.

(b) Concentrations of CO_2, CH_4, and N_2O now substantially exceed the highest concentrations recorded in ice cores over the past 800,000 years. The mean rates of increase in atmospheric concentrations over the past century are, with very high confidence, unprecedented over the last 22,000 years.

(c) It is extremely likely (95–100 percent probability) that human influence was the dominant cause of global warming between 1951 and 2010.

(d) Continued emissions of greenhouse gases will cause further global warming and changes in all components of the climate system. Limiting climate change will require substantial and sustained reductions of greenhouse gas emissions.

(e) The report explains the reduced rate of warming in the 15 years since 1998 (actually a cooling of 0.069°C according to the UK Met Office[61]) on the grounds that "Due to natural variability, trends based on short records are very sensitive to the beginning and end dates and do not in general reflect long-term climate trends," adding that a warming El Niño occurred in 1998. [62]

El Niño	An ocean-atmosphere event that occurs at irregular and unpredictable intervals every few years and is associated with a warming of sea temperatures across the equatorial Eastern Central Pacific Ocean by 0.5°C or more above the long-term average. It has extensive effects on weather and contributes to a warming of the global temperature. It is the complement of La Niña, which has cooling effects.
La Niña	An ocean-atmosphere event that occurs at irregular and unpredictable intervals every few years and is associated with a cooling of sea temperatures across the equatorial Eastern Central Pacific Ocean by 3–5°C. It has extensive effects on weather and contributes to a cooling of the global temperature. It is the complement of El Niño, which has warming effects.

Collectively El Niño and La Niña are opposite parts of what is called the El Niño-Southern Oscillation (ENSO) cycle. This also has a neutral phase. Scientists do not yet understand in detail what triggers an ENSO cycle. Not all El Niños are the same, and the atmosphere and oceans do not always follow the same pattern from one El Niño to another.

Speaking at a news conference to launch the summary for policymakers of the AR5 Working Group 1 report on the physical science of global warming, co-chair Thomas Stocker said that climate change ""challenges the two primary resources of humans and ecosystems, land and water. *In short, it threatens our planet, our only home* [my italics]."[63]

Just before the UN-sponsored climate talks in December 2018, the WMO issued a provisional report entitled "The State of the Global Climate in 2018."[64] It says that the previous four years had been the warmest on record, and 2018 was on course to be the fourth warmest year, with a rise of 0.98°C compared with pre-Industrial temperatures. The report highlights extreme weather events that impacted nearly 62 million people, such as the major flooding in parts of India and Japan, together with major wildfires in the USA. "We are not on track to meet climate change targets and rein in temperature increases," declared WMO Secretary-General Petteri Taalas. "Greenhouse gas concentrations are once again at record levels and if the current trend continues we may see temperature increases 3–5°C by the end of the century."[65]

The WMO report concedes that the past five years include the warming effect of the strong El Niño of 2015-2016. Nonetheless, it goes on to state that the IPCC SR15 Technical Summary of October 8, 2018, notes that "Since

2000, the estimated level of human-induced warming has been equal to the level of observed warming with a likely range of ±20% percent accounting for uncertainty due to contributions from solar and volcanic activity over the historical period."

On August 9, 2021 the IPCC published Working Group 1 of its Sixth Assessment Report entitled "AR6 Climate Change 2021: The Physical Science Basis" together with a Summary for Policy Makers and a Press Release.[66]

The report claims that:

(a) the past five years have been the hottest on record since 1850;
(b) it is "virtually certain" that hot extremes, including heatwaves, have become more frequent and more intense since the 1950s, while cold events have become less frequent and less severe;
(c) extreme heatwaves, droughts, and flooding will increase, and "their attribution to human influence has strengthened" over the past decade;
(d) the warming we have experienced to date has made changes to many of our planetary support systems that are irreversible on timescales of centuries to millennia.

According to Professor Ed Hawkins of the University of Reading in the UK and one of the report's authors, "It is a statement of fact, we cannot be any more certain; it is unequivocal and indisputable that humans are warming the planet."[67]

Past five years hottest on record?

Claim (a) appears to be contradicted by the National Oceanic and Atmospheric Administration/National Weather Service. Its data show that only the first third of 2016, the last third of 2018, and the first half of 2019 are hotter than the threshold of ±0.5°C for the Oceanic Niño Index, while a similar number of months are colder. From June 2019 to June 2020 the data are within this threshold. From June 2020 to June 2022, the data for four of these months are within this threshold, while the data for 20 of these months show colder temperatures.[68]

Extreme weather events

Claims (b) and (c) strengthen the view that human activity is the cause of global warming and reinforce the 2018 WMO provisional report that extreme weather events are due to climate change on the disputed grounds that the previous four years had been the hottest on record.[69]

Yet, as we saw (page 56), Working Group 1 of the IPCC's Fifth Assessment published in 2013 explains the reduced rate of warming from 1998 to 2012 (actually a cooling) on the grounds that 15 years is too short to reflect long-term trends.

The journal *Bulletin of the American Meteorological Society* (*BAMS*) explains this apparent paradox in a special annual supplement called "Explaining Extreme Events from a Climate Perspective." It concludes that human-induced climate change has increased the intensity or likelihood of almost all the heat-related events examined and has affected many other events, including heavy rainfall, tropical cyclones, and forest fires.[70]

Sophisticated satellite sensors first began monitoring wildfires globally in 1998. Analyses of these images showed that the burned area declined by 24.3 ± 8.8 percent from 1998 to 2015.[71] The number of acres burned by wildfires in the USA in 2019 was half that in 2017, 2015, and 2006.[72] Moreover, according to the National Park Service in 2018, nearly 85 percent of wildland fires in the USA were caused by humans through campfires left unattended, the burning of debris, equipment use and malfunctions, negligently discarded cigarettes, and intentional acts of arson.[73] It is misleading for *BAMS* to imply that such fires are attributable to human-induced climate change.

The most intense—and also the largest—tropical cyclone on record is Typhoon Tip in the northwestern Pacific Ocean in 1979.[74] The 1970 Bhola cyclone is considered to be the deadliest tropical cyclone, killing around 300,000 people after striking the Ganges Delta region of Bangladesh.[75] Furthermore, page 769 of Appendix 3 of the National Climate Assessment issued by the US government in 2014 states

> There has been no significant trend in the number of tropical cyclones nor has any trend been identified in the number of US land-falling hurricanes.[76]

Hence it is highly questionable that the devastation caused by the wildfires and tropical cyclones of late 2017 and 2018 was due to the preceding four years being the (disputed) hottest on record due to climate change.

Accuracy of climate model predictions

Climate models have become more sophisticated over the years. It is instructive to see how their predictions have compared with subsequent observations.

In October 2017 Carbon Brief, a UK-based website covering the latest developments in climate science, climate policy and energy policy, analyzed the performance of eight generations of climate models from 1975 to 2013 and compared their forecasts for the rate of surface warming for the period 1970–2016 with the observed rate (see Table 4.1).

Table 4.1 Accuracy of climate model predictions

Model	Difference in predicted 1970–2016 mean warming rate vs. observed warming rate
Broecker 1975	+30%
Hansen et al. 1981	−20%
Hansen et al. 1988	+30%
IPCC 1st Report, 1990	+17%
IPCC 2nd Report, 1995	−28%*
IPCC 3rd Report, 2001	−14%
IPCC 4th Report, 2007	+8%
IPCC 5th Report, 2013	+16%

*Differences calculated over the period 1990–2016 because estimates prior to 1990 are not readily available

Source: https://www.carbonbrief.org/analysis-how-well-have-climate-models-projected-global-warming

Carbon Brief concluded that climate models published since 1973 "have generally been quite skillful in projecting future warming."

Not all scientists would agree that predictions varying from +30 percent to −28 percent compared with observed outcomes show the models to be accurate. And while the 2007 prediction of a warming rate that was 8 percent greater than that observed suggests the IPCC climate models have improved, this is offset by the 2013 prediction that doubled this warming rate error to 16 percent.

Overall these figures show just how difficult it is to construct models that predict accurate global warming rates.

Challenges to the conventional predictions

Some scientists have challenged all the IPCC reports. Any impartial assessment must examine challenges to the current orthodoxy and attempt to ascertain to what extent, if any, they are valid.

Regrettably, reasoned debate has too often degenerated into opposing camps accusing each other of vested interests and propaganda. Many who support the IPCC's projections dismiss those climate scientists who question those projections as climate change deniers financed by industries like petrochemicals that stand to lose if the IPCC's recommendations are implemented and governments impose restrictions on petrol- and diesel-powered automobiles.

Hence I shall consider challenges from reputable scientists untainted, as far as I have been able to ascertain, by any such conflicts of interest.

In 2010 Judith Curry, Chair of the School of Earth and Atmospheric Sciences at the Georgia Institute of Technology, gave evidence to the US Congressional

Subcommittee on Energy and Environment. She asked whether the framing of the problem by the UNFCCC and the IPCC had marginalized research on broader issues surrounding climate change and resulted in an overconfident assessment of the importance of greenhouse gases in future climate change. "We know that climate changes naturally on decadal to century time scales, but we do not have explanations for observed historical and paleo climate variations, including the warming from 1910–1940 and the mid 20th century cooling."

Curry told the Congressional Subcommittee that her discussing concerns about how uncertainty is characterized by the IPCC resulted in her being labeled a climate heretic. It is, she said, important to broaden the scope of global climate change research beyond its focus on anthropogenic greenhouse warming to develop a better understanding of natural climate variability and to further explore the uncertainty of the climate models and the capability of those models to predict events such as catastrophic climate change. "And far more attention needs to be given to establishing robust and transparent climate data records (both historical and paleoclimate proxies)."[77]

In 2015 Curry said that she doesn't dispute for a moment that human-generated CO_2 warms the planet, but the evidence suggests this may be happening more slowly than the alarmists fear. The debate at the United Nations Climate Change Conference in Paris would be conducted on the basis that there is a known, mechanistic relationship between the concentration of CO_2 in the atmosphere and how global average temperatures will rise. She claimed that there isn't such a known, mechanistic relationship: any such projection would be meaningless unless it accounted for natural variability.[78]

On January 1, 2017, Curry resigned from Georgia Tech due to "my growing disenchantment with the academic field of climate science and scientists" in order to figure out new and better ways to apply weather and climate data through a company Climate Forecast Applications Network that she had cofounded with her husband, meteorologist and climate dynamicist Peter Webster.[79] In April 2018 TheBestSchools.org named her as one of the top 50 women in STEM (science, technology, engineering, and mathematics). She is the only one listed in the fields of geophysical sciences and climatology.[80]

IPCC methodology
Environmental economist Ross McKitrick was an expert reviewer for Working Group 1 of the IPCC for AR4. His experience led him to publish in 2011 a 45-page report "What is Wrong with the IPCC?" in which he criticized the IPCC Bureau for having a great deal of arbitrary power over the content and conclusions of the assessment reports.

In particular he found that the IPCC Bureau lacked transparency and had selected many lead authors who were employed by, or who served as advisors to, environmental activist organizations. He claimed that many of these lead authors review their own work and that of their critics, putting them in a conflict of interest. The IPCC's peer review rules give lead authors the final say, thus weakening the rigor of the system.[81]

Another critic of AR4 is a former IPCC Chair, Robert Watson, who said in February 2010 that all the errors in AR4, exposed by a simple checking of the sources cited by the 2,500 scientists who produced the report, resulted in several exaggerations of the impact of global warming and overstated the severity of the problem. For example, the report falsely claimed that Himalayan glaciers would disappear by 2035 when the evidence suggests that they will survive for another 300 years. It also claimed that global warming could cut rain-fed North African crop production by up to 50 percent by 2020; a senior IPCC contributor subsequently admitted that there is no evidence to support this claim.

Watson said "The mistakes all appear to have gone in the direction of making it seem like climate change is more serious by overstating the impact. That is worrying. The IPCC needs to look at this trend in the errors and ask why it happened." He maintained that the next report should acknowledge that some scientists believed the planet was warming at a much slower rate than has been claimed by the majority. If contrary evidence cannot be dismissed it should be included in the report.[82]

AR5 contained no such contrary views.

By 2016 the previously mentioned independent scientist and environmentalist James Lovelock had changed his view on climate change. He maintains that, unlike most environmentalists, he is a rigorous empiricist. The green movement is "a religion, really… It's totally unscientific." He went on to say that "CO_2 is going up, but nowhere near as fast as they thought it would. The computer models just weren't reliable."[83]

Reliability of IPCC's temperature datasets

Doubts have also been expressed about the reliability of the IPCC's temperature datasets, including by John Christy, Distinguished Professor of Atmospheric Science and Director of the Earth System Science Center at The University of Alabama in Huntsville, who received a Special Award from the American Meteorological Society "for developing a global, precise record of Earth's temperature from operational polar-orbiting satellites, fundamentally advancing our ability to monitor climate."

Christy, who had been a lead author for the IPCC, maintained in 2010 that the land-based weather stations around the world used by the IPCC to collect temperature data had been seriously compromised by local factors such as urbanization and changes in land use that produce temperature rises. He says he is not a climate change denier, but argues that predictions of future warming have been greatly overstated.[84]

In 2004 McKitrick also concluded that the IPCC's climate data are contaminated with surface effects from industrialization and data quality problems that add up to a warming bias. He subsequently published a summary of his papers, mainly co-authored with Patrick Michaels, on global warming and the quality of temperature data together with criticisms of those papers and his rebuttals of the criticisms.[85]

Essentially, Christy, McKitrick, and others argued that the land-based weather stations used to collect temperatures are sited in urban areas where industrialization and other factors produce temperatures higher than in rural areas—what became known as urban heat islands (UHIs).

On the other hand, Richard Black, then Director of the Energy and Climate Intelligence Unit, argued that, as researchers understand this phenomenon, they can remove any signal of urbanization from their data and indeed have done so.[86] In his 2018 book *Denied: The Rise and Fall of Contrarianism* he cites a 2013 study by Wickham et al. of Berkeley Earth.[87] This shows that, while the UHI effect is locally large and real, it does not contribute significantly to the average land temperature rise because the planet's urban regions amount to less than 1 percent of the land area. Black also found that while weather stations considered "poor" might be less accurate, they recorded the same average warming trend as other stations.[88]

However, a field experiment conducted by climate scientist Ronald Leeper and colleagues for the National Oceanic and Atmospheric Administration and published in June 2019 with the title "Impacts of Small-Scale Urban Encroachment on Air Temperature Observations" largely supported the UHI effect. It concluded that this effect results in daytime temperatures 0.5°C – 4.0°C higher and nighttime temperatures 1.0°– 2.5°C higher in urban areas than in rural areas. "The urban heat island effect will strengthen in the future as the structure and spatial extent as well as population density of urban areas change and grow (high confidence)."[89]

Reliability of IPCC's climate models
Several scientists have criticized the IPCC's climate models. Among them are John Christy and Roy Spencer, colleagues at The University of Alabama, who tested the rates of warming shown by 102 climate models used by the IPCC in its Fifth Assessment Report (AR5, 2013). They did so by comparing their consensus results of the temperatures in the bulk atmospheric layer (the

mid-troposphere, where greenhouse gases would be expected to play a major role) over the years 1979–2016 with actual observations of temperatures made using satellites, balloons, and reanalyzes (mergers of many observations made by independent major weather centers around the world). They found that the average climate model trend failed to represent the actual trend by a highly significant margin. Hence, Christy argued in 2017, these models should not be used for predicting future climate changes.

He claims that the IPCC's AR5 actually supported this conclusion by showing that (a) the tropical trends of climate models *with* extra greenhouse gases failed to match actual trends and (b) climate models without extra (i.e. anthropogenic) greenhouse gases agreed with actual trends. As an AR5 reviewer, Christy had insisted that the relevant figure be shown in the main text, but "the government-appointed lead authors decided against it. They opted to place it in the Supplementary Material where little attention would be paid, and to fashion the chart in such a way as to make it difficult to understand and interpret."[90]

In 2010 Terence C Mills, Professor of Applied Statistics and Econometrics at Loughborough University in the UK, examined the same data as the IPCC. He found that the warming trend reported over the past 30 years or so was just as likely to be caused by random fluctuations as by the impact of greenhouse gases.[91]

Simon Robertson of the University of New South Wales was appointed as a Working Group III Lead Author for Chapter 3 of the IPCC's Sixth Annual Report (AR6), which covers the IPCC's integrated assessment models (IAMs). In 2021 he pointed out that the cloaking of value-laden assumptions and output uncertainties in the IPCC's IAMs has been trenchantly criticized for approximately two decades. "This lack of transparency patently limits the credibility of the IPCC's modeling results and associated policy recommendations."[92]

In response to Robertson's paper, published during AR6's draft cycle, and similar criticisms, the Working Group III Co-chairs and colleagues published a response, which stated

IAMs require large arrays of input assumptions. Varying some may have little impact on results; others may make a big difference. Full transparency would require published documentation of all assumptions, but this is patchy in practice.[93]

This response shows that not even the non-IAM Lead Authors of the chapter had been granted access to the data for analysis during the AR6 drafting, which confirms Robertson's allegation.

Perhaps the most trenchant criticism of the IPCC has been made by Steven E Koonin, who served from May 2009 to November 2011 as President Obama's Undersecretary for Science in the US Department of Energy, where he helped guide the government's investments in energy technologies and climate science. He began by believing that we were in a race to save the planet from climate catastrophe.[94] Then, in late 2013, he was asked by the American Physical Society (APS) to lead an update of its public statement on the climate. In January 2014 he convened a workshop to stress test the state of climate science. He says he came away not only surprised but also shaken by what he discovered:

• Humans exert a growing, but physically small, warming influence on the climate. The deficiencies of climate data challenge out ability to untangle the response to human influences from poorly understood natural changes.

• The results from the multitude of climate models disagree with, or even contradict, each other and many kinds of observations. A vague "expert judgment" was sometimes applied to adjust model results and obfuscate shortcomings.

• Government and UN press releases and summaries do not accurately reflect the reports themselves. Distinguished climate experts (including report authors themselves) are embarrassed by some media portrayals of the science.

• In short, the science is insufficient to make useful projections about how the climate will change over the coming decades, much less predict what effects our actions will have on it.[95]

Concerned that public and political debates were being misinformed, Koonin published a 2,000-word article in the *Wall Street Journal* in September 2014 that outlined some of the uncertainties in climate science and argued that ignoring them could hinder our ability to understand and respond to a changing climate.[96] Some climate scientists said they agreed with him but dared not say so in public. Many of his scientific colleagues were outraged that, by highlighting problems with the science, he had given ammunition to the deniers.

More than six years of study since that APS workshop left Koonin increasingly dismayed at the public discussions of climate and energy, where climate alarmism had come to dominate US politics, especially among Democrats where he had otherwise felt at home, with President Biden proposing to spend almost 2 trillion dollars fighting this "existential threat to humanity."

In April 2021 Koonin detailed his findings in a book *UNSETTLED What Climate Science Tells Us, What It Doesn't, And Why It Matters.*[97] This dispassionate study concludes, among many other things

Projections of future climate and weather events rely on models demonstrably unfit for the purpose.[98]

One of many examples of false claims cited by Koonin is an article in *Foreign Affairs* entitled "Climate Change Is Already Killing Us" by the Director-General of the World Health Organization, Tedros Ghebreyesus. "Astoundingly," says Koonin, "the article conflates deaths due to ambient and household air-pollution (which cause an estimated 100 per 100,000 premature deaths each year, or about one-eighth of total deaths from all causes) with deaths due to human-induced climate change."[99]

He concludes

> It's clear that media, politicians, and often the assessment reports themselves blatantly misrepresent what the science says about climate and catastrophes. Those failures indict the scientists who write and too-casually review the reports, the reporters who uncritically repeat them, the editors who allow that to happen, the activists and their organizations who fan the fires of alarm, and the experts whose public silence endorses the deception. The constant repetition of these and many other climate fallacies turns them into accepted "truths."[100]

He attributes these to a self-reinforcing alignment of perspectives and interests that he persuasively amplifies by considering the media, politicians, scientific institutions, and individual scientists. His remedy is to advocate a fundamental reform of the ways in which the reports of the UN's IPCC and the US government are reviewed. He adds that the study that produced the alleged "97 percent consensus" among scientists on climate change has been convincingly debunked.[*]

Koonin says he has deliberately written his book in a descriptive manner rather than a prescriptive one: he has presented facts, the certainties and uncertainties of what they imply, and the options and choices to be made in response; this is the appropriate stance for a scientist to take. He concludes the book by moving to "what I think we *should* do, in short, is to begin by restoring integrity to the way science informs society's decisions on climate and energy... then take the steps most likely to result in positive outcomes for society, whatever the future might hold for planet."[101]

Global warming and CO$_2$ concentrations
The focus of the majority who warn of a catastrophic, if not existential, threat

---

[*] His source echoes the rebuttal of this "97% consensus" claim that I give in Chapter 6.

to the human species has been the correlation between rising temperatures and CO_2 concentration in the atmosphere produced by humans.

The UK Met Office estimates global mean temperatures.* If criticisms of their reliability are ignored and the global mean temperatures for each of the 23 years from 1997 to 2019 plotted against the concentrations of CO_2 in the atmosphere in parts per million measured from the observatory at the peak of the Mauna Loa volcano (the generally accepted measure), this results in Figure 4.5.

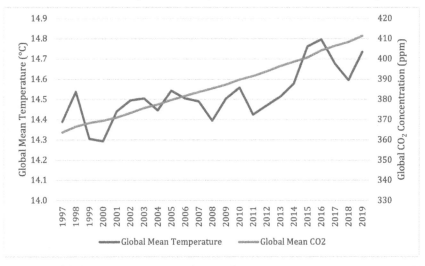

Figure 4.5 Global mean temperatures and atmospheric CO2 concentrations, 1997–2019[102]

This graph shows:

(a) an overall temperature rise of 0.346°C while the CO_2 concentration rises from 364 ppm to 411 ppm;
(b) the temperature fluctuates considerably over these 23 years while the CO_2 concentration rises steadily;
(c) at the end of 2017 the global temperature dropped back to the level before the warming effect of the strong El Niño of 2015–2016, and then began to rise with the El Niño of 2018–2019;
(d) a pattern of temperature rises and falls that correlates with the more moderate El Niños of 1997–1998, 2002–2003, 2004–2005, and 2009–2010.[103]

---

* These are calculated by adding the increase or decrease in temperature (referred to as the HadCRUT4 temperature anomaly taken from the latest dataset produced by the collaboration between the Hadley Centre of the UK Met Office and the Climatic Research Unit at the UK's University of East Anglia) relative to a 1961–1990 global mean of 14°C.

The temperature rise of 0.346°C is one third less than the rise of 0.540°C predicted by the IPCC's Fifth Assessment Report.* This suggests that the IPCC's predictions of temperature rises did not take into account these ocean–atmosphere events, which is understandable because such events are unpredictable. However, it does question the overall IPCC prediction of "a rate of increase of global-mean temperature during the next century of about 0.3°C per decade (with an uncertainty range of 0.2°C to 0.5°C per decade); this is greater than that seen over the past 10,000 years. This will result in a likely increase in global-mean temperature of about 1°C above the present value by 2025 and 3°C before the end of the next century."

This part of the IPCC's report subsequently qualifies this prediction by stating

> 3.1. There are many uncertainties in our predictions particularly with regard to the timing, magnitude and regional patterns of climate change, due to our incomplete understanding of:
> • sources and sinks of greenhouse gases, which affect predictions of future concentrations;
> • clouds, which strongly influence the magnitude of climate change;
> • oceans, which influence the timing and patterns of climate change;
> • polar ice sheets, which affect predictions of sea-level rises. [104]

However, nearly all reports in the media present only the summary prediction, while many climate warming alarmists claim without any evidence that this prediction underestimates climate warming.

Is a global temperature meaningful?

The concept of a global temperature is itself questionable. Land temperatures vary in different regions of the Earth, not just with latitude but also with altitudes and areas of industrialization. They differ from temperatures at the surface of the sea and at different altitudes in the atmosphere. And these differing temperatures fluctuate.

The orthodox view is that the Earth has been warming over the past half- century because there is an upward trend in the graph of a statistic called the "global temperature". This arises from projecting a sampling of the fluctuating temperature fields of the Earth onto a single number at discrete annual intervals.

---

* The IPCC's Fifth Assessment Report of 2013 predicts global temperature rises within upper and lower limits. The rise of 0.540°°C is calculated from the mean of the upper and lower predicted rises for 2019 and 1997, collated in https://www.carbonbrief.org/analysis-how-well-have-climate-models-projected-global-warming accessed 3 December 2020.

It assumes that this averaging of temperatures is a temperature itself and that the out-of-equilibrium climate system has only one temperature. Moreover, the global temperature statistic is also described as the average, as if there is only one kind of average. According to mathematician Christopher Essex and colleagues, whose 2007 paper in the *Journal of Non-Equilibrium Thermodynamics* considers the question of a global temperature in detail, there is an infinity of mathematically legitimate options, and over 100 different averages of temperatures have been used in meteorology and climate studies. They argue that there is no physical basis for choosing any one of these averages from the infinite number of mathematical options.[105]

It is certainly the case that there is no single temperature at any one time in the year at all locations on Earth, and that different areas will be affected differently by whatever warming has taken place, and some will be affected considerably more than others.

The science of climate change
Climate science comprises a vast and complex intersection of disciplines spanning meteorology, atmospheric chemistry, oceanography, geochemistry, glaciology, hydrology, geology, and economics, among others.

To its great credit the IPCC has sought to integrate the work of specialists in various disciplines to produce predictions for future warming and its consequences. However, compared with, say, physics and chemistry, climate science is a relatively young and inexact science for making predictions.

It is unsurprising that there should be challenges to the IPCC's predictions and a tendency by the institution of the IPCC, like any institution and its supporters, to defend those predictions. Moreover, among climate scientists the range of views is broader than the simplistic binary picture of IPCC supporters and climate change deniers that is frequently portrayed.

Species extinction threat
At the beginning of this section on climate change I summarized predictions that the human species faced extinction due to climate change.

Swedish school strike icon Greta Thunberg has very many admirable qualities. These include courage, unwavering practice of her beliefs, and a determination to hold governments and other organizations to account for reducing greenhouse gas emissions. She is not, however, a scientist, and indeed she took a year off school. Nonetheless she maintains that her existential predictions are based on science.

While the IPCC doesn't focus on humans, its Fifth Assessment Report does consider species extinction generally. Nonhuman species would be more vulnerable to climate change than humans because they lack our technologies to combat any such threat.

According to the IPCC:

> [A]cross all taxa there is only *low confidence* that rates of species extinctions have increased over the last several decades. Most extinctions over the last several centuries have been attributed to habitat loss, overexploitation, pollution, or invasive species, and these are the most important current drivers of extinctions…Overall, there is *very low confidence* that observed species extinctions can be attributed to recent climate warming, owing to the very low fraction of global extinctions that have been ascribed to climate change and the tenuous nature of most attributions [emphasis in the original].[106]

As for the future:

> [T]here is generally *very low confidence* that observed species extinctions can be attributed to recent climate change. Models project that the risk of species extinctions will increase in the future owing to climate change, but there is *low agreement* concerning the fraction of species at increased risk, the regional and taxonomic focus for such extinctions and the time frame over which extinctions could occur [emphasis in the original].[107]

These quotes contradict the claims made by Greta Thunberg that we are in the midst of the sixth mass extinction caused by climate change and, without immediate action, there will be an irreversible catastrophic chain reaction beyond human control by 2030. And they contradict the even more extreme predictions made by Extinction Rebellion cofounder Gail Bradbrook who was quoted as declaring that 95 percent of the world's species, including humans, would perish within her daughter's lifetime unless everyone on the planet stopped producing CO_2 by 2025.[108]

The long-term view
Commenting on possible existential threats to humankind, Peter Ulmschneider of the Institute for Theoretical Astrophysics at Heidelberg University observed that another likely danger might be a runaway greenhouse effect due to global warming from natural causes and human activity. However, he noted that for millions of years in the early Tertiary Period temperatures were considerably higher than those of today, coinciding with teeming life and allowing for tropical forests as far north as Egypt. He maintained that significantly higher temperatures may actually be more of a norm for our planet and that

we are presently in an unusually cold period of our planetary climate. He concluded that a runaway greenhouse effect does not seem to represent an overly convincing threat for the extinction of life.[109]

Conclusions

1. Previous predictions of the existential threats of a population explosion have been wrong and no evidence exists that this has changed.

2. Human actions since the Industrial Revolution began have increased the amounts of greenhouse gases in the atmosphere. These cause a warming at the surface of the Earth that will continue to increase in the future unless such human actions are restricted and/or countermeasures are implemented.

3. However, a multiplicity of interacting causes, each operating over different timescales, affect the climate, and some of these have a cooling effect. Some, such as solar activity and ocean-atmosphere events, are unpredictable. Hence it is difficult to predict with confidence what temperature rise will result in the future if human activities are not restricted or countered.

4. It is inconsistent for the IPCC to dismiss the lack of a global temperature increase from 1998 to 2013 (in fact this trend continued to 2018) on the grounds that 15 years is too brief a period to reflect long-term trends while in 2018 the WMO uses the four years 2014–2018 as the disputed warmest on record as the basis for predicting that a continuation of this trend could result in a global temperature increase of 3–5°C by 2099.

5. A future increase in temperature will cause sea level rises due to melting ice sheets. This will produce flooding with a consequent tragic loss of lives, crops, and infrastructure for underdeveloped communities least able to cope in the Arctic, parts of Africa, small islands, Asian megadeltas, and low-lying coastal areas.

6. The use of a statistically averaged annual global temperature is questionable. Land temperatures vary considerably in different regions according to latitude, altitude, and level of industrialization. Moreover, some regions will benefit from an increase in temperature while others will suffer. As a responsible global species, we humans should strive to protect our most vulnerable communities by working towards net zero greenhouse gas emissions in order to reduce one of the causes of global warming.

7. If we take a long-term view, we see that the warm interglacials of the Quaternary Period, with their much higher temperatures and

greater rise in sea levels than now, did not result in the extinction of our predecessor hominids or subsequent early humans, nor did the higher temperatures of the Holocene Maximum drive humans to extinction; to the contrary, that was a time when several great human civilizations began and flourished.

8. To answer the central question of this chapter, predictions that a population explosion or climate change—still less anthropogenic climate change—or a combination of the two will result in the extinction of the human species have a negligible probability of being realized.

5

Artificial intelligence

The development of full artificial intelligence could spell the end of the human race.
Stephen Hawking, 2014

A plausible default outcome of the creation of machine superintelligence is existential catastrophe.
Nick Bostrom, 2014

In December 2014 cosmologist Stephen Hawking said that efforts to create thinking machines pose a threat to our very existence. "The development of full artificial intelligence could spell the end of the human race. Humans, who are limited by slow biological evolution, couldn't compete, and would be superseded."[1]

Sir Clive Sinclair, inventor of the Sinclair ZX computers in the 1980s, agreed: "Once you start to make machines that are rivaling and surpassing humans with intelligence it's going to be very difficult for us to survive."[2]

Hawking repeated his warning in his posthumously published 2018 book *Brief Answers to the Big Questions*

> Success in creating AI would be the biggest event in human history. Unfortunately, it might also be the last, unless we learn how to avoid the risks… The concern is that AI would take off on its own and redesign itself at an ever-increasing rate. Humans, who are limited by slow biological evolution, couldn't compete and would be superseded. And in future AI could develop a will of its own, a will that is in conflict with ours.[3]

In January 2015 Microsoft cofounder Bill Gates contradicted the view of Microsoft Research Labs director Eric Horvitz, who had said he "fundamentally" did not see AI as a threat. According to Gates, "I am in the camp that is concerned about super intelligence. First the machines will do a lot of jobs for us and not be super intelligent. That should be positive if we manage it well. A few decades after that though the intelligence is strong enough to be a concern. I agree with Elon Musk and some others on this and don't understand why some people are not concerned."[4]

In 2020 the Global Challenges Foundation portrayed artificial intelligence as a global catastrophic risk.[5]

The power of AI

The public has become increasingly aware of the power of artificial intelligence in a number of ways.

In 1997 Deep Blue, a chess-playing computer designed by IBM engineers, defeated Gary Kasparov, probably the greatest chess player of all time, 3½ to 2½ in a six-game contest.[6]

In 2011 Watson, a question-answering computer system also developed by IBM engineers, competed on America's most popular quiz show *Jeopardy!* and defeated champions Brad Rutter and Ken Jennings to win the first-place prize of $1 million.[7]

Engineers at DeepMind Technologies, an AI company subsequently bought by Google's parent company, developed a computer program AlphaGo to compete at Go, an ancient Chinese strategy game played in more than 75 countries. It uses a board with a grid of 361 squares compared with chess's 8 × 8 grid of 64 squares and, on average, offers a far greater number of options per move than chess. In 2017 AlphaGo was pitted against Ke Jie, who had continuously held the world number 1 ranking for two years, and defeated him three games to nil.[8]

Of more direct impact on the public was the release in the second decade of the 21st Century of Apple's Siri, Amazon's Alexa, Microsoft's Cortana, and Google Assistant, computerized applications that can recognize spoken questions, have access to large databases, and respond using speech to answer a wide range of questions or to implement computer instructions.

As automatically driven cars developed, so too did their public awareness. Equipped with a range of data-collecting devices such as cameras, radar, GPS (Global Positioning System) receivers, optical recognition sensors, and infrared detectors, the vehicles' AI systems are programmed to process these data and drive such vehicles without human intervention.

Google, for example, began developing driverless cars in 2009, and in 2016 it spun off Waymo as a separate subsidiary of its parent company, Alphabet, for this purpose. In October 2018 it boasted that its fleet had self-driven more than 10 million miles of testing on public roads, with a human driver present and ready to take over if necessary, in order to develop its algorithms.

In November 2017 Waymo began testing its autonomous minivans around Phoenix, Arizona without a human driver on board.[9]

Many cars are assembled by robots. George Devol filed the first series of patent applications for robots in 1954, and two years later he and Joseph F Engelberger formed the company Unimation to make them. Today robots are used for a range of industrial tasks, including assembly, welding, painting, palletizing, packing and labeling, testing, and inspection. In 2018 the International Federation of Robotics estimated that 1,828,000 industrial robots were operating worldwide in 2016, and it predicted that this number would grow to more than 3 million by 2020.[10] This figure was achieved, despite the impacts of the Covid-19 pandemic.[11]

Such robots are distinct from a service robot, defined by the International Organization for Standardization as a robot "that performs useful tasks for humans or equipment excluding industrial automation applications."[12] Their use has also been growing.

Japan, for instance, faced with an aging population and a shrinking workforce, established its Robot Revolution Initiative in 2015. One product of this is Pepper, a 4-foot-tall semi-humanoid robot programmed to read and respond to emotions, which has been successfully employed in nursing homes for the elderly, many residents of which suffer from dementia.[13]

Japan planned to use English-speaking robots to help out in some 500 Japanese classrooms from 2019 as the country seeks to improve its English-language skills among both children and teachers.[14]

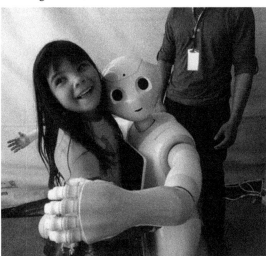

Figure 5.1 Pepper, a semi-humanoid robot programmed to read and respond to emotions

Robots have occupied the public imagination for many years through science fiction. Notable examples include Isaac Asimov's novel *I Robot* (1950) followed by a series of novels and short stories written between 1953 and 1985, while movie portrayals range from Stanley Kubrick's 1968 classic *2001: A Space Odyssey* through the six *Terminator* movies and the 2015 *Ex Machina* to the 2020 *Monsters of Man*. Most of these movies portray robots seeking to destroy humans.

The meaning of AI

AI is used loosely to mean many things. I define here the precise meaning used in this book, followed by two distinct types of AI that will help clarify any existential threat to humankind.

intelligence	The ability to learn facts and skills and apply them for a purpose.
artificial intelligence (sometimes called machine intelligence)	Intelligence demonstrated by machines: the ability to acquire and successfully apply knowledge for a purpose such as learning, planning, solving problems, recognizing speech, and manipulating and moving objects.
human-level AI (sometimes called strong AI)	Artificial intelligence that is indistinguishable from human intelligence.
superintelligence (sometimes called ultraintelligence)	Machine intelligence that vastly outperforms humans in every significant cognitive domain.

In order to function, intelligent machines use algorithms.

algorithm	A step-by-step procedure for solving a problem or accomplishing an objective.

A cake recipe or an IKEA manual is an algorithm, but I shall focus on their use in AI. Intelligent machines take a sequence of mathematical operations—using equations, arithmetic, algebra, calculus, logic, and probability—and translate them into computer code. Their designers set them an objective, feed them with relevant data, and set them to work crunching through the calculations to achieve their objective. [15]

Mathematical modeler Hannah Fry classifies two basic types of algorithm:

(a) rule-based algorithms, in which instructions are constructed by humans and are direct and unambiguous;

(b) machine-learning algorithms, which are inspired by how living creatures learn. Fry compares these to training a dog. This process does not involve giving the animal detailed instructions, but rather "reinforcing good behavior, ignoring bad, and giving her enough practice to work out what to do for herself." [16]

The outcome can be beneficial to humans. For example, an AI system developed by Professor Paul Leeson at Oxford University's John Radcliffe Hospital was given the objective of diagnosing an echocardiogram—a type of heart scan—and programmed to detect 80,000 subtle features invisible to the human eye. The results from trials in six cardiology units indicate that the system can perform far better than clinicians: of 60,000 heart scans carried out each year, 12,000 are misdiagnosed by cardiologists. [17]

In this chapter, however, I am evaluating the claimed harmful AI outcomes that pose an existential threat to the human species. To do so it is useful to summarize previous predictions about the development of AI.

Previous predictions about AI

Modern AI developed in the 1950s. The first generation of AI researchers were convinced that human-level intelligence, which they called "strong AI," would exist in just a few decades, and ultraintelligence would soon follow.

Pioneer Herbert Simon wrote in 1965 "[M]achines will be capable, within twenty years, of doing any work a man can do." [18]

British mathematician I J Good, who worked with Alan Turing on the design of computers, wrote in 1965

Let an ultraintelligent machine be defined as a machine that can far surpass all the intellectual activities of any man however clever. Since the design of machines is one of these intellectual activities, an ultraintelligent machine could design even better machines; there would then unquestionably be an "intelligence explosion," and the intelligence of man would be left far behind. [19]

He went on to say

It is more probable than not that, within the twentieth century, an ultraintelligent machine will be built. [20]

Marvin Minsky, cofounder of MIT's Computer Science and Artificial Intelligence Laboratory, predicted in 1970

> In from three to eight years we will have a machine with the general intelligence of an average human being. I mean a machine that will be able to read Shakespeare, grease a car, play office politics, tell a joke, have a fight. At that point the machine will be able to educate itself with fantastic speed. In a few months it will be at genius level and a few months after that its powers will be incalculable…Man's limited mind may not be able to control such immense mentalities. [21]

Eric Drexler, in his *Engines of Creation* (1986) considered in Chapter 2, asserted that

> thinking machines pose basic threats to people and to life on Earth… our machines are evolving faster than we are. Within a few decades they seem likely to surpass us. Unless we learn to live with them in safety, our future will likely be both exciting and short. [22]

Mathematician and science fiction writer Vernor Vinge wrote in his 1993 NASA paper "The Coming Technological Singularity"

> Within thirty years, we will have the technological means to create superhuman intelligence. Shortly thereafter, the human era will be ended. [23]

Current probability of human extinction by AI
Philosopher Nick Bostrom, founding director of Oxford University's Future of Humanity Institute, has been researching this topic, and also drawing on the work of others, since 1998. He compiled and developed his ideas in a 2014 book *SUPERINTELLIGENCE: Paths, Dangers, Strategies*. [24] In it he combines the results of four polls of different AI experts taken between 2011 and 2013. The respondents thought there is a 10 percent probability of human-level machine intelligence being achieved by 2022, a 50 percent probability by 2040, and a 90 percent probability by 2075.

Bostrom considers 2075 too distant for human-level machine intelligence. Furthermore, he thinks that once this goal is attained superintelligence will follow very quickly. A human-level intelligent machine will learn to design an improved version of itself more efficiently than human programmers can do (though Bostrom doesn't explain why this should be so). After this key first step has occurred, such a machine will rapidly construct increasingly intelligent versions of itself until superintelligence is attained.

Bostrom warns that we should understand the difference between super-intelligence and human intelligence as more like the difference between the intelligence of a human and the intelligence of a beetle or a worm. The goals of a superintelligent machine will necessarily be fundamentally different from human goals.

Moreover, he asserts that the first machine to achieve superintelligence will have a decisive strategic advantage over other AIs developing towards superintelligence, and that it will transform its lead into permanent control by disabling competing projects and establishing a "singleton."

A consequence of this could be the extinction of the human species. This could occur in either of two ways. If such a machine decided that humans could offer opposition to the achievement of its goals, it could destroy all humans by waging a war in which it would construct and unleash self-replicating biotech or nanotech weapons such as nerve gas dispensers or target-seeking mosquito-like robots.

Alternatively, if it considered that humans posed no threat, we could become extinct because our habitat would be destroyed when this machine begins massive global construction projects using nanotech factories and assemblers that would tile all of the Earth's surface with solar panels, nuclear reactors, supercomputing facilities with protruding cooling towers, space rocket launchers, or other installations in pursuit of the goals it has set itself. Human brains, if they contain information relevant to its goals, could be disassembled and scanned, and the extracted data transferred to some more efficient and secure storage format.

But what if humans built into the early AI machines values that would preserve if not foster the human species? Bostrom simply says that there is no known way of transferring human values to a digital computer.

He explores various ways of trying to prevent human extinction but finds none satisfactory. He compares humans at the later stages of this process, when many advanced AI machines are being developed, to children, each of whom holds the pin of a grenade. Most would keep their finger pressed tight on the pin, but the probability that we *all* have the sense to do that is negligible.

Limitations of current AI

Bostrom's predictions, like those of others, are projections from the then-current state of AI. But he, like those others, tends to ignore the limitations of AI.

The most fundamental limitation of today's intelligent machines is that each can achieve only the objective specified by its human programmers. However superior to any human AlphaGo is at playing Go, it cannot even play chess, still less write a novel or experience love or reflect on its own existence. A

4-foot-tall humanoid Pepper programmed to detect human emotions and respond in a positive way cannot jump, still less paint abstract art or decide to design a spacecraft to explore the solar system.

To achieve human-level intelligence, a machine must be as multifunctional as a human's intelligence.

Even when carrying out their programmed objectives, current AI systems are limited. In 2018 Stone Temple, a digital marketing company, put the question-answering ability of Apple's Siri, Amazon's Alexa, Microsoft's Cortana, and Google Assistant to a rigorous test. The results showed that Alexa tried to answer only 53.4 percent of the questions asked, while Siri attempted less than half. Google Assistant attempted the most answers. Of those questions attempted, the highest success rate was achieved by Google Assistant, which correctly answered only 74.6 percent, while Siri correctly answered a feeble 32.7 percent.[25]

In 2016 data science researchers Feng Liu, Yong Shi, and Ying Liu of the Chinese Academy of Sciences tested and ranked the IQs of AI systems compared with human IQs assessed in 2014. They found that Google has a higher IQ (47.28) than China's Baidu (32.92), Microsoft's Bing web search engine (31.98), and Apple's Siri (24.94), but Google's score was below that of an average 6-year-old human (55.5), an average 12-year-old human (84.5), and an average 18-year-old human (97).

To examine the existential threat posed to humans by AI machines, Liu's team classified the intelligence models of the systems into grades according to four criteria: input, output, mastery, and creation. Input means the system can obtain information from the outside world, output means it can feed the results generated internally back to the outside world, mastery means mastering and storing knowledge and having the innovative ability to solve problems, while creation means the ability to create knowledge.

Their classification ranges from a first-grade system to a sixth-grade system feared by Hawking, Rees, Gates, Musk, and Bostrom that "continuously innovates and creates new knowledge, with I/O [input/output] ability, knowledge mastery, and application ability that all approach infinite values as time goes on."

First-grade systems, such as water drops, cannot share information with humans, while second-grade systems include smart TVs and intelligent washing machines that can exchange information with humans, but their control programs cannot be upgraded and they lack the ability to learn automatically. Third-grade systems include computers and mobile phones, which can be programmed and upgraded. Fourth-grade systems have the additional functionality of sharing information and knowledge with other intelligent systems through a network. In 2011 the European Union funded a project called RoboEarth aimed at allowing robots to share knowledge through the

Internet. Other examples include Google Brain and Baidu Brain because of their ability to adapt based on information exchanged in the cloud.

Liu's team regard humans as possessing "special," naturally occurring intelligence that conforms to fifth-grade AI due to our capacity for creativity, which all lower-grade systems lack. They argue that AlphaGo is a third-grade system: despite beating humans at Go using exotic strategies, it cannot be considered as having creativity because it relies on humans for its training. [26]

I suspect that many futurists take insufficient account of the limitations of current AI because of the hyped claims made by companies who profit from selling their AI products.

For instance, claims have been made for a big leap forward in performance and accuracy of facial recognition systems in which a system scans an image and its algorithm builds a statistical description of the patterns of light and dark across the image. The system examines a vast dataset of faces, and its algorithm uses trial and error to match the patterns in order to identify the person.

However, as Hannah Fry pointed out in 2018, someone only has to wear a pair of spectacles with a disruptive pattern printed on the frames to fool the system. Moreover, by designing the specific disruptive pattern to signal the face of somebody else, say the actress Milla Jovovich, the algorithm would conclude that a man wearing such spectacles and Milla Jovovich were the same person. [27]

Another example of underreported limitations is driverless cars. The military historian Noah Yuval Harari states in his 2016 book *Homo Deus: A Brief History of Tomorrow*

> If we forbid humans to drive taxis and cars altogether, and give computer algorithms monopoly over traffic, we can then connect all vehicles to a single network, and thereby make car accidents virtually impossible. [28]

He reports that one of Google's self-driving cars was hit from behind by a sedan with a human driver, but "[t]his could not have happened if *both* vehicles were steered by interlinked computers." [29]

Omitted from such accounts, however, are the accidents caused by driverless cars. In 2016 a Google driverless car turned to avoid sandbags blocking its path and hit the side of a bus. Google, renowned for claiming it had test-driven its driverless cars more than 10 million miles,* reluctantly conceded

> we clearly bear some responsibility, because if our car hadn't moved there wouldn't have been a collision. [30]

---

* See page 74.

March 2018 saw the first recorded incident in the USA of a driverless car killing a pedestrian. An Uber Volvo modified with a self-driving system in computer control mode drove into a woman pushing her pedal bicycle at night across a road in Tempe, Arizona.[31]

In January 2018 a Tesla car, reportedly on autopilot, crashed into the back of a road-sweeping truck in China's Heibei Province. The Tesla driver was killed. The incident bore a striking similarity to an accident in Florida in May 2018 when a Tesla driver switched to autopilot and his car crashed into a tractor trailer turning onto the highway. The car's AI system had mistaken the white side of the tractor trailer for open sky, didn't stop, and killed the driver.[32]

In August 2021, speaking at Tesla's AI Day in Palo Alto, California, Elon Musk claimed that Tesla had become the "world leader in real world artificial intelligence" and its chief application, self-driving cars. That same month the National Highway Traffic Safety Administration opened an investigation into 11 crashes since 2018 involving cars driving under Tesla's autopilot or traffic- aware software. All the crashes, one of them fatal, involved emergency vehicles that used flashing lights, flares, and cones.[33]

In *Homo Deus* Harari asserts

> The idea that humans will always have a unique ability beyond the reach of non-conscious algorithms is just wishful thinking. The current scientific answer to this pipe dream can be summarized in three simple principles:
>
> 1. Organisms are algorithms. Every animal—including *Homo sapiens*—is an assemblage of organic algorithms shaped by natural selection of millions of years of evolution. 2. Algorithmic calculations are not affected by the materials from which you build the calculator. 3. Hence there is no reason to think that organic algorithms can do things that non-organic algorithms will never be able to replicate or surpass. As long as the calculations remain valid, what does it matter whether the algorithms are manifested in carbon or silicon?[34]

That he gives no citations to support his syllogism is unsurprising. This is not the current scientific answer.

The first proposition—the major premise—of this syllogism is false. *Homo sapiens* is not an assemblage of organic step-by-step procedures. Moreover, a human uses not only reasoning but also insight to solve a problem or accomplish an objective.[*]

---

[*] In *COSMOSAPIENS* pp. 500-509 I consider in detail these two human characteristics, giving examples of scientific and other kinds of insight.

reasoning	An attempt to understand the essence of a thing by a logical process based either on evidence or on assumptions taken as self-evident.
insight	Seeing clearly the essence of a thing, usually suddenly after disciplined meditation or following an unsuccessful attempt to arrive at an understanding through reasoning.

Moreover, Harari disproves his own first proposition by saying that practicing Vipassana meditation for 2 hours a day and in annual 60-day silent retreats enabled him to see the reality of human history of which he wrote in his previous book *SAPIENS*, and without such an insight he would still be researching mediaeval military history.[35]

Because his first proposition is false, Harari's conclusion is false.

For artificial (or machine) intelligence to achieve human-level intelligence, it must demonstrate the multifunctionality, flexibility, insights, and self-reflectivity of a human shown in the workings of the human brain.

Scientists of the international science project OpenWorm have so far failed to artificially reproduce the functioning of the 302 neurons within the brain of the tiny *Caenorhabditis elegans* worm.[36] An adult human has approximately 86 billion neurons passing signals to each other via some 500 trillion synaptic connections, making it the most complex thing in the known universe. Moreover these neurons can change their connections in response to new information and sensory stimulation as well as to damage or dysfunction.[37]

While it would be prudent to monitor the development of artificial intelligence, current predictions that AI will achieve human-level intelligence by the middle of this century, and shortly thereafter achieve superintelligence that will most likely make humans extinct, are no more realistic than previous predictions of AI development made from the 1950s onwards.

Conclusions

1. Since the 1950s developers of artificial intelligence have predicted dates when human-level intelligent machines would be achieved, followed by an intelligence explosion by those machines that would far outstrip human intelligence and end the human era. All these predictions have been wrong.

2. The fundamental reason for this is that, while an intelligent machine can be built and programmed to teach itself a particular skill that far

surpasses the most highly skilled humans in that field, this remains only one field. Human-level intelligence requires the multifunctionality, flexibility, insights, and self-reflectivity of a human shown in the workings of a human brain, the most complex thing in the known universe.

3. Current predictions that artificially intelligent machines built by humans will exceed human-level intelligence and thereafter bring about the extinction of the human species have no more probability of being realized than the previous failed predictions regarding AI.

6

Reflections and conclusions

Learning without reflection is a waste. Reflection without learning is dangerous.

Confucius

Reflections

Evaluating scientific probabilities or predictions for the future is even more difficult than evaluating scientific theories or hypotheses based on known data. For each of the four chapters examining the probabilities or predictions of the human species becoming extinct I sent the first draft of the chapter, or a section of it, to experts in the particular field and asked them to correct errors of fact, omissions, or unreasonable conclusions. I made a point of sending a draft to ones whose views about the future appeared to lack a reasonable foundation.

For the most part it was a stimulating experience to discuss these drafts. Apart from correcting errors, these specialists told me about developments and sent papers of which I was unaware, suggested improvements, while many praised the drafts. I am indebted to them and the time they spent. The vast majority of these experts are listed in the Acknowledgments section.

There were, however, some disappointing responses to my requests. Before drawing conclusions on these possible existential threats, I consider in more detail such responses and their implications by chapter for each threat.

Chapter 2 Natural disasters

One senior scientist at NASA Ames Research Center said the draft for Chapter 2 contained fundamental errors and that he "literally knows" of only one scientist who questions the fact that an asteroid hit the Earth at the end of the Cretaceous Period and caused a virtually instantaneous mass extinction. I asked him about the 25 other scientists quoted in the draft who challenged the Alvarez hypothesis (which he was defending), the fossil evidence indicating that the mass extinction certainly was not virtually instantaneous, and the growing evidence associating mass extinctions with supervolcanic eruptions and their consequences.

He replied that he had not personally done extensive work on that extinction event and relied on the judgment of others. He recommended I read a popular science book published in 1998.

The other specialists were very helpful from the start. This doesn't mean that they all agreed with my conclusions because some had genuine differences of opinion with each other, which is inevitable when hard data are not available.

Chapter 3 Warfare and accidents

Most respondents to the draft of this chapter were also very helpful. However, one whom I'd cited expressed disappointment with my section on the nuclear war threat. He said it was obvious I hadn't done my homework and that clearly I had no idea what a mass extinction was; he questioned whether I had ever read any papers on the nuclear winter hypothesis. He asserted that a US/NATO–Russian military conflict in Eastern Europe would quickly escalate to a nuclear conflict, and then escalate to a full-scale thermonuclear war that would leave the Earth uninhabitable and end human history.

At this point I should make a declaration of interest. I have been a life-member of the Movement for the Abolition of War since it was founded in 2001 following the Hague Appeal for Peace in 1999. However, my own conviction on the immorality of war, not just nuclear war, to solve disputes does not prevent me, as a trained scientist, from attempting an objective assessment of the evidence.

I supplied this critic with proof that I did know what a mass extinction was and that I was familiar not only with the nuclear winter hypothesis initially advanced in 1983 but also with the conclusions of named specialist scientists in that field (which he is not) who personally opposed nuclear weapons but found the nuclear winter hypothesis fundamentally flawed (see page 30). Nonetheless he continues to believe in the nuclear winter extinction hypothesis when most studies contradict it.

In a section of *COSMOSAPIENS* headed "Perpetuation of flawed theory" I discuss several theories that have hardened into dogma despite contradiction by evidence, a phenomenon that conflicts with the basic tenets of scientific methodology. [1] However laudable their motives, it is difficult to avoid the conclusion that for him, and the surviving proponents of the nuclear winter extinction hypothesis, this flawed hypothesis has become dogma.

Chapter 4. Population explosion and climate change

Another disappointing response came from one of the authors of the 1972 book *The Limits to Growth* and also *Limits to Growth: The 30-Year Global Update* of 2004. His initial reply asserted that my request was in bad faith because my draft manuscript had already been published, when very clearly it had not.

In a subsequent long email he wrote "I believe you have not actually read the text you are criticizing. It seems that your comments are based on the remarks of a few skeptics and on your personal beliefs and hopes about what you want to be true… We absolutely did note write on page 12, 'there would be a sudden and uncontrollable decline in both population and industrial capacity by 2072'. "

I had, of course, read *The Limits to Growth*. What the four authors wrote on page 23 is

> If the present growth trends in world population, industrialization, pollution, food production, and resource depletion continue unchanged, the limits to growth on this planet will be reached sometime within the next one hundred years. The most probable result will be a rather sudden and uncontrollable decline in both population and industrial capacity.

After summarizing the growth trends of the five variables the authors had used, what I actually wrote in that first draft was

> the most probable result would be a "sudden and uncontrollable decline in both population and industrial capacity" before 2072.

Before 2072 (not in quotation marks) simply gives a date to a 1972 publication saying "sometime within the next one hundred years."

He went on to state "You say that the five variables of our model grew linearly on page 13. Yet, surely you know that to be an error."

What I actually wrote in the draft I sent him was "Its computer model assumed that the five variables would grow *exponentially* [my italics] while the ability of technology to increase resources would grow only linearly. The opposite occurred."

That first sentence accurately summarizes the assumptions of their computer model. Moreover, page 34 of their book says "not only has the population been growing exponentially, but the rate of growth has also been growing. We might say that population growth has been super-exponential; the population curve is rising even faster than it would if growth were strictly exponential."

His email continued: "I do not imagine that any of the above will have the slightest effect either on your view of the future nor on your text." In fact draft chapters of this book underwent significant redrafting in the light of reasoned feedback from the specialists I consulted.

I think it's rather sad that someone should resort to misrepresenting what I've written in order to defend a prediction that evidently has no probability of being fulfilled.

The climate change section of Chapter 4 also produced some less than scientific responses.

Another declaration of interest: I gave up my car in 2004 in favor of cycling or, where this is not possible, using public transport. I have taken only one airplane journey since 2006. If I dine out and I'm offered meat, I will eat it, but when I have meals at home I eat red meat, pork, or poultry not more than once a week. I have taken whatever measures I can to reduce pollution, food waste, and energy use and will continue to do so because I want to minimize my contribution to any climate change that could prove disastrous for many communities on the planet.

When it came to assessing whether climate change could cause the *extinction* of the human species, rather than local disasters, I used my scientific training and attempted an impartial evaluation of current hypotheses and supporting data.

Among those nonscientific responses to the early drafts I sent for correction was one from an associate professor in a department of geological sciences whose paper I had cited. She began by marking the draft chapter with extremely helpful and assiduous comments, even correcting mistyped double-spaces between words. But when she reached the section "Challenges to the orthodox predictions", she commented

> What is the point of giving this so much space here when >99% of climate scientists agree with the IPCC on the whole?...Providing such an extended discussion here gives the dangerous and misconstrued impression that we should not trust the IPCC. This to me is analogous to the hopefully-now-outdated practice of staging 1 to 1 debates on climate change.

The ">99%...agree with the IPCC" is an exaggeration, but only a small one. A member of the IPCC Secretariat who commented on a draft said "non-IPCC studies have shown that 97% of scientists publishing on climate change support the [IPCC] assessments."

The origin of this claim is a letter conceived as a "citizen science" project by volunteers led by John Cook and published in 2013 in *Environmental Research Letters*, an online open-access website.

To arrive at the 97 percent figure, Cook says they examined 11,944 climate paper abstracts from 1991–2011 that matched the topics "global climate change" or "global warming." They found that 66.4 percent of abstracts expressed no position on anthropogenic global warming (AGW) [the theory that climate change is caused by human industry and agriculture], 32.6 percent endorsed AGW, 0.7 percent rejected AGW, and 0.3 percent were uncertain about the cause of global warming.

To conclude that, since 33 percent of the remaining 34 percent expressed the view that humans are causing global warming, and 33/34 = 97.1, then 97 percent of scientists constitute a consensus that humans are the principal, if not sole, cause global warming demonstrates, at best, an unfamiliarity with statistics.

The problem arises because this conclusion has been cited by 547 academic papers and referred to across social media: its claims have appeared on 306 Facebook pages and have been tweeted 3,258 times—including by Barrack Obama—and reported in 201 news outlets. Unsurprisingly many climate scientists now believe this 97 percent consensus claim. (For a detailed analysis of this claim see [2].) Richard Tol of the University of Sussex also debunks Cook's 97 percent consensus claim.[3]

As for my conclusion that the predictions of population explosion or climate change or a combination of the two will result in the extinction of the human species have a negligible probability of being realized, the geological sciences associate professor commented "I saw misleading, cherry picked arguments to cast aspersion on a claim that was not assessed [that of extinction] in those [IPCC] reports." In fact the latest IPCC Assessment Report *does* consider species extinction, saying "[T]here is generally *very low confidence* [the report's emphasis] that observed species extinctions can be attributed to recent climate change."[*]

Her email concluded by saying there was no need to cite her contribution to the chapter. I thanked her for her helpful comments and asked some questions about particular ones, including her offer to supply references, but she never replied despite my sending a reminder.

Another disappointing response came from a climate scientist who said he had absolutely no recollection of the quote from *The Times* article in

[*] See Chapter 4, page 70.

which he said, among other things, that errors in the Fourth Assessment Report of the IPCC overstated the impact of global warming and that the next report should acknowledge that some scientists believed the planet was warming at a much slower rate. He asked me to send him the article or delete these paragraphs, adding "You drastically underplay robustness of IPCC assessments. The skeptics or climate deniers have absolutely no scientific credibility."

I sent him the article headlined "UN Must Investigate Warming 'Bias', Says Former Climate Chief: 'every error exaggerated the impact of change'," which was jointly written by *The Times*'s environment editor and its energy editor, and contained extensive quotes from him. He responded by saying he would get back to me in three days with answers to the specific questions I had asked. Despite three reminders he never did.

The most disappointing response came from an emeritus fellow at an environmental change institute who had been a personal friend of mine for more than 40 years. She responded by dismissing the first draft of the chapter as unpublishable, saying it was not up to my usual standards and did not have the academic rigor and logic she expected from me. To justify these comments, she said the structure was poor, there was no clarity on which are the greenhouse gases, I was critical of some very old texts and did not cover the more recent publications, such as those from the IPCC.

I was shocked by this, but sent a friendly reply saying I was at a loss to understand her comments. I noted that the chapter structure was the same as that I'd used in *COSMOSAPIENS* and in five draft chapters sent for consultation on this book, and no one had ever commented on it having a poor structure. Pages 6 and 7 of the draft listed all the greenhouse gases by their percentage composition in the atmosphere, the processes by which they warm the atmosphere and the Earth's oceans and landmasses, and their role in the evolution of nonmicrobial life. Pages 11–14 explained what the IPCC is and briefly summarized its First Assessment Report and its Fourth Assessment Report before describing at greater length its latest, the Fifth Assessment Report. This was followed by an analysis of, among other publications, the World Meteorological Office "State of Global Climate" report of November 29, 2018, which quotes the IPCC SR15 Technical Summary of 2018, just 2 months before I sent her the draft chapter.

When no reply was forthcoming after a month, I sent a reminder asking how she was able to justify her comments. She replied "I gave my comments before, fairly instinctive, I admit. If you don't agree with them, so be it. I am afraid, I am not going to reply further."

I might have expected such a response from someone for whom climate change is a religion, not a science, but not from an academic, and certainly not from an academic who had been a close friend for more than 40 years.

Among the positive responses was one that said "I found the chapter to be both interesting and well written. I enjoyed reading it. Would it be possible to have a brief phone conversation? I have a few comments and suggestions that I hope you'll find useful, and for various reasons it would easier for me to relay these verbally."

When I phoned him, he said he was speaking off the record to say that my comments on the IPCC were absolutely correct. He felt that its role was to identify the problems and it should be for technologists to devise solutions. Instead it had politicized the debate into a binary choice: either believe, or your views are not valid. As a US government employee he couldn't say this publicly, but he assured me that many of his colleagues felt the same way.

Such a binary choice is the antithesis of science, which may be defined as:

science	The attempt to understand and explain natural phenomena by using systematic—preferably measurable—observation or experiment and to apply reason to the knowledge thereby obtained in order to infer testable laws and make predictions or retrodictions.

Unlike religion, belief has no place in science, which progresses when a current theory is revised after testing against its predictions or against new data, or else is replaced by a new theory that is consistent with all known data and makes testable predictions. Open-minded questioning, not belief, is at the heart of science.

It is difficult to avoid the conclusion that, for many, climate change has morphed from a science into a religion in which you either believe a particular view unquestioningly or else your views have no credibility.

Such beliefs have occurred many times in the past, from the belief that the Sun orbited the Earth to the more recent belief about the cause of the Earth's surface features. By the end of the 19th Century geologists had adopted the theory that, as the Earth cooled after its formation, it crinkled: this accounted for the mountains, valleys, volcanoes, and plains, all separated by vast and deep oceans. In the 20th Century Alfred Wegener questioned this, producing what later became the continental drift theory that accounted far better for the Earth's surface features. He was dismissed as having no credibility, as was Lawrence Morley who provided more data to support Wegener's theory. Scientific journals adhered to the orthodox belief and rejected Morley's paper in 1963. The *Journal of Geophysical Research* dismissed it as "not the sort of thing that ought to be published under serious scientific aegis." This theory, which developed into plate tectonics, is now accepted by nearly all geologists.[*]

Too many now seem to believe that only anthropogenic greenhouse gases, or even only anthropogenic CO_2, are the causes of climate change when there are very many other causes (see page 49 and following).

I sympathize with the vast majority of those who support Extinction Rebellion (XR) because they want to stop a climate warming that would result in the extinction of humans and other species. But I fear that most are being misinformed by the leaders of XR. As noted on page 70, in October 2019 XR cofounder Gail Bradbrook was quoted as asserting on BBC TV that 97 percent of the world's species, including humans, would perish within her daughter's lifetime unless everyone on the planet stopped producing CO_2 by 2025. XR's aim in 2019 was to force governments and other organizations to achieve net zero carbon emission by 2025.

I know of no climate scientist—as distinct from some scientists in unrelated disciplines—who thinks this is possible. Focusing on an overly simplistic and unrealistic target to tackle global warming distracts from implementing realistic targets for reducing anthropogenic greenhouse gases and from developing feasible technological solutions to the problem. Such solutions are being explored, like developing aviation fuel made from household waste and cooking oil instead of fossil fuels, and electric airplanes.

Chapter 5. Artificial intelligence

The feedback for this draft chapter was very positive, apart from in two instances. One came from an assistant of an academic to whom I'd sent the draft chapter, who said that the academic in question did not "have the bandwidth to commit to" commenting on the two pages that summarized his predictions.

Another was from a public relations team, who said that the academic to whom I'd send the draft did not have the time to review the three pages that summarized his conclusions.

I assume it was coincidental that in both cases I had said that I reached very different conclusions from them but had thought it only fair to give them the opportunity to correct any errors in my draft.

Those disappointing responses to early drafts of Chapters 3 and 4 emphasize that scientists are not a breed apart, but are little different from other people, with a wide range of personalities, attitudes, integrities, beliefs, insecurities,

---

[*] For a fuller account, see Hands (2017) pp. 172–176 and pp. 571–576 for other examples of orthodox theories hardening into beliefs before eventually collapsing under the weight of evidence.

egos, ambitions, levels of confidence, defensiveness, and so on. A scientific training should, and for the majority does, result in an objective approach to data. But for a minority, subjectivity takes over. In the chapter "Limitations of Science" in *COSMOSAPIENS*,[*] I examined a range of limitations both within the domain of science and of the domain of science. I suggested, not entirely mischievously

The Law	The degree to which scientists depart from an
of Data	objective interpretation of the data in their
Interpretation	investigation is a function of four factors: their
	determination to validate a hypothesis or confirm
	a theory; the length of time during which the
	investigation has occupied their life; the degree
	of their emotional investment in the project; and
	their career need to publish a significant paper or
	safeguard their reputation.

To this I would add that a scientific community is a human institution in which apprentice scientists are taught by—and have their grants, publications, and careers decided by—proponents of the current orthodoxy. The pressures to conform in any human institution are considerable.

I express my profound thanks to those specialist scientists who have been kind enough to correct errors, omissions, and unwarranted conclusions in early drafts and to supply me with papers of which I was unaware. Any remaining errors are, of course, my responsibility. My indebtedness to them does not imply that they necessarily agree with all my conclusions, or indeed with each other.

My attempt at an impartial evaluation of the probabilities and predictions that the future of the human species is extinction leads to the following.

Conclusions

1. Natural disasters (Chapter 2)
1.1. The first type of astronomical disaster—supernovae or gamma ray bursts—poses no existential threat to humans on Earth because no potential such candidates are sufficiently close for their energy releases to fatally damage Earth's atmosphere. Moreover, the probability of new such events arising sufficiently close is negligible.
1.2. Of the second type—asteroid and cometary impacts—the hypothesis that an asteroid was responsible for an end-Cretaceous sudden mass

* Ibid., pp. 561–579.

extinction 66 million years ago has been disproven. Furthermore, there are no sufficiently large asteroids in orbits that could potentially hit Earth. Cometary paths are more difficult to predict and track, and they leave less time to launch a nuclear bomb to deflect such a threatening comet. However, laser systems could be developed or repurposed to deflect such an approaching comet. Moreover, comets of all groups are estimated to be responsible for less than 1 percent of all impact events in the Earth's recent geological record. No comets of any size have been confirmed to have impacted the Earth in historical times, nor is one expected to impact in the foreseeable future. Hence it is safe to conclude that impacts from asteroids or comets pose no existential threat to humans.

1.3. The most dangerous geophysical threat is a series of pulsed eruptions over hundreds of thousands to millions of years of vast volumes of molten rock from deep cracks in the Earth that spread out from the cracks, cool, and solidify to form a large igneous province. These are claimed to be responsible for mass extinctions in the past. However, they are so rare—occurring approximately every 10–100 million years—that the future of the human species will be determined by other factors within this time frame. Supervolcanoes producing more than 1,000 square kilometers of ejected magma occur more frequently, roughly every 100,000 years. The most recent such eruption occurred 22,600 years ago, with no evidence of a global effect that reduced—still less posed an existential threat to—the human species. Consequently, geophysical events do not threaten the extinction of the human species.

1.4. The pandemic that caused the largest number of deaths in terms of death rate in human history, the 14th Century Black Death, was caused by an infectious agent that existed in a nonhuman host, enabling it to repeatedly infect the human population over some 60 years. Yet even at a time when no one knew what caused the Black Death or how to treat it and stop it spreading, it killed a maximum of 20 percent of the human population. Now we have this information and the means to combat plague, this death rate is minute. In 1918–1920, in the unusual conditions following the First World War and, crucially, with no antiviral drugs existing to treat the infection, nor antiviral vaccines to prevent it, the deadliest influenza pandemic killed some 2.5 percent of the global population, while the last influenza pandemic, in 2009, killed a maximum of 0.006 percent of the global population. The Covid-19 pandemic seems likely to account for the deaths of less than 6 percent of the human population. The HIV/AIDS pandemic has caused the deaths of a maximum of 0.5 percent of humans on the planet, and its death rate has plummeted in recent years. Although new pandemics may arise in the future, the continuing development of medical technology means it is safe to conclude that pandemics pose no existential threat to the human species.

1.5. I conclude that natural disasters pose no threat of extinguishing the human species.

2. Warfare and accident (Chapter 3)

2.1. Predictions that nuclear warfare, biological warfare, or bioterrorism will cause the extinction of the human species are contradicted by the scientific and sociological evidence.

2.2. Nuclear power plant accidents carry no threat of making humans extinct.

2.3. Predictions that self-replicating nanomachines, or nanorobots, could destroy all the Earth's biomass, including humans, are speculations lacking any scientific foundation.

2.4. Warfare and terrorism will continue to inflict devastation on some communities and a few countries in the foreseeable future, but the evidence strongly suggests deaths from these causes as a percentage of the human population will continue to decrease.

2.5. Warfare and accident will not cause human extinction.

3. Population explosion and climate change (Chapter 4)

3.1. Previous predictions of the existential threats of a population explosion have been wrong and no evidence exists to suggest that this situation has changed.

3.2. Human actions since the Industrial Revolution have increased the amounts of greenhouse gases in the atmosphere. These cause a warming of the Earth's surface that will continue to increase in the future unless such human actions are restricted and/or countermeasures are implemented.

3.3. However, a multiplicity of interacting causes, each operating over different timescales, affect the climate, and some of these have a cooling effect. Some, such as solar activity and ocean–atmosphere events, are unpredictable. Hence it is difficult to predict with confidence what temperature rise will result in the future if human activities are not restricted or countered.

3.4. A future increase in temperature will cause sea level rises due to melting ice sheets. These will produce flooding with a consequent tragic loss of lives, crops, and infrastructure for those underdeveloped communities least able to cope in the Arctic, parts of Africa, small islands, Asian megadeltas, and low-lying coastal areas.

3.5. The use of a statistically averaged annual global temperature is questionable. Land temperatures vary considerably in different regions according to latitude, altitude, and levels of industrialization. Some regions will benefit from an increase in temperature while others will suffer. As a responsible global species, we humans should strive to protect our most vulnerable communities by working towards net zero greenhouse gas emissions in order to reduce one of the causes of global warming.

3.6. The warm interglacials of the Quaternary Period, with their much higher temperatures and greater rise in sea levels than now, did not result in the extinction of our predecessor hominids or subsequent early humans, nor did the higher temperatures of the Holocene Maximum drive humans to extinction; to the contrary, this was a time when several great civilizations began and flourished.

3.7. Current predictions that a population explosion or climate change—still less anthropogenic climate change—or a combination of the two will result in the extinction of the human species have a negligible probability of being realized.

4. Artificial intelligence (Chapter 5)

4.1. Since the 1950s developers of artificial intelligence have predicted dates when human-level intelligent machines would be achieved, followed by an intelligence explosion by those machines that would far outstrip human intelligence and end the human era. All these predictions have been wrong.

4.2. The fundamental reason for this is that, while an intelligent machine can be built and programmed to teach itself a particular skill that far surpasses the most highly skilled humans in that field, this remains only one field. Human-level intelligence requires the multifunctionality, flexibility, insights, and self-reflectivity of a human that is shown in the workings of a human brain, the most complex thing in the known universe.

4.3. Current predictions that artificially intelligent machines built by humans will exceed human-level intelligence and thereafter bring about the extinction of the human species have no more probability of being realized than the previous failed predictions.

Summary of Part 1

I conclude with a high degree of confidence that the future of the human species is not extinction.

Part 2

SURVIVAL

7

Space colonization

We now have the technological ability to set up large human communities in space: communities in which manufacturing, farming, and all other human activities could be carried out.

Gerard K O'Neill, 1977

In Chapter 1 I noted that Martin Rees, Britain's Astronomer Royal, put the odds of humankind surviving the 21st Century at no better than 50 percent. He maintained that the only way we could avoid extinction on Earth is to expand into space. Previously, cosmologist Stephen Hawking had expressed a similar view. In 2001 he had warned that, by accident or design, human-made viruses would most likely wipe out the human species on this planet before the end of the millennium unless we set up colonies in space.[1] He reiterated this solution in 2006, this time warning that human civilization on Earth would be destroyed by disasters such as an asteroid collision or nuclear warfare, but once we spread out into space and establish independent colonies on other planets our future should be safe. No planets in our solar system are suitable, and so we must seek hospitable planets orbiting other stars in the galaxy. Because of the vast distances involved, Hawking thought that this would require spaceships powered by matter–antimatter annihilation that could achieve near-light speed velocities.[2]

Current plans
The Silicon Valley multibillionaire inventor, engineer, and entrepreneur Elon Musk is now devoting himself to two projects: replacing the world's polluting cars with electric vehicles through his Tesla company and colonizing Mars through his SpaceX company "to safeguard the existence of humanity in the event that something catastrophic were to happen [on or to Earth]."[3]

SpaceX began by making rockets at its Los Angeles factory to launch small commercial satellites and undertake cargo runs to the International Space

Station before developing rockets for human spaceflight. On February 6, 2018 Musk launched the Falcon Heavy rocket from the Kennedy Space Center in Florida on a course to send its payload of a Tesla car into an elliptical orbit round the Sun as far as the orbital distance of Mars. Two of the three first-stage boosters returned to Earth in controlled landings, ready to be used again; the third crashed. Musk claimed that the Falcon Heavy has more than double the power of the next most powerful rocket, the Delta IV Heavy, but it achieved this at one third of the cost because of its reusable first-stage boosters.[4]

These, however, are only the first steps in Musk's vision to establish a colony of thousands or tens of thousands of people on Mars by 2040 as a precursor to a million-strong, sustainable, genetically diverse civilization there.[5]

He is not the only one planning for Mars. In December 2017 Boeing chief executive Dennis Muilenburg predicted that the first person to set foot on Mars will go there in a Boeing rocket. The company is developing a next-generation rocket for NASA called the Space Launch System, the most powerful version of which will be comparable with the Saturn V rocket that sent Apollo astronauts to the Moon some 50 years ago.[6]

This is part of the North American Space Agency's (NASA) proposal to send humans to Mars in the 2030s, on which it is working with commercial partners as part of its Next Space Technologies for Exploration Partnerships (NextSTEP) program. One of these partners, Lockheed Martin, plans to build not a colony on Mars but a crewed space station in orbit around the planet: this will support long-term exploration by astronauts on 1,000-day missions. It will design a reusable, single-stage surface lander to ferry astronauts from the space station down to Mars's surface and back.[7]

Unlike Musk's plan, this current NASA project does not aim to establish an independent colony on Mars.

Problems

Health hazards

In October 2015 the NASA Office of Inspector General published a 48-page report that identified 30 human health and performance risks of space exploration, including a human mission to Mars. Among these are inadequate food and nutrition, space radiation, vision impairment, and intracranial pressure. The report found that long-duration missions would likely expose crews to risks for which NASA has limited effective countermeasures. Many of the health and performance risks associated with long-duration space travel are not fully understood. The Agency's risk mitigation schedule is optimistic, the report concluded, and NASA will not develop countermeasures for many deep-space risks until the 2030s at the earliest.[8]

I will include the principal hazards identified in the report, together with updates, in the following sections, because they also apply to any space colonization attempts.

Cosmic radiation

Studies had shown that the health risks to astronauts exposed to cosmic rays outside the protection of the Earth's magnetic field include cancer, central nervous system effects, cataracts, circulatory diseases, and acute radiation syndromes. Cosmic rays are particles with a wide energy range that move through space; most are charged atomic nuclei, mainly protons, but also a small percentage of the nuclei of heavy elements. Nuclei of heavy elements such as iron and titanium significantly damage the human cells they pass through.

Conventional risk models used by NASA and others assume that cancers are caused by this direct damage. Current levels of radiation shielding would, at best, modestly decrease the exposure risks in human missions to Mars, which will take 900 days or longer.

However, in May 2017 University of Nevada, Las Vegas radiation and space physics scientist Francis Cucinotta showed that the cancer risk for a human mission to Mars has effectively doubled. A nontargeted effect model—where cancer risk arises in bystander cells close to heavily damaged cells—leads to a twofold or more increase in cancer risk compared with the conventional risk model for a Mars mission.[9]

Microgravity

Studies of the effects of microgravity on the astronauts and cosmonauts in the space station Mir in low Earth orbit from 1986 to 2001 showed an average loss of bone mass of 1–2 percent per month.[10]

In 2006 James Pawelczyk, a physiology and kinesiology researcher who flew aboard the NASA STS-90 Space Shuttle mission as a payload specialist, warned of the effects of weightlessness on bones, muscles, the cardiovascular system, and the immune system. There is no evidence, he said, that bone loss ever slows* in space. During a voyage to Mars, unchecked bone loss could make an astronaut's skeleton the equivalent to that of a 100-year-old's. Bones weakened to such an extent would be highly susceptible to fractures, putting astronauts' health and the mission itself at risk. Exercise alone has not been

---

* In 2018 (personal communication) he modified this to say "stops," but doesn't alter his conclusion about the health risks of a long microgravity space journey.

sufficient to prevent loss of bone, muscle strength, and fitness capacity in space.[11]

Many astronauts suffer from poorer vision after space missions, some for years after. Magnetic resonance imaging (MRI) scans suggest that pressure changes in the brain and spinal fluid caused by weightlessness may be partly to blame.[12]

Such effects also imply that humans born and raised on Earth would suffer health hazards if they were part of a permanent colony on Mars, which has only two-fifths of Earth's gravity.

Gene pool

For a permanent space colony to preserve the human species away from Earth, population size will be critical. Breeding with too small a gene pool will produce later generations with physical and mental defects.

In 2014 Portland State University anthropologist Cameron Smith considered the factors determining the minimum population size of an interstellar starship to establish a colony on planets outside the solar system. He assumed a five-generation voyage and found that, based on the current understanding of human genetics and population dynamics, previously proposed populations of the order of a few hundred individuals are much too low.

He concluded that a properly screened and age- and sex-structured total founding population of 44,000 people would be a safe number to survive such journeys. This number would maintain good health over five generations despite (a) increased inbreeding resulting from a relatively small human population, (b) depressed genetic diversity due to the founder effect,* (c) demographic change over time, and (d) an expectation of at least one severe population catastrophe over the five-generation voyage.[13]

This figure, however, does not take into account the probability that there would be no planet at the target star capable of supporting a colony on its surface, and so the starship itself would have to remain as the colony in orbit around a planet.

Cost

The cost of establishing colonies in space will amount to billions if not trillions of US dollars. While the space visionaries argue that such colonies are vital to preserve the human species against existential threats on Earth, how much popular and political support can be garnered for such expenditure when there are pressing demands for money to solve immediate problems on Earth?

---

* The loss of genetic variation that occurs when a new population is established by a very small number of individuals.

Previous predictions

Many of the currently identified problems were addressed by NASA's first, and far more ambitious, plans for space colonization developed in the 1970s.

Three principal factors influenced these plans. The first was the rapid increase in space technology. This began on October 4, 1957 when the Soviet Union used an R-7 intercontinental ballistic missile to place Sputnik, the first artificial satellite, in Earth orbit, followed in 1959 when it sent the Luna 2 space probe to hit the Moon, and then on April 12, 1961 it won the race against the USA by sending the first human into space when cosmonaut Yuri Gagarin orbited the Earth once before it returned him safely.

NASA developed a series of manned spaceflights that led to the Apollo program and, in July 1969, the Apollo 11 mission in which Neil Armstrong became the first human to set foot on the lunar surface, watched live on TV by a worldwide audience.[14] Two years later the Soviet Union placed the first space station, Salyut 1, in Earth orbit and then sent three cosmonauts to stay there for 22 days.[15]

The second factor was the popular and political will to finance this government development of space technology. It was a space race between the two global superpowers: a proxy war with patriotic support on each side, made explicit in 1961 by US President John F Kennedy responding to the Soviet Union's achievements by asking Congress for the resources to put a man on the Moon and return him safely to Earth by the end of the decade.

The third factor was the mounting concern about the population explosion fueled by *The Population Bomb* (1968) and *Limits to Growth* (1972) discussed in Chapter 4. This created a climate of interest and support for the idea that, in order to escape such a fate and other existential threats, humankind's future lay in colonizing space, first within our own solar system by the beginning of the 21st Century and then spreading throughout the galaxy.

These three factors resulted in a series of publications and reports by space colonization advocates, including *The Next Ten Thousand Years* by Adrian Berry in 1974,[16] *Colonies in Space* by T A Heppenheimer in 1977,[17] *Space Settlements: A Design Study* by NASA in 1977,[18] *Space Colonies* edited by Stewart Brand in 1977,[19] *The Road to the Stars* by Iain Nicolson in 1978,[20] *Project Daedalus* by the British Interplanetary Society in 1978,[21] *Handbook for Space Pioneers*, an imaginary account of the colonization of eight planets outside our solar system,[22] by L Stephen Wolfe and Roy L Wysack in 1978, and *Space Resources and Space Settlements* by NASA in 1979.[23]

The most influential of these scientists, engineers, and science writers was Princeton physicist Gerard K O'Neill, who proposed the development of space colonies in 1969, the year that Armstrong walked on the Moon. He gained academic respectability by the publication of his proposals in *Nature*[24] and in *Physics Today*[25] in 1974, and he developed these proposals with other enthusiasts of different disciplines in a series of NASA project studies.

Space-based colonies

The majority of the space colony advocates adopted O'Neill's ideas, which he explained in his own 1977 book, *The High Frontier: Human Colonies in Space.*[26] In it he argued that these colonies should not be based on the Moon, where colonists would be subject to one-sixth of Earth's gravity, or on Mars, with two-fifths of Earth's gravity, but in orbit round what is called the L-5 [Lagrange] point in honor of the French–Italian mathematician and physicist Joseph-Louis Lagrange (1736–1813). Lagrange had shown there were five special points where a small mass can orbit in such a way as to maintain a constant position relative to two larger masses, and two of these, L-4 and L-5, are stable. Figure 7.1 shows the L-4 and L-5 points where the large masses are the Earth and the Moon.

However, for a small mass, like a space colony, to orbit the Earth and the Moon not only their gravitational pulls but also the gravitational pull of the Sun must be taken into account. When this is done, L-4 and L-5 are no longer stable points but become stable regions within which a small body can move in orbits of very large dimensions about L-4 and L-5.

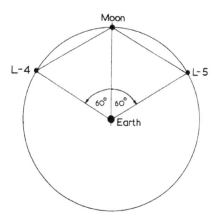

Figure 7.1 The Fourth and Fifth Lagrange Points of the Earth–Moon System
L-4 lies ahead of the Moon, making an equilateral triangle with the Earth and the Moon;
L-5 lies at a similar position behind the Moon.

O'Neill proposed that the space colonies be built in orbit around L-5. He reasoned that practically all the materials to build these colonies could be mined from the Moon, and it would be far cheaper to transport them from the Moon to L-5 orbit than to transport such materials from Earth.[27]

The first of these self-sufficient colonies, which O'Neill called Island One, comprises a sphere made of aluminum housing a population of 10,000. It rotates at such a speed as to simulate the effect of the Earth's gravity at its equator. Figure 7.2 shows a notional interior where a shallow river meanders along the equator, opening into occasional deep pools for swimming. Leading up from the river are grassy, treed areas in which the colony's housing is located. Walking up to low- or zero-gravity recreational areas near the rotation poles will be equivalent to climbing a gentle hill some 122 meters high.

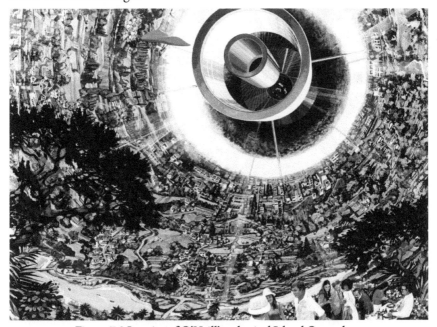

Figure 7.2 Interior of O'Neill's spherical Island One colony
A river bordered by housing by meanders along the 1.5km equator where the artificial gravity is Earth-like. At the poles the gravity is zero, allowing low-gravity recreation such as the pedal-powered flying machine with orange wings shown near the top of the image.

The first inhabitants would mainly be workers who will access the zero-gravity industrial and agricultural areas through a zero-gravity tunnel shown near the top of Figure 7.2. But living mainly in Earth-like gravity, O'Neill claimed, would allow the colony's inhabitants to retain normal muscle tone and strength without needing to follow special exercises.

Figure 7.3 depicts the proposed exterior of Island One, where mirrors surround the sphere to reflect sunlight through windows into the interior. The Sun provides power for the habitat and the agricultural and industrial regions.

Shielding against cosmic rays would be made of lunar soil or industrial slag packed between thin spherical shells spaced a few meters away from the rotating habitat.

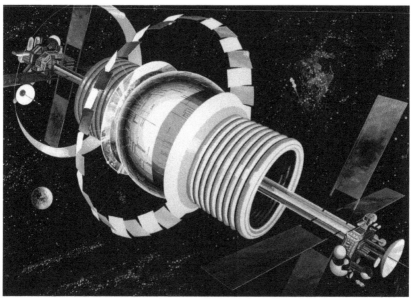

Figure 7.3 Exterior of O'Neill's Island One colony
The sphere is surrounded by mirrors that reflect sunlight into the interior, while sunlight supplies energy for the habitat and the agricultural and industrial regions.

Such colonies would not only be able to repay the initial investment from Earth but also generate new wealth by supplying low-cost energy to Earth, which would be facing a depletion of fossil fuel resources. The colonists would build large satellite solar power stations (SSPS) and ferry them to geosynchronous orbits, which mean above fixed points on the Earth's surface. At each station solar electric power would be converted into microwave energy that would be directed in a narrow beam to a fixed antenna on Earth.

O'Neill argued that not only would this energy be cheaper for Earth dwellers than current sources, it would also

(a) be much safer than using nuclear power stations with their radioactive waste and potential meltdown disasters;

(b) not deplete Earth's limited resources of fossil fuels such as oil, coal, and gas; and

(c) be more reliable than renewable sources like wind power, wave power, and terrestrial solar power.

O'Neill envisaged thousands of colonies orbiting L-5 and stated that all this could be achieved using then-current technology.

The second generation he labeled Island Two colonies, which would be home to around 100,000 people. His most ambitious plans were for the third-generation Island Three colonies with populations of tens of millions.

Figure 7.4 and Figure 7.5 illustrate an Island Three colony that comprises a coupled pair of rotating cylinders with their long axes parallel to each other and pointing towards the Sun. A large mirror at the end of each cylinder collects solar energy to provide the colony's power needs. Varying the angle of large external planar mirrors directed into the cylinders' windows simulates dawn, the slow passage of the Sun across the sky providing warmth and light, and sunset for the colonists inside. Rotation of each cylinder simulates Earth-like gravity at its inner surface. The cylinder circumference is divided into six regions: three "valleys" alternating with three arrays of windows. The curved interior would be covered as desired by lakes, hills, forests, and meadows.

O'Neill calculated that by using ordinary materials like iron and aluminum an Island Three colony could have a diameter of 4 miles and a length of 20 miles, supporting a population of several million people. The largest could be about 15 miles in diameter and 75 miles long.

Figure 7.4 Exterior of an O'Neill Island Three colony

Figure 7.5 Interior of an O'Neill Island Three colony

O'Neill predicted that the first Island One colony would be established between 1990 and 2005.

Peter Vajik of Science Applications Inc. developed a computer model in which construction of the first space colony of 10,000 people begins in 1982 and is completed in 1988. Using lunar resources the colony builds a duplicate of itself every two years or two power satellites every year, each delivering 5 million kilowatts of power to the Earth. By 1998 the number of colonies would grow to 16 and they would produce 32 power satellites every year. By 2007 the investment would be repaid and all revenues ploughed back into building more colonies and power satellites.[28]

While working on NASA's study of space colonization in the summer of 1975, Mark Hopkins also assumed 1982 to be the year for major construction in space to begin. According to his program the first power satellite for commercial use would be built in 1989, when the work crew begin constructing the colony, which would be completed in 1998. By 1999 all new and replacement power plants in the USA are built as antennas for receiving space-generated power. The entire cost of the project is repaid by 2019.[29]

Solar system exploration

In 1978 space science and astronomy author Iain Nicolson was sure that our curiosity would impel human exploration of the other planets in our solar system. He predicted that "we shall almost certainly see a lunar base established by the early nineteen-nineties... Manned expeditions to the nearer planets may commence about the end of this century, with a Mars landing mission being the obvious first step... The second Mars expedition, early in the twenty-first century, will almost certainly lay the foundations of a manned base on that planet, and manned bases are likely to be established far and wide in the Solar System as the century progresses."[30]

Galaxy exploration

Nicolson, like Adrian Berry, T A Heppenheimer, and others, forecast that the human urge to explore would result in interstellar voyages, initially with unmanned probes but later with manned starships.[31]

The problem here is the vast distances involved. The nearest star to us is Proxima Centauri, a red dwarf about 4.25 light-years away, which is some 275,400 times further than the distance from the Earth to the Sun.* O'Neill and NASA were designing colonies in space using then-current technology, including propulsion systems that are totally inadequate for galactic exploration, still less colonization. Hence innovative propulsion systems were needed to explore potentially attractive stellar systems. Nicolson described the principal possibilities discussed at that time.[32]

Nuclear-electric ion rocket

An ion rocket creates thrust by accelerating positive ions with an electric field. This version derives its electrical power from a fission reactor, but realistically it could only achieve about 1 percent of light speed for its payload.

Fusion rocket

Fusion power is released in a hydrogen bomb. Controlled nuclear fusion power would be a far superior and cleaner source of energy than nuclear reactors that use nuclear fission. However, some thirty years research since the late 1940s failed to find solutions to the daunting technical problems of producing controlled fusion power. The technical problems of designing a safe fusion rocket to achieve about 3 percent of light speed for a manned

---

* In 2016 a rocky planet slightly larger than the Earth was discovered to be orbiting very close to the relatively cool Proxima Centauri and probably has a surface temperature suitable for liquid water to exist. However, the intense radiation and flares from Proxima Centauri make it very unlikely that life could exist on that planet, named Proxima Centauri b.

starship are formidable, and a return flight would have to rely on refueling at its target.

Nuclear pulse rocket

As first proposed in the 1950s a nuclear pulse rocket basically involves exploding a series of atomic bombs out of the back of the vehicle, with part of the momentum of the explosion being absorbed by a pusher plate. This offered the prospect of attaining velocities in excess of 10 percent of light speed. The very detailed Project Daedalus plausibility study undertaken by the British Interplanetary Society between 1973 and 1978 aimed to design an unmanned scientific probe to Barnard's Star, a red dwarf 6 light-years from Earth. The study proposed using a much more sophisticated nuclear pulse rocket powered by very large numbers of very small thermonuclear explosions detonated by intense pulses of laser light to achieve a cruise velocity of 12–13 percent of light speed. Using such a method, it would take about 50 years to reach Barnard's Star without decelerating at its target.[33]

Interstellar ramjet

The problem with rockets is that they have to carry their fuel with them, and so they waste much of the energy they produce in accelerating this remaining fuel. An ideal solution is a rocket that collects its fuel en route. In the interstellar ramjet's theoretical design, enormous electromagnetic fields scoop up and compress hydrogen from the interstellar medium until thermonuclear fusion occurs, with the resulting energy being directed as exhaust from the rear of the craft in order to accelerate it. The technical problems are, once more, formidable, but Nicolson felt that this approach offered the best hope for long-range interstellar travel.

Antimatter rocket

As noted, Stephen Hawking thought that the enormous energy released by the annihilation of matter by antimatter could propel a vehicle to near light speed. While the starship *Enterprise* in *Star Trek* uses such an engine, the reality is that there are enormous technical problems facing such an approach. Nicolson pointed out that part of the energy released would be in the form of neutrinos that would penetrate everything, including the vessel and its inhabitants, and neutrinos cannot be directed by electric or magnetic fields. Most of the rest of this energy would be produced as gamma rays, and attempts to convert such energy into useful thrust have been unsuccessful.

Moreover, producing, manipulating, and storing sufficient quantities of antimatter lie way beyond current technology. Antimatter can be contained by powerful electromagnetic fields, but even a brief power failure in these fields leading to antimatter coming into contact with any part of the starship would be catastrophic.

Galaxy colonization

Most of those 1970s studies and books assume that humans would go on to colonize other star systems when once more advanced propulsion systems had been developed. But even if the technical problems of the propulsion systems outlined above could be solved, manned starships would still take hundreds of years to reach their destinations.

Too little consideration was given to a viable founding population size and structure, and how such pioneers would survive the voyage. The two options for the latter seem to be putting them into deep freeze or some other form of suspended animation before resuscitating them on arrival (but see the problems with this procedure detailed in Chapter 9, page 151), or else one generation begins the voyage while a much later generation, who didn't choose to be colonists, arrives at the destination after a voyage in which there would have to be zero population growth.

The destination might be an Earth-like planet, but realistically the chances of finding such a planet are remote. The alternative is a space-based colony. As for the vehicle itself, to which the propulsion system is attached, the two main proposals at the time were a hollowed-out asteroid or else an O'Neill-type space colony.

Conclusions

1. Most of the space colony advocates of the 1970s predicted that the first colony of some 10,000 people would be built in near-Earth orbit before the end of the 20th Century, that it would be self-financing by selling the power it generated to nations on Earth, and that it would use its revenues from these power sales to construct rapidly increasing numbers of solar power-generating stations and even larger space colonies supporting several million people. Another prediction was that a lunar base would be established by the early 1990s followed by manned expeditions to the nearer planets by the end of the 20th Century. None of these predictions has been realized.
2. More recent identification of health hazards facing humans on long-duration space missions, which apply also to colonies in space or on other planets, have not been solved.
3. Forecasts that human colonization of space would expand throughout

the galaxy fail to provide hypothetical means for the propulsion needed to achieve this objective.

4. Consequently the probability that the future of humans lies in space colonization is vanishingly small.

8

Extending healthspan

*For the first time in all time a living creature understands its origins
and can undertake to design its future.*
Robert Sinsheimer, 1969

*It is cybernetic immortality in particular that will be able to grant
people real freedom… Moreover, it's possible that this scenario will
become a reality sooner than other such possibilities for extending
lifespan all the way to immortality.*
Dmitry Itskov, 2011

*CRISPR has been hailed as the breakthrough that will finally elimi-
nate disease.*
Jennifer Doudna, 2017

Another set of forecasts predict that the future of the human species lies not in
escaping to extraterrestrial colonies but in using technology to repair and heal
human bodies, enabling us to live much healthier and longer lives, referred to
as extending healthspan. They fall broadly into two categories: (1) replacing
diseased or missing body parts, and (2) genetic engineering, which is altering
an individual's genetic makeup in order to improve the functioning of her or
his body or that of an offspring.

Replacing defective body parts
The earliest reference to replacing a body part appears in the Rig Veda, the oldest
sacred text in the world, written in Sanskrit in India between 4000 and 2000
BCE.* It tells of how Queen Vishpala lost a leg in battle and, after the wound had
healed, she had an iron leg fixed to the stump so that she could return to the fray.[1]

The oldest physical evidence of replacing a body part is displayed in the

---

* For dating of the Rig Veda see Hands (2017) p. 9.

Egyptian Museum in Cairo. An artificial big toe belonging to Tabeketenmut, a priest's daughter who lived sometime between 950 and 710 BCE, comprises three interconnected parts: two made of wood and the third possibly of leather. Most likely she lost her toe due to gangrene. [2]

The seventh book of Pliny's *Natural History* recounts how the Roman general Marcus Sergius had a hand cut off in the Second Punic War (218–201 BCE). He had a replacement one made of iron so that he could return to the campaign. [3]

Replacements for limbs lost in wars in the Middle Ages show little technological improvement since Roman times. It was only in the 16th Century that Ambroise Paré constructed a hinged prosthetic hand and a leg with a locking knee joint. He also designed replacement eyes made of enameled gold, silver, porcelain, and glass. [4]

Improvements in the design, materials, and methods of attaching replacement limbs were slow to arrive. The first microprocessor-controlled prosthetic knees were produced in 1993 by Chas A Blatchford & Sons Ltd of Great Britain, a company that had responded to the mobility needs of Second World War amputees by developing a prosthetic knee that allowed for stabilized weight bearing and flexion when walking. [5]

It is not just diseased or amputated limbs that have been replaced, nor have the replacements always been artificial.

The cornea is the transparent tissue at the front of the eye that helps the eye focus images. When the cornea becomes cloudy or misshapen, vision dramatically decreases and can lead to blindness. Eduard Zirm performed the first successful cornea transplant in 1905 from a living donor who had been blinded by a penetrating injury to the white of his eye. [6]

Developments in medical technology from the middle of the 20th Century resulted in the replacement of more diseased organs by ones transplanted from other individuals. The first successful kidney transplant took place in 1950, the first successful lung transplant in 1963, and the first successful liver transplant in 1967, which was also the year in which the South African cardiac surgeon Christian Barnard carried out the well-publicized first heart transplant.

Many of these transplant firsts were short-lived successes. The first person to be given a heart transplant regained consciousness but lived only for 18 days before dying of pneumonia, most probably caused by the anti-rejection drugs suppressing his immune system. [7] However, these transplants paved the way for improvements in techniques. Barnard's longest-surviving patient lived for 24 years after her surgery. [8]

The next technological advance was the replacement of diseased organs by artificial ones.

A total artificial heart is a pump that is surgically installed to provide circulation and replace heart ventricles that are diseased or damaged. Two ventricles pump blood out of the heart to the lungs and other parts of the body. Machines outside the body control the implanted pumps, helping blood flow to and from the heart.[9]

In 1969 Denton Cooley performed the first implantation of a temporary total artificial heart, and the primitive device sustained the patient for almost three days until a donor was found for a heart transplant. Robert Jarvik claims that he invented the first permanent total artificial heart. Made of plastic and aluminum, it was surgically implanted in 1982 into Barney Clark, a Seattle dentist with severe congestive heart failure. He lived for 112 days tethered to an external pneumatic compressor before dying of circulatory collapse and secondary multiple organ system failure.[10]

Figure 8.1 illustrates a modern total artificial heart compared with a normal heart. It is usually implanted to bridge the period between imminent heart failure and finding a suitable heart for transplant or when all clinical signs indicate that a replacement heart would be rejected.

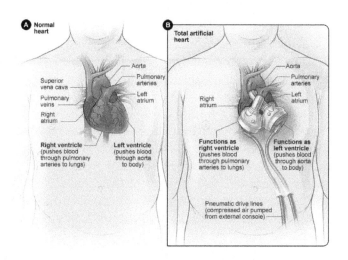

Figure 8.1 Total artificial heart
(A) shows the normal heart and (B) shows a modern total artificial heart, including the tubes that exit the body and connect to a machine that powers and controls the total artificial heart.

In October 2017 a Swiss team, led by Nicholas Cohrs and Anastasios Petrou, 3D-printed a mold to construct an artificial heart made of soft, flexible silicon capable of pumping fluid with comparable viscosity to blood, thus replicating a human heart beating. The design was at proof of concept stage, unable to beat for longer than half an hour. The team's goal is to develop an artificial heart that is roughly the same size as a patient's own and can replace the diseased heart. They believe this could potentially improve the lives and health of around 26 million people worldwide who suffer from various heart conditions. [11]

Technology that allows prostheses—or artificial body parts—to be controlled by the brain is progressing at a rapid rate.

In February 2017 Stanford University investigators reported that a brain-to-computer hookup enabled people with paralysis to type via direct brain control at the highest speeds and accuracy levels reported to date. Three study participants with severe limb weakness each had one or two baby-aspirin-sized electrode arrays placed in their brains to record signals from the motor cortex, the region of the brain controlling muscle movement. These signals were transmitted to a computer via a cable and translated by algorithms into point-and-click commands guiding a cursor to characters on an onscreen keyboard. One participant was able to type 39 correct characters per minute, equivalent to about eight words per minute, without the use of automatic word-completion assistance. [12]

At the annual meeting of the Society for Neuroscience in November 2017 Jacob George of the University of Utah announced that his team had fitted an amputee with a prosthetic hand that the amputee could control with his thoughts, decoded from electrical signals from his remaining arm muscles. The team implanted electrodes into his arm's remaining nerves that had previously detected somatosensory input from the hand. Stimulating these electrodes caused the amputee to feel natural sensations in his missing hand, and he could use these sensations to guide movements such as opening a door and to discriminate between soft foam blocks and hard plastic blocks. [13]

For people no longer able to move any of their limbs, brain–machine interfaces (BMIs) represent a hope that they could regain their lost motor and communication abilities. Sofia Sakellaridi of the California Institute of Technology reported that a woman with tetraplegia was implanted with a 96-electrode array in her anterior interparietal cortex, a brain region involved in the planning of movement. She learned to control an on-screen cursor using her thoughts alone. [14]

Predictions for the future
Many forecast that the development of current BMI technology, in which the brain controls a single artificial body part, will lead to the brain controlling a complete disease-free artificial body.

This is one step in the goal of the 2045 Initiative, an organization founded by Russian entrepreneur Dmitry Itskov in February 2011 to develop a network of specialists in neural interfaces, anthropomorphic robotics, artificial organs, and systems. Its main science project aims to create technologies enabling the transfer of an individual's consciousness to a more advanced nonbiological carrier and extending life to the point of immortality.

Its roadmap predicts

(1) the emergence and widespread use of affordable human-looking robots controlled by brain-computer interfaces during 2015 to 2020;
(2) the creation by 2025 of an autonomous life-support system for the human brain linked to a robot for people whose body is completely worn out or irreversibly damaged, enabling those with an intact brain to return to a fully functioning bodily life;
(3) the creation by 2035 of a computer model of the brain and human consciousness with the subsequent development of transferring an individual consciousness into an artificial carrier, giving everyone the possibility of cybernetic immortality;
(4) by 2045 substance-independent minds will receive new bodies with capacities far exceeding those of ordinary humans, marking a fully managed evolutionary transition in which humans will have become a new species. [15]

The organization hosted an international conference in New York in 2013 where its goals and roadmap were supported by some prominent voices in a range of disciplines, including Ray Kurzweil, futurologist and Google's director of engineering, and Hiroshi Ishiguro, director of the Intelligent Robotics Laboratory in Osaka. Ishiguro brought along an android, or humanoid robot, made as a replica of himself (see Figure 8.2). This robot can be remotely operated using the Internet, but it was not being controlled by a brain–computer interface (BCI). [16]

In 2016 Ishiguro's team were able to use a BCI system to move the left hand or right hand of the android. [17] This simple maneuver is very far from completely controlling an android BCI.

Although there have been advances in robotics since 2013, the first predicted stage of the roadmap did not happen by 2020, and the second seems unlikely, if not impossible, to achieve by 2025. As for the third and fourth stages, I will consider these in more depth in Part 3: Transformation of the human species.

Figure 8.2 Hiroshi Ishiguro with an android replica of himself

Genetic engineering

Human genetic engineering aims to alter an individual's genotype in order to change his or her phenotype or that of a future generation.

genotype	The genetic makeup of an organism, as distinct from its physical characteristics.
phenotype	The observable characteristics of an organism, such as shape, size, color, and behavior.

In 1969 Caltech biophysics professor Robert Sinsheimer described human genetic modification as "potentially one of the most important concepts to arise in the history of mankind… For the first time in all time a living creature understands its origins and can undertake to design its future." [18]

Genetic modification raised the prospect of curing genetic diseases, providing immunity to infections, enhancing the human body, and even improving mental faculties like memory and intelligence.

Its first application was gene therapy, involving the replacement of the defective genes involved in some 3,000 illnesses, many of which are incurable and fatal.

gene	The fundamental unit of inheritance, which normally comprises segments of DNA; the sequence of the bases in each gene determines individual hereditary characteristics, typically by encoding for protein synthesis.

120

DNA   Deoxyribonucleic acid, located in cells, contains the genetic instructions used in the development and functioning of all known independent organisms and some viruses. Each DNA molecule normally consists of two long chains of four nucleotides in a characteristic sequence; the chains (usually referred to as strands) are twisted into a double helix and joined by hydrogen bonds between the complementary bases adenine (A) and thymine (T) or cytosine (C) and guanine (G) so that its structure resembles a twisted ladder. A, T, C, and G are commonly referred to as DNA letters.

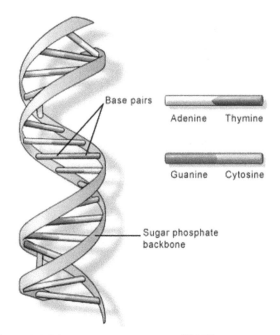

Figure 8.3 Schematic representation of DNA's structure

genome   All the genetic material of an organism. It comprises DNA (or RNA in RNA viruses) and includes the genes, noncoding DNA, mitochondrial DNA, and chloroplast DNA.

The first authorized attempt at performing gene therapy was for two young girls suffering from adenosine deaminase (ADA) deficiency, a form of severe combined immune deficiency (SCID). Affected children are born with mutations in both copies of their *ADA* genes,* which produce nonfunctional ADA enzymes, thereby preventing a crucial chemical reaction from taking place within living cells. This results in a buildup of chemicals in the blood that are lethal to specialized white blood cells called T cell lymphocytes, that orchestrate the immune system's defense against invading organisms. Such children are consequently susceptible to chronic and repeated infections. In most cases one of these infections will prove fatal during childhood.

In September 1990 a team of 19 scientists at the National Institutes of Health (NIH) led by French Anderson, Michael Blaese, and Kenneth Culver treated the first of these girls, four-year-old Ashanti DaSilva. From her blood they isolated some of her white blood cells, used a retroviral vector to insert normal *ADA* genes into them, and infused these cells back into her body.

Ashanti experienced no harmful side effects, and so in January 1991 they repeated the process on the second girl, nine-year-old Cindy Cutshall.

Ashanti received 11 infusions over the course of nearly two years. To much acclaim the investigators announced that she showed evidence of the *ADA* gene in about 30 percent of her lymphocytes. Two years after receiving her last infusion of genetically altered cells, Ashanti began to attend school regularly and lead a relatively normal childhood. [19]

It was less widely reported that the gene was present in only about 1 percent of Cindy's cells. Moreover, both girls had continued their treatment of regular injections of PEG-ADA, an artificial version of the enzyme, and so it was difficult to judge to what extent the gene therapy alone contributed to their improved health. [20]

The favorable publicity that followed the investigators' announcement led to a boom in gene therapy investigations for a wide range of diseases. By 2000 researchers had launched more than 400 such clinical trials. In September 2000 the US Food and Drug Administration (FDA) concluded that "the hyperbole has exceeded the results" and "little has worked." [21]

One of these human trials was led by James Wilson, director of the Institute for Human Gene Therapy at the University of Pennsylvania, who wanted to cure a genetic disease of the liver, ornithine transcarbamylase (OTC) deficiency, a metabolic disorder that was thought at the time to affect around 1 in 40,000 newborns. Most of these babies become comatose within 72 hours of birth and experience severe brain damage. Half die within a month of birth, and half of the survivors die before reaching their fifth birthday.

18-year-old Jesse Gelsinger had a milder form of the disease and altruistically volunteered to join the trial in order to help those for whom the disease

* By convention, a gene is written in italics while the protein it codes for is written in normal type.

is life threatening. In 1999 he was injected with an adenoviral vector carrying an unmutated *OTC* gene in order to test the safety of the procedure. Four days later he died of multiple organ failures after suffering a massive immune response triggered by the use of the adenoviral vector to transport the gene into his cells.

Investigations by the University of Pennsylvania, the NIH, and the FDA revealed that details of the deaths of monkeys in preceding animal trials had been removed from the informed consent document Gelsinger had been asked to sign and that two other participants in the human trial had reported adverse reactions. Moreover, Wilson had a conflict of interest. He had founded Genovo, a company developing liver gene therapies, that had received a reported $37 million from Biogen for the rights to market products in this area of medicine. In a letter to Wilson dated November 30, 2000 the FDA initiated procedures to have Wilson disqualified from clinical investigation because he committed "repeatedly or deliberately violations governing the proper conduct of clinical studies."[22]

Other clinical trials aimed to cure the most common type of Severe Combined Immune Deficiency known as SCID-X1. In March 1999 Selima Hacein-Bey-Abina led a team at the Necker Hospital for Sick Children in Paris that began treating infant boys by infusing them with their own blood cells into which the *IL2RG* gene had been inserted using a retroviral vector. A similar technique was used by Adrian Thrasher and his team at the Institute for Child Health in London.

In the April 2002 issue of the *New England Journal of Medicine* the Paris team reported the results of their treatment of the first five boys they treated. They concluded that the procedure "can safely correct the immune deficiency of patients with X-linked severe combined immunodeficiency."[23]

Although 18 of the 20 boys treated in Paris and in London were cured of SCID-X1, five of them developed leukemia between three six years after their treatment and subsequently one of them died of it.[24]

Reflecting in 2009 on these developments, Wilson concluded that

The hyperaccelerated translation to the clinic that occurred in the field of gene therapy in the 1990s was driven by multiple factors, including: (i) a straightforward, if ultimately simplistic, theoretical model indicating that the approach "ought to" work; (ii) a large population of patients with disabling or lethal diseases and their affiliated foundations harboring fervent hopes that this novel therapy could help them; (iii) unbridled enthusiasm of some scientists in the field, fuelled by uncritical media coverage; and (iv) commercial development by the biotechnology industry during an era in which value and liquidity could be achieved almost entirely on promise, irrespective of actual results.[25]

The underlying, and unforeseen, problem was the use of a retroviral vector to deliver the correct gene. The gene inserted randomly into the genome. For five of the 18 SCID-X1 patients it inserted near to, and activated, an oncogene (cancer-causing gene), which triggered the development of leukemia.

Other researchers began investigating ways to target the insertion of a gene into a safe part of the genome. Two methods of what became known as genome editing developed, ZFN and TALEN. They took several months to perform and were expensive.[26]

In an echo of the response that greeted the announcement of Ashanti DaSilva's gene therapy treatment some 20 years previously, a 2013 report of the first successful gene editing of human cells in a laboratory dish[27] was hailed as the dawn of a new era in molecular biology. The technique was called CRISPR (pronounced "crisper").

CRISPR

Jennifer Doudna, co-inventor of CRISPR, declared in 2017 "As long as the genetic code for a particular trait is known, scientists can use CRISPR to insert, edit, or delete the associated gene… Practically overnight, we have found ourselves on the cusp of a new age in genetic engineering and biological mastery—a revolutionary era in which the possibilities are limited only by our collective imagination."[28]

As for its therapeutic use, Doudna noted that "Because of the ease with which it can find and repair any sequence of DNA, CRISPR has been hailed as the breakthrough that will finally eliminate disease."[29]

CRISPR stands for Clustered Regularly Interspaced Short Palindromic Repeats, meaning repetitive sequences of DNA interspersed with fragments of viral DNA. CRISPR "spacer" sequences are transcribed into short RNA sequences ("CRISPR RNAs") capable of guiding the system to matching sequences of DNA. When the target DNA is found, Cas9—one of the enzymes produced by the CRISPR system—binds to the DNA and cuts it, shutting off the targeted gene. Using modified versions of Cas9 researchers can activate gene expression instead of cutting the DNA, or they can target and modify "typos" in the sequence of 3 billion DNA letters contained in the human genome in an effort to treat genetic disease.[30]

What later became known as CRISPRs were first identified in archaea[*] in 1987. In 2005 several scientists, including Francisco Mojica, a microbiologist at the University of Alicante in Spain, realized that they contained viral

---

[*] Single-celled organisms similar to bacteria in size and simplicity of structure but radically different in molecular organization. They are now believed to constitute an ancient organism intermediate between bacteria and eukaryotes (cells or organisms that possess a clearly defined nucleus).

sequences. Mojica hypothesized that they are the mechanism by which these single-celled organisms defend themselves against attacks by viruses. They do so primarily by chopping up and destroying the DNA of the invader. But it was not until 2012 that scientists adapted and developed CRISPR as a programmable DNA-cutting tool. In June of that year Doudna, a professor of biochemistry and molecular biology at University of California, Berkeley, and Emmanuelle Charpentier, then associate professor at the Laboratory for Molecular Infection Medicine Sweden (MIMS) at Umeå University, published evidence that the bacteria-derived CRISPR system could cut targeted DNA.[31]

In February of the following year a team led by Feng Zhang at the Broad Institute of MIT and Harvard demonstrated targeted genome cleavage using CRISPR in human and mouse cells.[32]

According to Doudna, with CRISPR an organism's entire DNA content, including all its genes, has become almost as editable as a simple piece of text.[33] Moreover CRISPR's low cost and ease of use finally made gene editing available to all scientists. "[W]hat used to require years of work in a sophisticated biology laboratory can now be performed in days by a high school student."[34]

Scientists involved at the early stages of CRISPR's development formed companies to exploit this potential. Many applications were filed in US, European, and other patent offices by institutions on behalf of these scientists for various uses of CRISPR technology, including eukaryotic gene editing. Patents that could result not only in academic prestige but also potentially huge financial returns were challenged, dividing the small gene-editing community. The Broad Institute filed several patent applications for inventions enabling mammalian cell use of CRISPR on behalf of its researchers who claimed to have made key advances. Lawyers representing the University of California contested these on behalf of Doudna and her team, who claimed they were the first to use CRISPR as a "programmable" tool to cut DNA[35] (although a team at Lithuania's Vilnius University reported similar results at about the same time[36]) and that this invention conflicted with the Broad Institute's patent.

On September 10, 2020 the USA's Patent Trial and Appeal Board ruled that the Broad Institute has "priority" in its already-granted patents for uses of the original CRISPR system in eukaryotic cells, which covers potentially lucrative applications in lab-grown human cells or in people directly. However, this ruling doesn't settle the dispute, but instead requires the University of California group and Emmanuelle Charpentier to provide more evidence at a future hearing that they were first to cut DNA using this tool.[37]

In a twist to this conflict, a month later the Royal Swedish Academy of

Sciences decided to award the Nobel Prize in Chemistry jointly to Charpentier and Doudna "for the development of a method for genome editing."[38]

Industries—from pharmaceuticals, agriculture, and energy to materials manufacturing—have ploughed huge amounts of money into developing CRISPR tools for their sectors, while businesses building gene-editor design tools and shipping synthetic guide RNAs or premade Cas9-expressing cell lines have boomed.[39]

Thus far scientists are using CRISPR gene editing to try and produce disease-resistant crops, mosquitoes that are unable to transmit malaria, cows that no longer grow horns, and ultra-muscular dogs that make fearsome partners for police and soldiers.[40]

Application to humans

As far as we humans are concerned, a key potential benefit of CRISPR is to cure disease. To achieve this, any new therapy has to go through three stages to ensure that it works and produces only acceptable side effects: first, testing in human cells in a laboratory dish; second, testing in animals; and third, testing in clinical trials.

As noted above, in 2013 Feng Zhang of the Broad Institute led a team that used CRISPR-Cas9 to target genome cleavage in human and mouse cells in a laboratory dish. They also showed that the system could be programmed to target multiple genomic loci and could drive homology-directed repair.[41] A team from Harvard Medical School led by George Church reported similar findings in the same issue of *Science*.[42]

In December 2013 Jinsong Li and a team of researchers at the Shanghai Institutes for Biological Sciences programmed the same CRISPR molecules to achieve the first CRISPR-based cure of a genetic disease in a live animal. They found and fixed a single-letter mutation among the 2.8 billion DNA letters of the mouse genome that had caused congenital cataracts, a disorder causing eye cloudiness and a decline in vision, in 24 mice.[43] Subsequently scientists used CRISPR to cure live mice of muscular dystrophy (a severe muscle-wasting disease) and various metabolic disorders affecting mouse livers.[44]

As of December 2020 there were 43 registered human clinical trials using CRISPR technology. 17 were in the USA, with two suspended, one terminated, and one completed. The completed study was the first stage of modifying a live strain of a bacterium that causes acne, with the aim of testing its safety, tolerability, and clinical impact in five patients.[45] Of the remainder, one was recruiting patients to treat beta thalassemia, an inherited blood disorder, and 12 were recruiting patients to treat different types of cancer.[46]

18 of the human trials were in China, with two withdrawn and two

completed. Each completed study was the first stage of modifying T cells (part of the immune system) with the aim of evaluating their activity and safety in programming the death of cells, the first causing esophageal squamous cell carcinoma and the second causing non-small cell lung cancer.[47] The 14 other trials were recruiting or planning to recruit patients suffering from a wide range of illnesses, from different cancers through pneumonia, tuberculosis, and HIV to eye infections that lead to blindness.[48]

In the USA and Europe some researchers hold major stakes in startup companies planning human trials that have received hundreds of millions of dollars in venture capital backing. These include Intellia Therapeutics (Jennifer Doudna and colleagues), Editas Medicine (Feng Zhang and his Broad Institute colleagues), and CRISPR Therapeutics (Emmanuelle Charpentier and her colleagues).[49]

CRISPR Therapeutics' program listed several proposed clinical trials in 2018, including what it labeled CTX001 for sickle cell disease set to commence later in 2018 in the USA, and another trial for β-thalassemia in Europe.[50] However, on May 30, 2018 the FDA called a halt to the CRISPR Therapeutics' sickle cell disease trial before it began.[51]

Potential dangers

CRISPR has been assumed to be reasonably specific, and so clinical trials using CRISPR-Cas9 to edit cells would be safe.

However, in July 2018 Allan Bradley of the Wellcome Sanger Institute in the UK warned against using CRISPR in humans. CRISPR-Cas9 gene editing relies on the Cas9 enzyme cutting DNA at a particular target site. The cell then attempts to reseal this break using DNA repair mechanisms. But in studies of mice and human cells Bradley's team had found that in some 20 percent of cells CRISPR causes unintended large deletions—often several thousand DNA letters long—and complicated rearrangements of DNA sequences in which previously distant DNA sequences were stitched together.[52]

Some groups are developing treatments that would involve using CRISPR to edit billions of cells inside the human body. Such unintended deletions and rearrangements could activate cancer-causing genes in some of these cells. According to Bradley, "There's a risk of causing cancer sometime in a patient's lifetime. We need to understand more before rushing into human clinical trials."[53]

These results were published a month after two other studies reported that using CRISPR-Cas9 gene editing may inadvertently increase cancer risk in cells for a different reason. The first study was a collaboration between the University of Cambridge in the UK and Sweden's Karolinska Institutet. The research team found that cutting the genome of retinal cells activated the p53 protein, which triggers the cellular repair mechanism, and makes editing much more difficult. By decreasing the activity of p53 in a cell they could more efficiently edit the cells. The second study by researchers at the pharmaceutical company Novartis independently obtained similar results with pluripotent stem cells.[54]

Mutations in the *p53* gene have been found in almost every type of cancer. These two studies suggest that where CRISPR-Cas9 gene editing works most effectively, it does so in cells that have a mutated *p53* gene, and if such edited cells are injected into a patient, they are more likely to become cancerous.

Several researchers who are committed both emotionally and financially to developing CRISPR gene editing therapies say that it is premature to assume that this technique causes cancer in humans. They maintain that these studies simply reinforce the need to monitor the p53 pathway status and that of other oncogene-related pathways, and that any risks should be carefully weighed against potential benefits as trials are designed and then progress.[55]

The reception among scientists, the media, large pharmaceutical corporations, and venture capitalists to the CRISPR gene-editing tool was similar to that following the announcement of Ashanti DaSilva's gene therapy 20 years previously. If you take the reflections of the investigator of the clinical trial that resulted in Jesse Gelsinger's death quoted above[*] and replace "gene therapy in the 1990s" by "CRISPR gene editing in 2017–2020", the circumstances are strikingly comparable.

In the light of the failed predictions and the consequences of gene therapy in the 1990s, Bradley's warning against "rushing into human clinical trials" using CRISPR is apposite.

Future developments
Advocates of CRISPR argue that it should be used not just to treat diseases in existing humans but also to edit germline cells in order to prevent disease in future generations and also to enhance future humans.[56]

germline cells (human)	Any cells whose genome can be inherited by subsequent generations. They include egg and sperm cells, and also the progenitors of these mature sex cells plus stem cells from the very early stages of the developing embryo.

[*] See page 123.

somatic cells (human)	Cells whose DNA cannot be transmitted to offspring. They are the majority of cells in a body and comprise organs and tissues such as the heart, brain, and skin.

In cases of dominant genetic disorders, such as Huntington's disease or the familial form of early-onset Alzheimer's disease, a single copy of the mutated gene is sufficient to cause disease, regardless of whether it comes from the mother or the father.

Where each parent suffers from the same recessive genetic disorder, such as cystic fibrosis or sickle cell disease, each parent carries two mutated copies of the gene and so every single child they produce would be fated to have the same disease because each child would inherit one mutated copy of the gene from its father and one from its mother.

Although these diseases could still be treated with therapeutic gene editing in the body's cells, Doudna claims that germline editing would prevent children developing these diseases in the first place and thus could prevent suffering.

Such diseases are relatively rare. Much more common are cases where genetic disease is a risk but not a certainty. Doudna gives several examples of these and claims that intervening with CRISPR in such cases could benefit future generations.[57] In the last two of her examples that follow I note that such interventions could come at a cost.

Editing the *APOE* gene could lower the risk of developing Alzheimer's disease, while altering sequences in the *IFIH1* and *SLC30A8* genes could lower the risk of developing type 1 and type 2 diabetes, respectively. The gene *PCSK9* produces a protein that regulates a person's level of low-density lipoprotein cholesterol (LDL cholesterol, commonly called bad cholesterol). A high level of LDL cholesterol is currently considered a major contributor to heart disease. CRISPR could be programmed to tweak this gene and save unborn people from high cholesterol. However, doing so would increase body weight and modestly increase the risk of type 2 diabetes.[58] Editing the gene *CCR5* with CRISPR could confer in offspring lifelong resistance to HIV, but at the cost of susceptibility to West Nile virus infection, which can prove fatal.[59]

On November 28, 2018 a young Chinese researcher Jiankui He claimed at the Second International Summit on Human Genome Editing in Hong Kong that he had made the first CRISPR-edited babies. He had used CRISPR-Cas9 to disable the *CCR5* gene in 31 embryos and had implanted two of these in the mother, resulting in the birth of twin girls. The father was HIV-positive, but the mother wasn't.[60]

Jiankui He didn't inform his university about this work, and the results weren't published in an academic journal, although reportedly he had hired an American PR consultant and made five promotional YouTube videos. Scientists' responses were hostile on the grounds that he appeared to have attempted to give the twins resistance to a disease they didn't have, the gene editing was poorly executed, he operated in secrecy, and it was irresponsible to use such techniques outside the lab because not enough is known about their risks. [61] The Chinese Vice Minister of Culture was quoted as saying that He's experiment "crossed the line of morality and ethics adhered to by the academic community and was shocking and unethical." [62]

The next step in germline gene editing is to enhance a newborn's abilities. For example, CRISPR-edited mutations in the *LRP5* gene could endow individuals with extra-strong bones. Mutations in the *EPOR* gene could confer exceptional levels of endurance. Mutations in the *MSTN* gene could produce leaner muscles and greater muscle mass, just as it has already produced super-muscular dogs and pigs. [63] Such a step raises ethical implications of designer babies compared with the rest of the population.

More radical still are the forecasts that genetic engineering will extend human healthspan indefinitely, which I will consider in the next chapter entitled Immortality.

Conclusions

1. The construction of custom-made artificial hearts that could improve the lives of those suffering from various heart conditions is distinctly possible.

2. The development of brain-machine interface (BMI) technology could prove to be of considerable help to those suffering from paralysis.

3. However, past predictions that BMI technology will lead to the widespread use by people with irreversibly damaged bodies using their brains to return to a fully functioning bodily life via robots have not been realized. Moreover, none of these technological developments applies to the human species as a whole.

4. The enthusiastic use of genetic engineering to cure specific existing diseases has been fraught by failures of predicted results and the unexpected development of other diseases.

5. Proposed use of the latest technique not only to treat existing diseases but also to prevent disease in future generations is questionable on both practical and ethical grounds.

6. It is highly improbable that the future of the human species lies in extending the healthspans of individuals genetic engineering.

9

Immortality

What you seek you shall never find.
For when the Gods made man,
They kept immortality to themselves.
                    The Epic of Gilgamesh, c. 1300–1000 BCE

We have the means right now to live long enough to live forever.
                    Ray Kurzweil, 2005

From its very start human history has been replete with accounts of individuals trying to achieve immortality. Generally regarded as the earliest example of literature, *The Epic of Gilgamesh* describes the quest to defeat death by the Sumerian king of that name who ruled the Mesopotamian city of Uruk sometime between 2800 and 2500 BCE.

In 221 BCE 38-year-old Ying Zheng declared himself the first Emperor of China and adopted the title Qin Shihuang. Obsessed with wanting to live forever, he sent emissaries to seek out the elixir of eternal life. He died aged 49, reportedly from being poisoned by one such elixir.[1] Numerous later Chinese rulers and nobles suffered the same fate after ingesting elixirs prepared by alchemists.[2]

Alchemists throughout the Indian subcontinent and Europe similarly attempted to concoct the elixir of eternal youth. They all failed.

Will recent developments in biotechnology prove more successful?

National Academy of Medicine Grand Challenge

In 2017 the US National Academy of Medicine launched a Grand Challenge in Health Longevity, offering at least $25 million for breakthroughs in the field.

The launch, held at the Los Angeles home of 94-year-old TV writer and producer Norman Lear, was attended not only by scientists, but also by movie stars, Silicon Valley billionaires, and biotech company executives. A *New*

Yorker article, "Silicon Valley's Quest to Live Forever", describes the launch and quotes several of the speakers. Martine Rothblatt, the founder of United Therapeutics, a biotech firm that intends to grow new organs from people's DNA, is quoted as saying, "Clearly, it is possible, through technology, to make death optional."[3]

Unity Biotechnology

In the fall of 2016 a Silicon Valley start-up called Unity Biotechnology founded by four researchers raised $116 million from investors including Amazon chief executive Jeff Bezos and PayPal founder Peter Thiel, multi-billionaires who believe in using science and technology to defeat death caused by aging.

Unity Biotechnology aims to develop drugs that will slow, halt, or reverse the diseases of aging. It is investigating the role of senescent microglial cells in neurodegenerative diseases, but its most developed program is focused on age-related eye diseases. In March 2022 it planned to assess the safety, tolerability, and biological activity of a repeat injection into the back of the eye of a small molecule, UBX1325, in 46 patients.[4]

Unity Biotechnology's fundraising pales, however, in comparison to the funds available to another company, Calico.

Calico

Calico (the CAlifoniaLIfeCOmpany) was cofounded in 2013 by company executive Arthur D Levinson, Chair of Apple and Google (now part of Alphabet Inc), which supplied $1 billion in launch funding. Levinson is the company's chief executive officer. Its mission is to harness advanced technologies and model systems to improve our understanding of the biology that controls human aging, and to use that knowledge to devise interventions that enable people to lead longer and healthier lives.[5]

In January 2018 two of Calico's scientists published a paper on the planet's longest-lived rodent, the naked mole-rat, based on Calico's colony of nearly 4,000 mole-rats. They found that a substantial proportion have a 30-year lifespan and, significantly, unlike all other mammals studied to date, their age-specific hazard of mortality did not increase with age. The scientists concluded that this uniquely identifies the naked mole-rat as a non-aging mammal, confirming its status as an exceptional model for biogerontology.[6]

In November 2019 another team of Calico's scientists claimed that the naked mole-rat is also unusually cancer-resistant. They hypothesized that the naked mole-rat's immune system had evolved unique features, and they compared it to that of the short-lived, cancer-prone mouse. They found that, surprisingly, it lacked canonical natural killer cells.* The team's comparative genomics analyses showed key differences in the naked mole-rat's immune system compared to those of other mammals that may contribute to its remarkable healthspan.[7]

In September 2019, using Ancestry.com, Calico scientists conducted meta-analyses of genetic variants associated with human lifespans. Such a study is extremely difficult to perform because many sociocultural factors play a large role in human lifespans. Nonetheless Calico claimed to have identified 11 paternal and 4 maternal lifespan-associated genome loci, two of which had not previously been associated with parental lifespan.[8]

In April 2022 Calico scientists developed a comprehensive platform to score aging-dependent changes in mouse physiology and behavior using a multi-dimensional longitudinal phenotyping approach. Their data collection and analysis revealed a diversity of trajectories in aging-related physiological and behavioral changes and helped to disentangle biological aging from chrono-logical aging, providing a pioneering reference for future studies aimed at large-scale aging multidimensional phenotyping.[9]

SENS

Aubrey de Grey, an English computer scientist-turned-biomedical geron-tologist, developed from around 2000[10] what he calls SENS (Strategies for Engineered Negligible Senescence) to reverse human aging by curing seven types of aging damage.

(1) Mitochondrial mutations

mitochondrion	A membrane-bound organelle found in the cytoplasm of almost every eukaryotic cell (a cell with a clearly defined nucleus), the primary function of which is to generate useable energy in the form of adenosine triphosphate (ATP) for the cell.

In the course of generating energy for a cell, mitochondria produce free radicals that attack DNA within the mitochondria causing mutations that impair the cell's functioning. Indirectly these mutations may accelerate many aspects of aging. SENS plans to make copies of mitochondrial DNA in the DNA of the cell nucleus, where it would be at a safe distance from the damaging mitochondrial free radicals.

---

* Natural killer cells (NK cells) form part of the body's immune system. They help the body fight infec-tion and cancer.

(2) Intracellular junk

When a cell functions it generates waste products, or junk. This is usually broken down and recycled by a specialized organelle called a lysosome, which contains enzymes for that purpose. Some types of junk—like proteins, fats, and metals—are not broken down by normal lysosome enzymes. This junk accumulates with age inside cells and prevents the cell from operating properly, causing aging diseases like macular degeneration of the eye, narrowing and blocking of arteries due to the buildup of deposits known as plaque, and several types of neurodegenerative disease, like Alzheimer's. SENS aims to produce additional enzymes that would remove this junk and restore full functioning of the affected cells.

(3) Extracellular junk

As cells age they also produce junk on the outside, the most notorious of which are amyloid plaques that hinder communication between cells and are associated with Alzheimer's disease. SENS will investigate ways of using the immune system to eliminate this junk, thereby allowing brain cells to communicate efficiently with each other once more.

(4) Cell loss

As tissues and organs age they either fail to replace dead cells or replace them less efficiently, producing a net loss of cells. This in turn causes tissues and organs to stop functioning properly and results in diseases such as Parkinson's; it also impairs the immune system. SENS will use stem cell therapies to restore cells and their tissues.

(5) Cell senescence

Cells that age and no longer divide but also do not die produce inflammatory substances that contribute to many aging diseases. SENS will eliminate senescent cells by inducing such cells to commit suicide, known as apoptosis.

(6) Extracellular protein crosslinks

Cells bind to each other by special linking proteins to form tissues. As tissues age these proteins form crosslinks with sugars. The accumulation of such crosslinks causes the tissues to lose their elasticity resulting in diseases like presbyopia, where the eye loses its ability to focus on close objects. SENS aims to discover enzymes that will break down these harmful crosslinks.

(7) Cancer-causing mutations and epimutations

cancer	A group of diseases in which cells in a specific part of the body grow and reproduce uncontrollably. The cancerous cells can invade and destroy surrounding healthy tissue, including organs, or spread to other parts of the body.
epimutation	A heritable change that does not affect the DNA sequence but results in a change in gene expression.

Each time a cell replicates it loses part of the non-coding DNA sequences, known as telomeres, that protect the ends of the chromosomes inside the cell's nucleus.

chromosome	A structure that contains the genetic information of a cell. In a human cell it consists of threadlike strands of DNA wrapped in a double helix around a core of proteins within the cell nucleus; in addition to this nuclear chromosome, the cell may contain other small chromosomes within, for example, a mitochondrion.

A diseased cell normally would not survive after loss of its telomeres. Cancer cells, however, express an enzyme called telomerase that replaces the telomeres, enabling them to replicate uncontrollably. SENS would eliminate all telomerase genes from the human genome to prevent this uncontrolled replication, thereby producing cancer cell death.

Stem cells also express telomerase and replicate continually in order to differentiate into new specialized cells that replenish specialized tissues. Without this replenishment these tissues would atrophy. Accordingly, SENS would replenish stem cells about every 10 years with cells engineered to have telomeres long enough to sustain them for 10 years but minus any telomerase genes.*

Instead of telomerase, a few cancers use what is referred to as an ALT (Alternative Lengthening of Telomeres) mechanism in order to replicate uncontrollably. SENS will identify this mechanism and apply the same strategy as it would for telomerase.

Criticisms of de Grey

In 2005 28 biogerontologists wrote a withering criticism of de Grey in *EMBO Reports*, the journal of the European Molecular Biology Organization, stating, among other things, that "the items of the SENS programme in which de Grey

---

* I will consider the role of telomeres and telomerase in more detail later in this chapter. See page 139.

expresses such blithe confidence are not yet sufficiently well formulated or justi-fied to serve as a useful framework for scientific debate, let alone research."[11]

de Grey responded in the same issue with equal acerbity, claiming that "their knowledge of SENS is woeful."[12]

Later that year the Massachusetts Institute of Technology, in its *Technology Review*, announced that it was offering a prize of $20,000 to anyone who could demonstrate that SENS was "so wrong that it was unworthy of learned debate."

The result was published in *Technology Review* on 11 July 2006. The judges unanimously agreed that one submission, by Preston W Estep III and eight other biogerontologists, was the most eloquent. This entry concluded that

(1) SENS is based on the scientifically unsupported speculations of Aubrey de Grey, which are camouflaged by the legitimate science of others;
(2) SENS bears only a superficial resemblance to science or engineering;
(3) SENS and de Grey's writings in support of it are riddled with jargon-filled misunderstandings and misrepresentations;
(4) SENS's notoriety is due almost entirely to its emotional appeal;
(5) SENS is pseudoscience.

de Grey rebutted the submission, claiming that Estep and colleagues' diatribe blurred the distinctions between the methods of science and of technology, and that they had attempted to mislead readers by selectivity.

The judges' verdict was that no entry had succeeded, but Estep and colleagues would be awarded half the prize in recognition of their careful scholarship. They also noted that de Grey had not convincingly defended SENS and that many of his ideas seemed somewhat fanciful.

Estep and colleagues complained that the judges were self-appointed and that people of relevant experience had not been included. They maintained that what set SENS apart from nascent science or engineering were

(1) SENS's direct contradiction of key claims by much available and generally accepted evidence;
(2) de Grey's pervasive falsehoods and misrepresentations;
(3) de Grey's demonstrated misunderstanding of relevant science and engineering.[13]

SENS Research Foundation
In 2009 de Grey moved from the University of Cambridge to California's more receptive Silicon Valley where he co-founded and became chief science officer of the SENS Research Foundation, a public charity. It operates by

giving grants to researchers at other institutions and by conducting research at its base, the Mountain View Research Center, to pursue the SENS program.

In 2011 de Grey inherited some $16.5 million on the death of his mother. He gave $13 million of this to fund SENS research over a period of five years, doubling its budget from $2 million annually to $4 million. [14] Its publicity and fundraising activities resulted in a donation in 2016 of $1 million from PayPal founder and multibillionaire Peter Thiel, as well as donations from other rich entrepreneurs like Jason Hope. [15]

Longevity escape velocity
In 2007 de Grey published a book, *Ending Aging: The Rejuvenation Breakthroughs That Could Reverse Human Aging in Our Lifetime*, co-written with his assistant, Michael Rae, that details the SENS program, its social challenges, and its politics.

In it he states "I expect many people alive today to live to one thousand years of age and to avoid age-related health problems even at that age." [16]

To justify this claim he introduces the term "longevity escape velocity" (LEV). According to this, if you are 60 years old you will benefit from advances in anti-aging treatments, so that by the time your calendar age is 90 your biological age will be 60. Those intervening 30 years will have produced even greater leaps forward in biomedical technology. Consequently you will then have access not just to the therapies of 30 years ago but also to improved ones that the first generation of therapies couldn't treat. They will still not be perfect, but they will be sufficient to rejuvenate you back to a biological age of 60 when your calendar age is 120, and so on to an indefinitely long healthspan. It is not necessary to know what the specific developments in the next 30 years will be, but simply to assume that funding is available that will enable the current rate of progress to continue. In fact it gets even better: the required rate of progress actually diminishes over time because the more comprehensive the repairs to your body become, the longer it takes for the remaining, still-unrepairable damage to accumulate to a pathogenic level. [17]

Futurist and Google engineering director Ray Kurzweil is even more optimistic. In 2017 he said "I predict it's likely just another 10 to 12 years before the general public will hit longevity escape velocity." [18]

de Grey has reiterated his assertion about reversing aging and achieving a 1,000-year healthspan in numerous appearances and publications since 2007, [19] and even more confidently since 2017 due to claimed SENS breakthroughs.

Claimed breakthroughs

In a July 12, 2017 interview for the Billionaire.com website, de Grey claimed that

> Over the past two years we've had a slew of breakthrough publications in journals such as *Science, Nature Communications* and *Nucleic Acids Research* that reported key advances against the most intractable components of aging. It's no exaggeration to say that in at least a couple of cases we have broken through logjams that have stalled key areas for over 15 years. [20]

The first of these breakthroughs was in extracellular protein crosslinks, published in a *Science* research report of 2015. But this was only a synthesis in the lab of a protein crosslink and not a method of breaking such crosslinks in animals, still less in humans. [21]

The second was in mitochondrial mutations, reported in 2016 in *Nucleic Acids Research*. This was an exploration of re-engineering mitochondrial genes and expressing them from the nucleus as an approach to remedy defects arising from mitochondrial DNA mutations. Again this was work done in laboratory tissue culture dishes and not in animals, still less in humans. [22]

Unrealistic predictions?

In December 2017 I asked de Grey that if this is the progress since the SENS program was developed 13 years previously, does it not render unrealistic the first step in the longevity escape velocity, namely that if you were 60 years old you could receive anti-aging therapies resulting from the rate of progress over 30 years in the seven SENS categories that would make you biologically 60 when you have reached a calendar age of 90?

In response de Grey modified his claim by saying that the age of people who would live 1,000 years was now 65 rather than 60. However, this isn't the average person but someone who is running maybe 25 years biologically younger than their calendar age and so would expect to reach 110 with today's medicine. [23]

Claimed acceptance by gerontologists

In response to the criticisms from biogerontologists published in *EMBO Reports* and the MIT *Technology Review* some 10 years previously, de Grey claimed in 2017 that he had been proved right because a number of these critics had now come round to his point of view, as evidenced by their joining SENS's 30-strong Research Advisory Board. [24]

None of the *EMBO Reports* signatories and only one of the *Technology*

Review signatories has joined the SENS Research Advisory Board. About a dozen members of this board have received or are receiving funding from SENS. de Grey points out that the SENS Research Foundation is an atypical funding body in that the overwhelming majority of its funding of external labs comes from its own initiative: it approaches the researcher and proposes a project rather than the researcher submitting an application.[25]

As another example of how SENS has become mainstream, de Grey refers to a paper published in *Cell* in 2013, "The Hallmarks of Aging", as a reinvention of SENS and which has been cited in more than 100 scientific papers. It covers five of the seven SENS categories plus four others. One of its five authors, Linda Partridge, was one of the *EMBO Reports* signatories, while another, Maria Blasco, is a member of the SENS Research Advisory Board, although their paper does not cite de Grey or SENS.[26]

When one of the members of the Research Advisory Board in receipt of a SENS grant, Judith Campisi of the Buck Institute for Research on Aging, was asked about de Grey's 1,000-year healthspan claim, she replied, "Aubrey has two hats. One he wears for the public when he's raising funds. The other hat is when he talks to a scientist like me, where he doesn't really believe that anyone will live to 1,000 years old. No." She suspects there is a natural maximum human lifespan. "Like you'd say there's a limit to running a marathon. You aren't going to ever run one in 30 seconds…we think the upper limit we could get to is around 115 to 120 years old."[27]

Having met de Grey I think he genuinely believes that SENS will eventually eliminate death due to aging. Whether his predictions are well founded is a different matter entirely.

The telomerase solution

In his 2015 book *The Telomerase Revolution: The Enzyme That Holds the Key to Human Aging…and Will Soon Lead to Longer, Healthier Lives*, Michael Fossel, a researcher in aging and also a clinician for more than 30 years, sets out his proposals for ending human aging based on his 1996 book *Reversing Human Aging*.[28]

He considers de Grey's seven types of aging damage plus a raft of other hypotheses that attribute aging to entropy, explaining aging in terms of wear and tear, damage, and waste products. In his view, while each of these contains a germ of truth, they all underestimate a cell's capacity to repair itself and regenerate. Moreover, they address the results of aging, not the primary cause. He believes that the cause of aging is the shortening and ultimate loss of telomeres; the solution is telomerase.

telomere	A region of repetitive DNA structures that protects the end of a chromosome from deterioration or from fusion with neighboring chromosomes in a cell; it shortens with each cell division.
telomerase	The enzyme that re-lengthens shortened telomeres.

Fossel claims that a human ages when his or her organs, bones, and tissues age, and each of these ages when its cells age; its cells age when they divide, telomeres shorten, gene expression changes, cellular repair and recycling slow down, and errors accumulate, leading to cell failure. The symptoms of aging we experience—everything from wrinkles through increased cancer risk to Alzheimer's disease—reflect the aging and failure of these cells.

Certain kinds of cell, including single-cell organisms, germ cells,[*] and most cancer cells, express the enzyme telomerase that rebuilds their telomeres so that they can continue to repair themselves and divide indefinitely. These cells never age.

Hence employing telomerase to re-lengthen telomeres restores gene expression to its most healthy state, enabling cells to function fully as they did when they were young. A rejuvenated body consists of rejuvenated organs, bones, and tissues, which consist of rejuvenated cells.

In humans and all other vertebrates, telomeres consist of repetitive sequences of noncoding nucleotides whose bases are thymine, thymine, adenine, guanine, guanine, guanine (TTAGGG).

nucleotide	A subunit of DNA or RNA made up of three parts: a phosphate group, a 5-carbon sugar, and a nitrogenous base. The four nitrogenous bases in DNA are adenine, cytosine, guanine, and thymine. RNA contains uracil instead of thymine. Thousands of nucleotides are linked to form a DNA or an RNA molecule.

Every time a cell replicates by dividing, its chromosomes lose the end sequence of their telomeres until no telomeres remain, at which point cell division stops, illustrated by Figure 9.1.

---

[*] Reproductive cells of the body: egg cells in females and sperm cells in males.

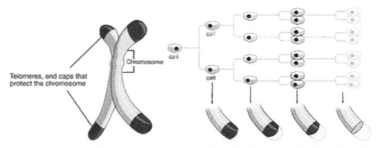

As cells divide over time...telomeres shorten, and eventually cell division stops.

Figure 9.1 Telomere shortening

The scientific research on which Fossel's telomerase hypothesis is based was conducted primarily by Elizabeth Blackburn, Carol Greider, and Jack Szostak in the 1980s and 1990s, for which they jointly received the 2009 Nobel Prize in Physiology or Medicine.

According to Fossel there was almost no interest in the clinical implications of this discovery apart from that of Michael West, who established the Geron Corporation in 1990. Carol Greider, for instance, disagreed with Fossel's telomere hypothesis of human aging, telling him in 1996

> Telomere shortening is correlated with cell age; there is yet no evidence that telomeres in any way cause cellular senescence. Further, there is no direct link between cell aging and aging of humans.[29]

In 2000, however, Geron's scientists showed in laboratory tests that aged human skin cells could be made young again by using telomerase to reset their telomere lengths. Moreover, conferring replicative immortality in this way not only made the cells young again, they also formed skin tissue typical of young human skin.[30]

Research into aging diseases

Current research into aging diseases has produced no successful treatments. For example, by the beginning of the 1990s it had been shown that the dementia of Alzheimer's disease correlates with the buildup of beta-amyloid protein plaques between brain cells and tangles of tau protein inside brain cells.[31] Apart from trials of drugs intended to provide some amelioration of the effects of dementia, like acetylcholinesterase inhibitors, most trials of drugs aimed at slowing or even stopping the progress of Alzheimer's disease have been targeted at these plaques and tangles.

None has succeeded.

In January 2018 one of the world's largest pharmaceutical companies, Pfizer, announced it was pulling out of research into drugs to treat Alzheimer's disease. Axovant Sciences also announced that its experimental drug, which in late 2017 failed in an Alzheimer's trial, had also failed to treat a different form of dementia. This was the latest in more than 400 failed clinical trials since the last Alzheimer's disease drug (which only aims to treat temporarily the symptoms of the disease) was approved by the US Food and Drug Administration more than a decade previously. [32]

The telomerase strategy

In Fossel's view these failures are predictable because they aim to treat the results, not the cause, of aging diseases. He claims the telomerase strategy

(1) clearly explains the mechanism that drives the aging process at the cellular level over time;
(2) explains why some cells age and some do not;
(3) incorporates the proven elements of the other various theories of aging;
(4) can successfully address the various objections to the theory; and
(5) perhaps most importantly, provides a clear path to clinical interventions, taking us beyond the theory to an actionable map for improving our health.

The strategy is to activate telomerase in all replicating cells in order to restore telomere length to youthful levels and so reverse aging damage throughout the body.

In the case of direct aging diseases such as osteoarthritis, osteoporosis, pulmonary disease, and skin aging, the cells in the cartilage, bones, lungs, and skin replicate. The more they replicate the shorter their telomeres become, the pattern of gene expression changes, and the cells become increasingly less efficient and slower at replacing other lost cells. The aging tissue becomes dysfunctional, producing joint pain, brittle bones, breathing difficulties, and wrinkled and blotched skin. Resetting telomere lengths in such cells would reset the pattern of gene expression, making these cells functionally young again.

Many age-related deaths, such as those from heart failures and strokes, involve organs like the heart and the brain, but heart cells and brain neurons replicate rarely if at all. However, these organs depend for their survival on parts of the body whose cells do replicate and age. The heart depends on coronary arteries to supply it with blood. The lining of the coronary arteries consists of replicating cells whose telomeres shorten with age to a dangerous level when the cells can no longer dispose of waste products. Deposits of these waste products build up to block the arteries and cause the heart to fail. We die of blocked arteries, referred to clinically as atherosclerosis.

atherosclerosis	A disease in which plaque builds up inside arteries, which are blood vessels that carry oxygen-rich blood to the heart and other parts of the body. Plaque is made up of fat, cholesterol, calcium, and other substances found in the blood. Over time, plaque hardens and narrows the arteries.

Telomerase would restore telomere length to the cells lining the arteries enabling them to dispose of this plaque.

Cerebral arteries supply oxygen-rich blood to the brain. When they become blocked with age, and blood flow stops, we die of a stroke. If these arteries become constricted and blood flow is reduced rather than blocked completely, tissue in parts of the brain dies. This produces a mini-stroke, which affects memory and cognitive ability. A series of tissue deaths results in what is clinically known as multi-infarct dementia. If the dead tissue is in the substantia nigra region of the midbrain, this impairs motor function and results in Parkinson's disease.

Generally speaking, people who suffer from a heart attack or a stroke in middle age rather than old age correlate with one or more of four lifestyle risk factors: smoking, high blood pressure, high cholesterol, and diabetes. An exception to this correlation is instructive. Children with progeria have none of these risk factors, and yet they age rapidly and die of a stroke or a heart attack, often before they are 10 years old. They are born with very short telomeres. Their skin wrinkles, their bones are brittle, and, although their blood serum is normal, the cells lining their arteries are unable to dispose of even slight levels of cholesterol in their blood.

Neurons in the brain do not replicate, but they depend on supporting cells that do replicate. Glial cells comprise some 90 percent of all cells in the brain.

glial cell	A supportive cell in the central nervous system. Unlike neurons, glial cells do not conduct electrical impulses; they surround neurons and provide support for, and insulation between, them.

Microglia are a type of glial cell.

microglia	A type of glial cell located throughout the brain and spinal cord (the central nervous system); they account for 10–15 percent of all cells within the brain. They provide an immune response in the central nervous system by acting as macrophages, removing cellular debris and dead neurons by engulfing and digesting them.
macrophage	A large, white blood cell that is an integral part of the immune system. It detects, engulfs, and digests harmful microscopic bodies, including worn-out or dead cells and other debris.

When microglia are located near to neurons in the brain they remove waste products like beta-amyloid protein and tau protein, but when their telomeres shorten they lose the ability to do this.

Cancer

Certain cells, like stem cells, naturally express telomerase, which enables them to keep replicating and prevents them from aging. As noted earlier, however, cancer cells also express telomerase, allowing them to replicate indefinitely and invade and destroy healthy surrounding tissue or spread to other parts of the body.

Hence most clinicians and scientists are opposed to activating telomerase in any cell. If a cell becomes corrupt the body's immune system will normally kill it. If, however, a malignant cell escapes death, then telomerase will enable that cell to continue replicating indefinitely. It takes only one such cell to start the spread of cancer.

Fossel, however, takes a different view. Cancer cells are corrupt because they have very short telomeres, which cause a very high rate of mutation. Activating telomerase in all cells to restore telomere length so that they function as young, healthy cells will prevent them from becoming corrupt and hence cancerous.

According to Fossel, extending telomeres in a patient with cancer might well be beneficial in that the cells may once again be capable of repairing their DNA damage and reversing early cancerous changes. One promising avenue would be to activate a telomerase inhibitor to prevent the replication of cancer cells; this would lead to their death, thus curing the disease. It would have the unfortunate side effect of also inhibiting telomerase in our stem cells, which are important for our long-term survival, but this may be a small price to pay in order to cure the cancer.[33] However, Fossel has doubts that telomerase inhibitors will prove effective. His bottom line is that telomerase is generally protective against cancer.[34]

Recent progress

Fossel claims it is now widely accepted that telomerase prevents cells from aging, although it is not yet accepted that it prevents organisms from aging. He attributes this to a failure on the part of investors, management, and researchers to get their minds around the conceptual changes. "The key problem remains: people find it almost impossible to really believe that aging can be reversed."[35] However, he points to two recent studies that support his telomerase strategy for reversing aging.

In 2010 a team led by Ronald DePinho of the Dana-Farber Cancer Institute and Harvard Medical School in Boston, Massachusetts artificially aged mice by switching off the telomerase enzyme. When the telomerase enzyme was switched back on, the mice appeared rejuvenated. They showed increased brain size, improved cognition, restoration of hair to a healthy sheen, restored fertility, and recuperation of organs. DePinho did point out, though, that prolonged telomerase reactivation or application in later life could provoke cancer.[36]

In 2012 Maria Blasco and colleagues from CNIO, Spain's National Cancer Research Centre, infected adult (one-year-old) and aged (two-year-old) mice with a modified virus containing the telomerase enzyme. This increased the lifespan of the adult mice by an average of 24 percent and that of the aged mice by 13 percent, delivering a rejuvenating effect without increasing the incidence of cancer. It led Blasco to propose that further such trials be carried out in larger mammals.[37] She continued with this work and in November 2019 published the results of an analysis of the blood of dolphins, goats, reindeer, American flamingos, and griffon vultures. She concluded that, as cells accumulate DNA damage and their telomeres shorten, they enter into a state of senescence, thus accelerating the aging process and shortening lifespan.[38]

A claimed telomerase activator has been given to humans in capsule form. Known as TA-65, it was derived from a plant and patented by Geron. It was sold under license to the public by Telomerase Activation Sciences (TA Sciences) as a health supplement; as such it does not come under the jurisdiction of the US Food and Drug Administration. It generated an annual revenue of $6 million in the USA alone.[39] Calvin Harley, chief scientific officer of Geron in which he owns stock, led a study of its effects. The first report, published in *Rejuvenation Research* 2011, analyses data from the first year of the study and focuses on the immune system. It concludes that TA-65 lengthens critically short telomeres.[40] The second report, in which Harley is listed as a consultant to TA Sciences, was published in the same journal in 2013, and concludes that TA-65 may improve biomarkers of metabolic, bone, and cardiovascular health.[41]

However, this was not a conventional double-blind study, and the number of people examined was low. In Fossel's opinion "the results were neither overwhelming nor inarguable." The changes seen were only in biomarkers, like lowering the level of cholesterol, rather than in an actual disease, like a reduction in the rate of heart attacks. Moreover, there is no evidence that anyone on TA-65 or any other telomerase activator ever got any younger. According to Fossel the best estimate is that such compounds as TA-65 are only about 5 percent as effective as they need to be if we want, for example, to cure or prevent Alzheimer's disease.[42]

In early 2015 Fossel founded a company called Telocyte to show that telomerase could not only halt but also cure Alzheimer's disease. It planned to use adeno-associated viral vectors* to deliver the telomerase gene to the body's cells. The company signed a memorandum of understanding with CNIO's Maria Blasco to take its therapy through to FDA-approved human trials.

In June 2016 Telocyte prepared a protocol for FDA approval. It planned the FDA-required animal toxicity study for 2017 followed by the first human trial to cure Alzheimer's in 2018. However, funding problems prevented any progress on the FDA-required toxicity study. In January 2021 Telocyte planned to conduct a dog study later that year to refine dosages, provide a proof of concept in a large animal model for potential investors, and establish patent rights. In September 2022 it was still negotiating with two potential investors.[43]

Fossel's prediction
In his 2015 book *The Telomerase Revolution* Fossel predicts that

We can at least double the human lifespan and will likely extend the average lifespan several centuries of active, healthy life…The notion of healthy human lifespans in the range of, say 500 years is an entirely rational point for argument, even in terms of what we now understand about possible interventions in the aging process.[44]

The method he proposes—using telomerase to restore telomere lengths in all of the body's replicating cells—is the same that he proposed in his 1996 book *Reversing Human Aging*. Page 1 of this book declares that "We will be able to prevent, even reverse, aging within two decades."[45]

---

* Adeno-associated viruses are small viruses that infect humans and some other primates. They are currently not known to cause disease, have features that make them attractive candidates for gene therapy, and are currently undergoing clinical trials for that purpose.

146

That clearly has not happened. His current prediction appears similarly over-optimistic.

Limit to human lifespan?

In *COSMOSAPIENS* I summarized from the best available evidence human life expectancy at birth, which ranged from 21 years in Neolithic times—some 10,500 years ago in the Middle East—to 78 years in the early 21st Century for scientifically developed countries like the USA. Most striking was the increase in life expectancy by two-thirds, from 47 years to 78 years, over the last 100 years or so in those scientifically developed countries. The most reasonable explanation is the correlated evolution of medical science that produced an understanding of the causes of diseases and developed measures such as clean drinking water and vaccines that have almost eliminated previously common diseases like diphtheria, tetanus, poliomyelitis, and smallpox.[46]

So, could a development of the understanding of the causes of aging diseases lead to treatments that would eliminate them and vastly extend human lifespan as de Grey, Fossel, Kurzweil, and others claim?

Jan Vijg, a geneticist at the Albert Einstein College of Medicine in New York City and a member of the SENS Research Advisory Board, and his colleagues set out to answer this question. They examined three sources: the Human Mortality Database, which spans 38 countries and is run jointly by US and German demographers; the International Database on Longevity, which focuses on the oldest people worldwide; and another database run by the international Gerontology Research Group.

They reasoned that, if there is no upper limit on lifespan, then as medical science and technology improved over the years, the biggest increase in survival should be experienced by ever-older age groups. They found, however, that while the age with the greatest improvement in survival became steadily higher since the early 20th Century, it started to plateau at about 99 in 1980. (The age has since increased by a very small amount.) Vijg concludes that there is a natural limit to human lifespan of about 115 years. There will be occasional outliers, but he calculates that the probability of a person exceeding 125 years of age in any given year is less than 1 in 10,000.[47]

In 2017, Vijg defended his conclusions against critics who accused him of misinterpreting the data and of failing to account for biotechnology developments that had resulted in significant lifespan increases in mice and other animals.[48]

Suitability of animal studies

Many of those claiming that human healthspan will be vastly increased assume that the techniques acquired in extending the lifespans of mice and other animals can be applied to humans. Christopher Turbill, senior lecturer in animal ecology at Western Sydney University, disagrees. He points out that the species most frequently studied by biologists—such as mice, worms, and flies—are chosen precisely because their short lifespans and fast generational turnovers make them quicker and easier to work with. But their short lives and adaptable reproductive strategies actually make them unsuitable models for testing drugs or other anti-aging interventions aimed at slowing human aging.[49]

In the early 1990s research on *Caenorhabditis elegans*, a tiny nematode worm that resembles a fleck of lint, showed that a single gene mutation extended its life, and that another mutation blocked that extension. The idea that age could be manipulated by genetic intervention generated a research boom. Experiments increased the worm's lifespan by a factor of 10 and that of lab mice by a factor of 2. The scientific consensus was transformed: aging could be manipulated by genetic and other interventions.

Reflecting on this in 2017, Gordon Lithgow, a leading *C. elegans* researcher, said

> At the beginning, we thought it would be simple—a clock!—but we've now found about five hundred and fifty genes in the worm that modulate life span. And I suspect that half of the twenty thousand genes in the worm's genome are somehow involved.[50]

This is for a very simple creature that lacks a respiratory and a circulation system, the adults of which have only about 1,000 cells[51] compared with adult humans who have around 40 trillion cells.[52] Lithgow was one of the 28 biogerontologists who had criticized de Grey in *EMBO Reports*.*

In a 2017 book chapter "The Search for the 'Anti-Aging Pill': A Critical Viewpoint," University of Toulouse biogerontologist Éric le Bourg also challenges the view that aging interventions in animals can be applied to humans. He argues that because humans are not giant mice and mice are not miniature humans, a treatment increasing the lifespan of mice will always fail to get a similar result in humans because the lifespan of long-lived mammals is less plastic than that of mice.

> Showing that a treatment increases lifespan in mice does not offer any clue for a positive result on human aging or longevity. This rationale could be extended to nematodes, flies, and other species with life-history strategies very different from that of humans.[53]

---

* See page 135.

Rodrigo Calado of the São Paulo University School of Medicine and Bogdan Dumitriu of the US National Heart, Lung, and Blood Institute Hematology Branch studied telomere dynamics in mice and humans. They, too, question the applicability of mouse models to human aging and diseases.

They found that mice have exactly the same telomere nucleotide sequence as humans, and telomeres play the same role of protecting chromosomes and genetic information from damage and erosion in both species. However, the telomeres of most laboratory mice are 5 to 10 times longer than those in humans, but their lifespan is 30 times shorter.

They also found that a complete absence of telomerase shows little change in observable characteristics over several generations of mice, whereas telomerase mutations in humans are sufficient to cause organ regeneration defects and cancer development. Humans with telomerase deficiencies and very short telomeres may develop a disease in which the bone marrow stops producing enough blood cells, a respiratory disease in which scars form in the lung tissues leading to serious breathing problems, or a disease of the liver marked by degeneration of cells, inflammation, and fibrous thickening of tissue, whereas mice with no telomerase show only a modest deficiency in the production of blood cells.

In summary, Calado and Dumitriu conclude that telomerase deficiency in both humans and mice accelerates telomere shortening, but its consequences in the different organs and in the different organisms diverge, mainly due to telomere length differences.[54]

I would also point out that most of these life-extension studies are of animals kept in laboratory conditions, which are very different from life in the wild where every species of animal has evolved its own natural survival strategy when confronted by existential threats like predators or a lack of food. Some hibernate. Some migrate.

A dramatic example of the unsuitability of animal trials as models for humans occurred in 2002. One of the seven SENS categories for reversing human aging is to develop vaccines that stimulate the immune system to eliminate extracellular junk such as beta-amyloid plaques. It was claimed that a successful anti-beta-amyloid vaccine would not only prevent but also cure all but the most advanced cases of Alzheimer's disease. Elan Pharmaceuticals developed such a vaccine, codenamed AN-1792. In a series of animal studies, mice were injected with human beta-amyloid and then given this vaccine. The studies proved astonishingly successful. Plaques quickly regressed from the mice's brains with no side effects. Their memory function—evidenced by the animals' ability to find hidden platforms in flooded mazes—became more like that of younger, healthy animals.

The FDA was so impressed that it approved placebo-controlled clinical trials. A few months after these human trials began, disaster struck. Of more than 300 patients recruited from 28 clinical centers across Europe and North America, about one in 15 developed a life-threatening swelling of the brain, even though they had been treated much less aggressively than had the mice. The trials were halted.

de Grey claims that subsequent sifting of the trial data showed that amyloid immunization fundamentally does work in humans and that further animal studies suggested ways to avoid this disastrous side effect. [55]

However, a 2014 paper reports that human trials of an anti-beta-amyloid antibody were modified to halt a dosage of 2.0mg per kg weight of the patient because brain swelling had been reported in another study. Results from patients given a smaller dosage did not show this side effect, but neither did they show any clinical improvement in contrast with the many mice models that have shown benefit with various dosages. [56]

Cryonics

Another way of achieving immortality was proposed in 1962 by Michigan college physics teacher Robert Ettinger in a privately published book *The Prospect of Immortality*, which was subsequently published in 1964 by Doubleday. This claimed that very soon after you have been pronounced dead your body could be preserved indefinitely until science is able to repair or replace the damaged tissues or organs responsible for your death and then revive you. [57]

Ettinger was instrumental in forming the Cryonics Society of Michigan, which eventually was renamed the Immortalist Society. In the 1970s he and three others founded the Cryonics Institute, where more than 250 individuals have now been preserved (after the 68th by a process called vitrification*) and then stored in cryostats at the temperature of liquid nitrogen.

Ettinger continued to write and campaign for cryonics. When he died in 2011 aged 92 he was cryopreserved. Also preserved at the Institute are his mother and his first and second wives.

By March 2018 five facilities existed for cryopreservation, four in the USA and one in Russia. More than 375 people had undergone cryopreservation, although some paid for only their heads to be preserved, with over 2,700 signed up to be frozen after their deaths. Alcor is the other major cryonics institute in the USA. Founded in 1972, by January 2021 it had 181 "patients" and 1,317 members. [58] One of those members paying for cryopreservation when he dies is futurist Ray Kurzweil, who said in 2002 that "I believe we'll have

* A process of cooling to very low temperatures without ice formation.

the technology for reanimation in 50 years. My best guess would be 40, but probably not more than 50."[59]

According to Dennis Kowalski, President of the Cryonics Institute in 2018, "Cryonics is much more than just the science of 'freezing,' because our objective is life after revival, with renewed youth and extended lifespans. We want to make this a reality." Their website points to prominent companies, like Google* that are now attempting to retard and reverse aging.

In 2004 the Cryonics Institute prepared a letter saying "there is a credible possibility that cryonics performed under the best conditions achievable today can preserve sufficient neurological information to permit eventual restoration of a person to full health." It obtained 61 signatories of mainly current or retired academics in a wide range of specialties. They included Martine Rothblatt, Aubrey de Grey, and Michael West mentioned above, as well as Nick Bostrom, whose predictions are considered in Chapter 11.[60]

On the other hand, many scientists are critical of claims that people cryopreserved for perhaps centuries could be revived with their minds intact. In a 2015 MIT *Technology Review* article "The False Science of Cryonics," neuroscientist Michael Hendricks of McGill University concludes that "reanimation or simulation is an abjectly false hope that is beyond the promise of technology and is certainly impossible with the frozen, dead tissue offered by the 'cryonics' industry."[61]

This was echoed in 2016 by Clive Coen, professor of neuroscience at King's College London: "The main problem is that [the brain] is a massively dense piece of tissue. The idea that you can infiltrate it with some kind of antifreeze and it will protect the tissue is ridiculous." Since the brain is so densely organized and so well shielded by the blood-brain barrier and the fatty myelin coating around the neurons, the cocktail of cryonic chemicals would need to be vigorously pumped in to ensure that every nook and cranny is infiltrated. Achieving full vitrification would most likely rupture membranes and neuronal connections. Moreover, within a few minutes of the brain being deprived of oxygen hippocampal neurons die: global brain damage would be inevitable. "Would you really want to wake up in 100 years' time and be basically a cognitive vegetable and have your cancer fixed?"[62]

Almost certainly the damage caused to cells, neurons, and their connections during the freezing of those currently in cryostorage is irreparable. It is a vain hope that some future technology will repair that damage so that the corpse restored to his or her former self with the same memories and cognitive abilities.

The prediction that humans can achieve immortality through cryopreservation is based on an unfounded speculation that unknown future developments

* See page 132.

in medical technology will provide a viable means of reanimating both body and mind.

Conclusions

The current paradigm in gerontology is that defeating death through aging and thereby achieving an indefinite human healthspan is not possible. Science is not fixed and progresses through paradigm changes. As *COSMOSAPIENS* showed, advocates of the current paradigm in their field resist or deny evidence that challenges that paradigm until the weight of contradictory evidence builds up to the point that the paradigm collapses and a new theory with new predictions is required to explain all the evidence.[63] It does not follow, however, that anyone who challenges the current paradigm is necessarily correct. Those who predict that, spared death through violence or a sudden overwhelming disease, humans will achieve immortality have so far failed to provide any evidence to support their predictions, which are no more than hopeful speculations.

The forecasts for future human survival examined so far apply speculated technological advances within human bodies. Other forecasts predict that humans will survive through technological transformation. I will consider such forecasts in the next part of the book.

10

Reflections and conclusions

For a successful technology, reality must take precedence over public relations, for Nature cannot be fooled.

Richard Feynman

Reflections

By contrast to those exceptional disappointing responses to the early drafts of Chapters 3 and 4, the comments on the first drafts of Chapters 7, 8, and 9 were all extremely helpful. Many specialists and those whom I'd cited provided detailed corrections and suggestions not only to a particular chapter section but also to whole chapters. Several engaged in lengthy exchanges when I followed up with consequential questions.

Some clearly wanted me to adopt their interpretations of the data and predictions. However, this was impossible if only because these differed significantly from those of others. It was gratifying to receive fulsome praise for a draft, particularly those responses that said I'd struck the right balance when evaluating opposing views.

The chapters in Part 2 benefited immeasurably from these respondents who are listed in the Acknowledgments section of the book.

Conclusions

1. Space colonization (Chapter 7)

1.1. Most of the space colony advocates of the 1970s predicted that the first colony of some 10,000 people would be built in low Earth orbit before the end of the 20th Century, that it would be self-financing by selling the power it generated to nations on Earth, and that it would use its revenues from these power sales to construct rapidly increasing numbers of solar power-generating stations and even larger space

153

colonies supporting several million people. Another prediction was that a lunar base would be established by the early 1990s, followed by manned expeditions to the nearer planets by the end of the 20th Century. None of these predictions has been realized.

1.2. More recent identification of health hazards for humans on long duration space missions, which would apply to colonies in space or on other planets, have not been solved.

1.3. Forecasts that human colonization of space would expand throughout the galaxy fail to provide hypothetical means of propulsion needed to achieve this objective.

1.4. Consequently, the probability that the future of humans lies in space colonization is vanishingly small.

2. Extending healthspan (Chapter 8)

2.1. The construction of custom-made artificial hearts that could improve the lives of those suffering from various heart conditions is distinctly possible.

2.2. The development of brain-machine interface (BMI) technology could prove a considerable help to those suffering from paralysis.

2.3. However, past predictions that BMI technology will lead to the widespread use by people with irreversibly damaged bodies using their brains to return to a fully functioning bodily life via robots have not been realized. Moreover, none of these technological developments applies to the human species as a whole.

2.4. The enthusiastic use of genetic engineering to cure specific existing diseases has been fraught by failures of predicted results and the unanticipated production of other diseases.

2.5. Proposed uses of the latest techniques not only to treat existing diseases but also to prevent disease in future generations is questionable on both practical and ethical grounds.

2.6. It is highly improbable that the future of the human species lies in extending the healthspans of individuals by technological means.

3. Immortality (Chapter 9)

3.1. The current paradigm in gerontology is that defeating death through aging and thereby achieving an indefinite human healthspan is not possible. Science is not fixed and progresses through paradigm changes. As *COSMOSAPIENS* showed,[*] advocates of the current paradigm in their field resist or deny evidence that challenges that paradigm until

---

[*] See, for example, Hands (2017) pp. 172–174, 388, 409, 573–576

the weight of contradictory evidence builds up to the point that the paradigm collapses and a new theory with new predictions is required to explain all the evidence. It does not follow, however, that anyone who challenges the current paradigm is necessarily correct.

3.2. None of the programs undertaken to halt or reverse aging diseases in humans has produced any results that suggest it is feasible to prevent death by aging.

3.3. Techniques that extend lifespans in mice are not applicable to humans because their physiology is different from ours and their average lifespan is 30 times shorter.

3.4. The various techniques for freezing a human immediately after death so that the person can be unfrozen and restored to full health in the future when a cure for the death-causing disease has been found represent a vain hope because the damage done to the brain in the freezing processes will almost certainly be irreparable.

3.5. It may safely be concluded that the future of the human species does not lie in using speculative and unfounded technologies to achieve immortality for individual humans.

Summary of Part 2

I conclude with a high degree of confidence that the future of the human species does not lie in colonizing space or in using technology to extend the healthspans of individuals, still less to make them immortal.

Part 3

TRANSFORMATION

11

Transforming humans

The intelligence that will emerge [after the Singularity in 2045] will continue to represent the human civilization, which is already a human–machine civilization. In other words, future machines will be human even if they are not biological.

Ray Kurzweil, 2005

In Part 1 I examined the principal predictions that the human species would become extinct, and in Part 2 the predictions that the human species would survive. What they have in common is that they forecast the future for individual humans as we know them. In Part 3 I will consider predictions that individual humans will be transformed.

For clarity's sake I make a distinction between the terminal extinction of humans discussed in Part 1 and their transformational evolution considered in Part 3, which I define as follows.

human terminal extinction	Humans cease to exist without leaving any successors.
human transformational evolution	Humans evolve by being transformed into a new species.

This is a change not in degree but in kind, just as modern humans (*Homo sapiens*) are different in kind from their hominid predecessors, which in turn are different in kind from their primate predecessors, which are different in kind from preceding mammals, and so on back through preceding vertebrates, preceding animals, preceding eukaryotes, and preceding bacteria and archaea.[*]

All the predictions in this chapter are based on humans using technology to transform themselves into a new species of posthuman, but rarely do the

---

[*] For a more detailed discussion of the evolutionary transitions from the first life on Earth to humans, see Hands (2017) pp. 334–340 and 427–445

predictors define what a posthuman is. Nick Bostrom, Director of Oxford University's Future of Humanity Institute, says

> An explication of what has been referred to as "posthuman condition" is overdue. In this paper, the term is used to refer to a condition which has at least *one* [my italics] of the following characteristics:
> • Population greater than 1 trillion persons
> • Life expectancy greater than 500 years
> • Large fraction of the population has cognitive capacities more than two standard deviations above the current human maximum
> • Near-complete control over the sensory input, for the majority of people for most of the time
> • Human psychological suffering becoming rare occurrence
> • Any change of magnitude or profundity comparable to that of one of the above[1]

To say that such a definition is vague and arbitrary, as Bostrom freely concedes, is somewhat of an understatement. To classify population size, the cognitive capacities of a large fraction of the population, human psychological suffering becoming rare, life expectancy, and "[a]ny change of magnitude or profundity comparable to that of one of the above" as alternative characteristics of a species lacks coherence.

After examining all the proposed mechanisms for achieving this evolutionary transformation, I define a posthuman as follows.

posthuman	A member of an immortal species evolved from a human and distinguished from it by having its mind and personality uploaded from its body to a new substrate such as a robot, avatar, or a computer, or whose mind is able to roam freely through the universe.

Evolutionary processes take time and hitherto have involved changes of degree before a critical change of kind emerges. Some predictions refer to an intermediate transhuman stage, which I define as

transhuman	An individual in the process of evolving from a human to a posthuman and who possesses faculties far exceeding those of humans today.

Transhuman

The 2045 Initiative was established by Russian entrepreneur Dmitry Itskov in February 2011. In 2014 it hosted an international conference in New York at which prominent figures in the fields of computer science, cybernetics, robotics, human cognitive development, and artificial intelligence (AI) supported its 4-stage roadmap to the development of posthumans:

(1) the emergence and widespread use of affordable human-looking robots controlled by brain–computer interfaces by 2020;
(2) the creation of an autonomous life-support system for the human brain linked to a robot for people whose body is completely worn out or irreversibly damaged, enabling those with an intact brain to return to a fully functioning bodily life by 2025;
(3) the creation of a computer model of the brain and human consciousness with the subsequent development of transferring an individual consciousness into an artificial carrier, giving everyone the possibility of cybernetic immortality by 2035; and
(4) substance-independent minds receiving new bodies with capacities far exceeding those of ordinary humans, marking a fully managed evolutionary transition in which humans will have become a new species by 2045.

Figure 11.1 shows a diagrammatic representation of this.

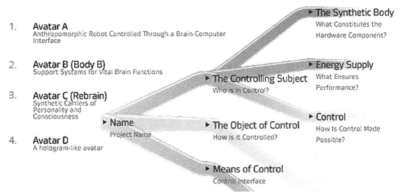

Figure 11.1 2045 Initiative's Four-Stage Roadmap to Posthumanity

The 2045 Initiative uses the word "avatar" to mean the embodiment of the person. The first two stages are examined in Chapter 8.*

The third stage is a transhuman stage (because Initiative 2045 doesn't claim the development of a new species until Stage 4), where the avatar is a synthetic carrier of a human's personality and consciousness (others consider this as posthuman). Figure 11.1 shows the questions that the 2045 Initiative team consider need answering in order to reach this stage.

* <fn>See p. 119.</fn>

Witali L Dunin-Barkovsky, head of the Department of Neuroinformatics at the Centre for Optical Neural Technologies of the Scientific Research Institute for System Analysis of the Russian Academy of Sciences, has been working on the human brain for many years. Itskov appointed him their project manager for "reverse engineering" the human brain.

reverse	Taking apart an object or system to see how is
engineering	works in order to duplicate or enhance it.

Dunin-Barkovsky said in 2011 "If the job is to be taken seriously, we can get a detailed model of a brain prototype within five years or so. And since many research areas concerned with the subject develop in parallel, it may well be that we can achieve these results even faster." [2]

Itskov claims that not only will this third stage of the 2045 Initiative's project give everyone the possibility of cybernetic immortality, but also it will create a friendly AI, expand human capabilities, and provide opportunities for ordinary people to restore or modify their own brain multiple times. [3]

Posthuman

2045 Initiative

The fourth and final stage of the 2045 Initiative is vague and lacks coherence. Its website says that humanity, for the first time in its history, will make a fully managed evolutionary transition and eventually become a new species. It will be the time when substance-independent minds will receive new bodies with capacities far exceeding those of ordinary humans, bodies consisting of nanorobots will become affordable and capable of taking any form, and body holograms feature controlled matter. Moreover, prerequisites for a large-scale expansion into outer space will be created as well. A key element in this is the achievement of immortality. [4]

Ray Kurzweil

One of the experts that Itskov recruited to his cause is computer engineer and entrepreneur Ray Kurzweil, employed since 2012 as Google's director of engineering. Unlike those who predict that the increasing power of technology, and in particular AI, will lead to the extinction of the human species (see Chapter 5), Kurzweil says that humans will harness technology in order to bring about their own evolutionary transformation.

He maintains that, as a consequence of his law of accelerating returns, the rate of technological development is increasing exponentially. Humans will augment their bodies and minds with genetic engineering, nanotechnology, computers, robotics, and AI until an evolutionary change of kind occurs. Using a concept that has been around for many years, Kurzweil adopts the term "Singularity" to define this point.

He discusses this in his 2005 book, *The Singularity Is Near: When Humans Transcend Biology*,[5] which expands on two of his previous books, *The Age of Intelligent Machines* (1990)[6] and *The Age of Spiritual Machines: When Computers Exceed Human Intelligence* (1995).[7]

In common with most other predictors of a human transformation, Kurzweil envisages the process as using technology to upload a human mind onto a future high-speed computer or network of computers. He quotes Anders Sandberg, then a computational neuroscientist at Sweden's Royal Institute of Technology: "The brain…is an existence proof that a certain arrangement of matter can produce mind."[8] He then goes on to assert

> There are no inherent barriers to our being able to reverse engineer the operating principles of human intelligence and replicate these capabilities in the more powerful computational substrates that become available in the decades ahead. The human brain is a complex hierarchy of complex systems, but it does not represent a level of complexity beyond what we are already capable of handling.[9]

Moreover, Kurzweil forecasts that the nanobot era will arrive in the 2020s. Then we will be able to send "billions of nanobots through [the brain's] capillaries [to] enable us noninvasively [sic] scan the entire working brain in real time."[*][10]

nanobot	A robot whose size is approximately one nanometer (10–9 meters). Such a small scale requires a robot to be constructed from single atoms or molecules. See nanotechnology.

He predicts that by the end of the 2020s machine intelligence will be indistinguishable from that of humans, when a machine will pass the Turing test.[†][11] By 2045 the Singularity will have been achieved, when the power of AI will be a billion times that of all human intelligence in 2005.[12] By 2099 it will be trillions of trillions times that. But, according to Kurzweil, this will not be a

---

[*] See Chapter 3 page 36 et seq. for a discussion of the development of nanotechnology, which includes Kurzweil's prediction of a two-phase attack by uncontrolled self-replicating nanobots that could destroy all Earth's biomass (including humans) very rapidly.

[†] The Turing test, proposed by mathematician and polymath Alan Turing in 1950, maintains that if a machine can answer questions in a way indistinguishable from how a human answers, then the machine is capable of humanlike thinking. It may be criticized for, among other things, failing to differentiate between behavior and other kinds of thinking such as self-reflection, belief, and imagination.

separate path from human evolution. The intelligence that will emerge will continue to represent human civilization: "future machines will be human even if they are not biological." [13]

Kurzweil asserts that, although the contemporary universe acts more like a simple machine than a conscious being, at the Singularity

> the matter and energy in our vicinity will become infused with the intelligence, knowledge, creativity, beauty, and emotional intelligence (the ability to love, for example) of our human–machine civilization. Our civilization will then expand outward, turning all the dumb matter and energy we encounter into sublimely intelligent—transcendent—matter and energy…the Singularity will ultimately infuse the universe with spirit.

> Evolution moves towards greater complexity, greater elegance, greater knowledge and greater levels of subtle attributes such as love. In every monotheistic tradition God is likewise described as all these qualities, only without any limitation… as it explodes exponentially [evolution] moves inexorably towards this conception of God, although never quite reaching this ideal. We can regard, therefore, the freeing of our thinking from the severe limitations of its biological form to be an essentially spiritual undertaking. [14]

The book doesn't adequately distinguish between brain and mind, and in 2013 Kurzweil published *How to Create a Mind: The Secret of Human Thought Revealed*. [15] As philosopher of mind Colin McGinn points out in his review of the book for *The New York Review of Books*, Kurzweil has no background in neuroscience, psychology, or philosophy. [16] He is a computer engineer whose specialty is voice recognition technology, which depends on pattern recognition. Hence it is unsurprising that, according to Kurzweil, the secret of human thought is pattern recognition as it is implemented in the hardware of the brain.

Kurzweil considers the neural architecture of the neocortex, which is the thin, wrinkled outer layer that is the most recently evolved part of the human brain and which processes higher cognitive functions such as short-term memory, perception, innovation, language, reasoning, and self-reflection.

He claims pattern recognition occurs when neurons fire in response to stimuli from the world, and that there are some 300 million neural pattern recognizers in the neocortex arranged in hierarchies. For example, in order to recognize words, pattern recognizers at a lower level respond to shapes like straight lines and curves. These feed up to a higher level that recognizes patterns like letters of the alphabet that are constructed from combinations of these shapes. These in turn feed up to a higher level that recognizes word patterns such as APPLE or PEAR from letters of the alphabet.

These recognizers are "intelligent" in that they are able to anticipate and correct for poverty and distortion in the stimulus. This process mirrors our human ability to recognize a face, say, when it is in shadow, partially occluded, or drawn in caricature.

Kurzweil contends that such pattern recognizers are uniform across the brain, so that all regions of the neocortex work in basically the same manner. This uniformity of anatomy and function leads to the further claim that he has a general theory of the mind—the pattern recognition theory of mind (PRTM)—because pattern recognition is the essence of mind, and all pattern recognition is implemented by the same basic neural mechanisms. And since we can duplicate these mechanisms in a machine there is nothing to prevent us from creating an artificial mind: we just need to install the right pattern recognizers. Hence, to upload a human's mind we simply need to duplicate her or his brain's pattern recognizers in an artificial substrate.

Nick Bostrom

In 2014 Nick Bostrom, founding Director of Oxford University's Future of Humanity Institute, found no satisfactory way of preventing human extinction by artificial intelligence.* However, he took the opposite view when he co-authored a paper in 2008 with Anders Sandberg entitled "Whole Brain Emulation: A Roadmap."

In the paper they say that, by analogy with a software emulator, a brain emulator is software (and possibly dedicated non-brain hardware) that models the states and functional dynamics of a brain at a relatively fine-grained level of detail. In particular

(a) a mind emulation is a brain emulation that is detailed and correct enough to produce the phenomenological effects of a mind;
(b) a person emulation is a mind emulation that emulates a particular mind.

They claim that, in order to emulate a whole brain, we do not need to understand the whole system but rather we just need a database containing all necessary low-level information about the brain and knowledge of the local update rules that change brain states from moment to moment. [17]

The following year Bostrom published a paper "The Future of Humanity." In it, he, like Kurzweil, proposes using technology to transfer a human mind onto a computer, known as "uploading."

* See Chapter 5 (page 78).

Such mind emulation involves the following steps. First, create a sufficiently detailed scan of a particular human brain, perhaps by feeding vitrified brain tissue into an array of powerful microscopes for automatic slicing and scanning. Second, from these scanning data, use automatic image processing to reconstruct the 3-dimensional neuronal network that implemented cognition in the original brain, and combine this map with neurocomputational models of the different types of neurons contained in the network. Third, emulate the whole computational structure on a powerful supercomputer or cluster of supercomputers. "If successful, the procedure would [be] a qualitative reproduction of the original mind, with memory and personality intact, onto a computer where it would now exist as software." This mind could either inhabit a robotic body or live in virtual reality.

He considers two paths towards a posthuman future. One is a slow, gradual growth into the posthuman level and beyond. The other is a period of extremely rapid growth due to extremely rapid technological development in which humans abruptly transition into posthumans. He notes that proponents of the latter—the Singularity hypothesis—believe that this transition will take place within a few decades.[18]

Humanity+

In 1998 Bostrom and philosopher David Pearce founded the World Transhumanist Association (WTA) as a nonprofit organization dedicated to promoting and guiding the development of human-enhancement technologies and to combating those social forces opposed to such technological progress. In 2008 WTA changed its name to Humanity+ in order to project a more humane image, and it amended its Articles of Incorporation in 2011.

Currently, Humanity+ aims to "deeply influence a new generation of thinkers who dare to envision humanity's next steps." In addition to Bostrom and Pearce, those who have developed its ideas about the future include philosopher Max More (President and Chief Executive of the cryonics organization Alcor*), artistic designer and polymath Natasha Vita-More (Humanity+'s Executive Director), Anders Sandberg, and Eliezer Yudkowsky (see later), plus Aubrey de Grey and Martine Rothblatt (see Chapter 9).

One of Humanity+'s predictions is achieving an indefinite lifespan through uploading, which it defines as "the process of transferring an intellect from a biological brain to a computer." In addition to a good three-dimensional map of a brain, it says such uploading will require progress in neuroscience to develop functional models of each species of neuron (how they map input stimuli to

---

* See Chapter 9 (page 150).

outgoing action potentials and how their properties change in response to activity during learning). It will also require a powerful computer to run the upload, and some way—as yet unspecified—for the upload to interact with the external world or with a virtual reality.

Humanity+ proposes three possible methods of uploading.

(a) Analyze pieces of the brain slice by slice in an electron microscope with automatic image processing. In addition to mapping the connection patterns among the 100 billion or so neurons, the scan would also have to register some of the functional properties of each of the synaptic interconnections, such as the efficacy of the connection and how stable it is over time.
(b) A gradual method of replacing one neuron by an implant or by a simulation in a computer outside of the body, then another neuron, and so on until eventually the whole cortex has been replaced and the person's thinking is implemented on entirely artificial hardware. To do this for the whole brain would almost certainly require nanotechnology.
(c) Scan the synaptic structure of a particular brain and then implement the same computations in an electronic medium. A brain scan of sufficient resolution could be produced by disassembling the brain atom for atom by means of nanotechnology.

Humanity+ claims that an upload's experience could in principle be identical to that of a biological human. An upload could have a virtual (simulated) body that gives it the same sensations and the same possibilities for interaction as a non-simulated body. With advanced virtual reality, uploads could enjoy food and drink, and "upload sex could be as gloriously messy as one could wish." Moreover, uploads wouldn't have to be confined to virtual reality: they could interact with people in the non-virtual world and even rent robot bodies in order to work in or explore physical reality.

Furthermore, uploads would not be subject to biological senescence. Backup copies of uploads could be created regularly so that you could be rebooted if something bad happened. Thus your lifespan would potentially be as long as the universe's.

If you were running on a computer a thousand times more powerful than a human brain, then you would think a thousand times faster, and the external world would appear to you as if it were slowed down by a factor of a thousand. You would thus get to experience more subjective time, and so live more, during any given day. You could travel at the speed of light as an information pattern.[19]

In common with Kurzweil and others, Humanity+ discusses the Singularity, which it describes as "a point in the future when the rate of technological development becomes so rapid that the progress-curve becomes nearly vertical. Within a very brief time (months, days, or even just hours), the world might be transformed almost beyond recognition. The most likely cause of this hypothesized Singularity would be the creation of some form of rapidly self-enhancing greater-than-human intelligence." [20]

Humanity+ says those posthumans who jettison their bodies altogether and live as information patterns on vast, super-fast computer networks may have minds that are not only more powerful than those of humans but also may employ different cognitive architectures or include new sensory modalities that enable greater participation in their virtual reality settings. Such posthuman minds might be able to share memories and experiences directly, greatly increasing the efficiency, quality, and modes in which posthumans could communicate with each other. The boundaries between posthuman minds may not be as sharply defined as those between humans. [21]

Yuval Noah Harari

In his bestselling 2016 book *HOMO DEUS A Brief History of Tomorrow,* [22] the sequel to *SAPIENS*, military historian Yuval Noah Harari has surprisingly little to say about the long-term future of *Homo sapiens*. In the first chapter he mentions, somewhat skeptically, the predictions of Aubrey de Grey and Ray Kurzweil on achieving immortality.[*]

In 2017 he was quoted in *The Guardian* as saying

> I think that *Homo sapiens*as as we know them will probably disappear within a century or so, not destroyed by killer robots or things like that, but changed and upgraded. The point at which the increase in artificial intelligence (AI) surpasses human intelligenceed with biotechnology and artificial intelligence into something else, into something different. The timescale for that kind of change is maybe a century. [23]

Singularity

Distilling the essence of the many descriptions of the Singularity leads to the following definition:

---

[*] See Chapter 9 for an examination of the predictions of de Grey, Kurzweil, and other immortalists.

| Singularity (technological) | The point at which the increase in artificial intelligence (AI) surpasses human intelligence; thereafter the exponential growth of such superintelligence achieved by technological self-improvement becomes incomprehensible to human biological intelligence. |

Polymath and computer scientist John von Neumann (1903–1957) was probably the first to articulate the concept of the Singularity. Mathematician Stan Ullam quotes him as referring to

> the ever accelerating progress of technology and changes in the mode of human life, which gives the appearance of approaching some essential singularity in the history of the race beyond which human affairs, as we know them, could not continue.[24]

Although he didn't use the term "Singularity," mathematician I J Good predicted what I've defined as the Singularity would most probably be achieved within the 20th Century.[*]

Likewise, Marvin Minsky, cofounder of MIT's Computer Science and Artificial Intelligence Laboratory, predicted in 1970 that such a point would be achieved before 1980.[†]

In 1986 theoretical nanotechnologist Eric Drexler forecast that it would be achieved within a few decades.[‡]

In 1993 mathematician and science fiction writer Vernor Vinge said the technological Singularity would be achieved by 2023.[§]

In 1996 Eliezer S Yudkowsky, cofounder of the Machine Intelligence Research Unit and a founding member of Humanity+, predicted that the Singularity would be achieved by 2021[25] (although he now considers everything he produced before 2002 as obsolete[26]).

As we saw above, Kurzweil predicted in 2005 that the Singularity would be achieved by 2045.

Flaws in predictions

Exponential development of technology (Kurzweil)
One of Kurzweil's basic assumptions in his forecasts is that information-related

* See page 77.
† See page 77.
‡ See page 78.
§ See page 78.

technologies are developing and will continue to develop at an exponential rate. By using such exponentially developing technologies to replicate the workings of a human brain, we will be able to upload that human's mind onto another substrate.

This assumption is rooted in what he calls his law of accelerating returns (LOAR), which says that "an evolutionary process inherently accelerates... and that its products grow exponentially in complexity and capability." This "pertains to both biological and technological evolution."[27]

Reviewing this law, Kurzweil argues that such evolutionary change is "a doubly exponential phenomenon (that is, exponential growth in which the rate of exponential growth—the exponent—is itself growing exponentially)."[28]

For a statement to qualify as a natural or a scientific law, all the phenomena it describes must follow the law, which produces accurate predictions. But this clearly is not the case for biological and technological evolution. From the very many exceptions I give two striking examples previously described in this book.

The growth rate in the complexity and capability of space technology from 1961, when Yuri Gagarin became the first human to orbit the Earth, to 1969, when Neil Armstrong became the first human to walk on the Moon, led NASA, individual scientists, and science writers to predict that human colonization of space would start within our own solar system by the beginning of the 21st Century and then spread throughout the galaxy.*

Such technological evolution has not occurred; colonization of space has regressed. There has been no manned Moon landing since 1972. As of 2020 only the International Space Station (which is only capable of supporting a crew of around six people for three to six months) and stations resulting from China's space program exist in low Earth orbit. China launched its first space laboratory, Tiangong-1, into low Earth orbit in 2011 followed by Tiangong-2, a more advanced laboratory complete with a cargo ship, in 2016, and this program will culminate in a large orbital station capable of supporting three astronauts for long-term habitation scheduled for completion by 2022, just as the International Space Station is due to be retired.[29]

The same is true of the complexity and capability of nuclear weapons technology. The power of the first nuclear bomb, used in Hiroshima in 1945, was equivalent to 15 kilotons of TNT. By 1961 the Russian Big Ivan bomb, evolved from fission to more complex fusion technology, had a power of more than 50 megatons of TNT, an increase in capability of more than 3,000-fold in 16 years. But this power subsequently decreased, so that now the power of nuclear bombs rarely exceeds 100 kilotons of TNT.†

---

* See Chapter 7, (page 104 et seq.).

† See Chapter 3, (pages 25 and page 29).

What increased exponentially was not technology but human reflective consciousness. We humans took the conscious decision to drastically reduce the resources we invested in human space exploration. Similarly, although it was by no means a smooth process, we decided that the possibility of humankind's destruction by nuclear weapons was so high that we agreed to dramatically reduce not only their explosive power but also their numbers.

Only a small part of the genome is needed for brain reproduction (Kurzweil)

Although Kurzweil concedes that the human brain is highly complex, he claims that the initial design of the brain is based on the human genome, which "consists of eight hundred million bytes [where a byte is a group of eight consecutive bits], but most of it is redundant, leaving only about thirty to one hundred million bytes…of unique information…which is smaller than the program for Microsoft Word [in 2003]." Moreover, "highly repetitive patterns are found in each specific brain region, so it is not necessary to capture each particular detail" to successfully model the human brain.[30]

Kurzweil is correct to say that the entire human genome consists of 800 million bytes. However, he is wrong to say that most of it is redundant, leaving only about 30–100 million bytes (4–13 percent) of unique information. This echoes the view held for around 50 years that 98 percent of the genome consisting of non-protein-producing DNA is junk. Since the human genome was analyzed in 2007, studies have shown that some 80 percent of this "junk DNA" is functionally active, including portions of repeat elements; much of it involves complex collaborative networks that regulate gene expression.[31]

Methods of uploading a brain (Humanity+)

The three methods of uploading a human brain described by Humanity+ are totally impractical.

For method (a), in addition to mapping the neural connection pattern among the 86 billion (not "100 billion or so") neurons in a human brain, Humanity+ says that it would have to register some of the functional properties of each of the synaptic interconnections, such as the efficacy of the connection and how stable it is over time. The human brain has some 500 trillion synaptic connections that change in response to new information and sensory stimulation. Unsurprisingly, Humanity+ offers no suggestions as to how to register the functional properties of each of these 500 trillion connections.

For method (b), if it takes only one second to replace one neuron by an implant or by a simulation in a computer outside of the body, then another neuron, and so on, this would take 86 billion seconds or 1,500 years to complete.

As for method (c), it beggars belief than anyone should even suggest scanning the synaptic structure of a particular brain by disassembling the brain atom for atom when no one even knows how many atoms there are in the 86 billion neurons plus the 85 billion non-neuronal cells, which include glia and other cells like endothelial cells. [32]

Operational brain reproduced from genome bytes (Kurzweil)

Kurzweil is wrong to assume that the design and operation of the brain can be reproduced from bytes in the genome. The brain is not like a computer with billions of identical transistors in regular memory arrays that are controlled by a central processing unit with a few different elements. The brain is not a fixed structure; rather, the adult male human brain contains approximately 86 billion neurons of basically three different types dynamically passing signals to each other via some 500 trillion synaptic connections, making it the most complex thing in the known universe. Furthermore, these neurons have the capacity to change their connections in response to new information and sensory stimulation as well as to damage or dysfunction. This phenomenon, known as neuroplasticity, increases behavioral flexibility and is associated with learning and innovation. [*][33]

As Microsoft cofounder Paul Allen and colleague Mark Greaves point out in a comprehensive critique of Kurzweil's prediction, for Kurzweil's law of accelerating returns to apply and the Singularity to occur in 2045, advances in capability have to occur not only in a computer's hardware technologies (memory, processing power, bus speed, etc.), but also in the software we create to run on these more capable computers.

To achieve the Singularity, it isn't enough just to run today's software faster. We would also need to build smarter and more capable software programs. Creating this kind of advanced software requires a prior scientific understanding of the foundations of human cognition, and we are just scraping the surface of this. "[A]s we learn more and more about the actual complexity of how the brain functions, the main thing we find is that the problem is actually getting harder... The amazing intricacy of human cognition should serve as a caution to those who claim the Singularity is close. Without having a scientifically deep understanding of cognition, we can't create the software that could spark the Singularity." [34]

Kurzweil's assumption that reproducing the structure of a human brain on a computer will reproduce its functioning is further undermined by the

---

[*] See Hands (2017,) pp. 396–405 for a consideration of the brain and its operations.

practical experience of OpenWorm. This international open science project was established in 2011 to recreate the world's first whole organism in a computer by simulating all 959 cells of the tiny *Caenorhabditis elegans* nematode worm in order to understand complex systems like the human brain. The first stage is to model the worm's locomotion by simulating its 302 neurons and 95 muscle cells.

As OpenWorm's leaders say, "Despite decades of effort, we struggle to describe how individual neurons give rise to such organismal behavior [as simple crawling and swimming]."[35]

By 2018 OpenWorm had established collaborations with six university research laboratories in four countries and had a map of the connections between the worm's 302 neurons. It had achieved the impressive feat of designing a simplified software program to give a crude simulation of those connections and had built a prototype OpenWorm robot consisting of nine articulated segments, with each segment mounted on a pair of unpowered wheels. Microprocessors with wireless communication capabilities are fastened to several of the segments. Locomotion is achieved, as in *C. elegans*, by moving the segments in a snake-like manner that relies on surface friction.

OpenWorm claims that the robot behaves in ways similar to those of *C. elegans*. Stimulation of the robot's nose stops forward movement. Touching the anterior and posterior touch sensors makes the robot move forward and back accordingly.[36]

Nonetheless, completion of OpenWorm's first stage has still not been achieved, and the requirements to do so are formidable. Progressing from 302 neurons to 86 billion neurons of basically three different types dynamically passing signals to each other via some 500 trillion synaptic connections involves meeting requirements that are vastly more formidable than Kurzweil proposes.

Neural pattern recognizers will reproduce a mind (Kurzweil)
Kurzweil claims that he has produced a general theory of mind because pattern recognition is the essence of mind and all pattern recognition is implemented by the same basic neural mechanisms. And since we can duplicate these mechanisms in a machine, we can reproduce a mind by creating an artificial version: we just need to install the right pattern recognizers.

In a withering critique of Kurzweil's *How to Create a Mind*, Gary Marcus, professor of cognitive science at New York University, notes that the basic theory of pattern recognition was standard in the field of AI in the 1980s when it was called neocognitron. Marcus points out that Kurzweil's attempt to differentiate his Pattern Recognition Theory of Mind (PRTM) from that of Jeff Hawkins's Hierarchical Temporary Memory System proposed several years previously will convince no one.

Marcus is disappointed that Kurzweil never bothers to build a computer model to instantiate his theory and then compare the predictions of the model with real human behavior. Kurzweil's deepest problem is that he wants badly to provide a theory of the mind and not just the brain. But any theory that seriously engages with what the mind is has to reckon with human psychology—with human behavior and the mental operations that underlie it. "Here, Kurzweil seems completely out of his depth."

Marcus concludes that "Ultimately Kurzweil is humbled by a challenge that has beset many a great thinker extending far beyond his field—Kurzweil doesn't know neuroscience as well as he knows artificial intelligence, and doesn't understand psychology as well as either. (And for that matter he doesn't know contemporary A.I. as well as the A.I. of his heyday, when he was running his companies thirty years ago.)."[37]

In an equally withering criticism, Colin McGinn says Kurzweil's claim that reproducing neural pattern recognizers will reproduce a mind is obviously false. Pattern recognition pertains to perception specifically, not to all mental activity: the perceptual systems process stimuli and categorize what is presented to the senses, but that is only part of the activity of the human mind. In addition to perceiving there are such mental phenomena as conceiving, reasoning, willing, intending, believing, imagining, remembering, and feeling pain, pleasure, or depression. None fits the pattern recognition theory of mind.

One example McGinn gives is thinking about London when he is in Miami. He is not perceiving London with his senses: there is no perceptual recognition in thinking about an absent object. "So pattern recognition cannot be the essential nature of thought. This point seems totally obvious and quite devastating, yet Kurzweil has nothing to say about it, not even acknowledging the problem."[38]

Moreover, not even all perception involves pattern recognition. When you see an apple as red, you don't recognize the color as a pattern because color is not a geometric arrangement of shapes; rather it is a homogeneous sensory quality. Likewise the sweetness of sugar or the scent of a rose.

To create or reproduce a human mind you need at a minimum to create or reproduce consciousness. Kurzweil believes—he calls it a leap of faith—that if a machine can pass the Turing test,* then it is conscious.[39] This conflates talking like a conscious being with possessing all the other attributes of human consciousness—free will, belief, imagination, feeling, etc.—mentioned previously.

Kurzweil's claim does not even address the self-reflection and flashes of insight that characterize a human mind.

* See page 163.

Chapter 11

Mind, memory, and personality uploaded intact (Bostrom)

Bostrom claims that a person's brain can be emulated as software that models the brain's states and functional dynamics at a relatively fine-grained level of detail and that this person's mind can be emulated with sufficient detail and correctness to produce the phenomenological effects of a mind. Moreover, this person's mind, memory, and personality can be uploaded intact onto a computer where it would exist as software. This mind could either inhabit a robotic body or live in virtual reality.*

I won't repeat the fatal flaws in the predictions that a brain—still less a mind—can be uploaded.

Bostrom implies that a brain is the same thing as a mind and encompasses personality. It is not and does not. For example, if you decide to shoot your neighbor, this mental decision causes the activation of neurons in your brain that send signals to activate muscles in your arm and fingers to pick up a loaded gun, point it at your neighbor, and pull the trigger. But it is not the neurons of your brain that make that decision. If you plead not guilty in court on the grounds that it wasn't you but the neurons of your brain that took the decision, I somehow doubt that the judge and jury would be impressed.

As for uploading a memory intact, this implies that memory is a fixed thing, like unchangeable data. In fact human memory constantly adapts to new information and inputs. On November 12, 2007 I saw a production of *Macbeth* at the Gielgud Theatre in London—an unchangeable fact. For the next few years my memory was that it was a magnificent production. Since then, my appreciation of the production has been changed by external factors such as seeing other productions, and I no longer think it magnificent. Moreover, I can no longer remember most details of that performance. Memory is not intact in the generally accepted sense of being untouched and having no missing parts.

Furthermore, even if the memory of an individual human could be uploaded, it would not be the intact memory of that individual because it would be subject to inputs on the substrate different from those experienced by the biological human, and so it would differ from that of the person from whom it was uploaded.

A human's personality comprises the characteristic ways in which an individual thinks, feels, and behaves. It encompasses moods, attitudes, and opinions, and is most clearly seen in their interactions with other people.[40]

Although some believe that your personality results, at least in part, from your genetic makeup, personality is not fixed: an individual's personality traits often change in response to that individual's interactions with other people and with the environment.

All the arguments exposing the flaws in the claim that an individual's memory

* See page 165.

175

can be uploaded intact onto a computer apply with even greater force for the claim that an individual's personality can be uploaded intact.

Assumption of physicalism

Underlying all these predictions is the assumption—whether acknowledged or not—that mind and consciousness are nothing but neurons and their interactions. This is an example of physicalism.

physicalism	The speculation or belief that only physical matter is real and that all other things, such as mind or consciousness or thoughts, will eventually be explained as physical things or their interactions.

This is self-evidently false because the speculation or belief is not itself a physical thing or an interaction of physical things.

There are many attributes of the mind that cannot be reduced to physical things or the interaction of physical things. For example, we can establish scientifically that neurons transmit electrochemical impulses just as we can establish that a telephone landline wire transmits pulses of electricity. We may say that the telephone wire transmits information, but this is only a metaphor. By itself, the telephone wire does nothing. Information is transmitted only when one human mind conveys that information to another human mind at the other end of the telephone wire. Similarly, neurons by themselves do nothing. It requires a conscious mind to activate the neurons, as I illustrated above in the decision to shoot a neighbor.

Even if it is assumed that our minds are generated by, or emerge from, our neurons and their interactions, a mind is not the same thing as the 1.5kg of jelly-like matter that constitutes a human brain. Those who claim that it is fail to provide independently verified observations or experiments that explain what it is like to have subjective experiences of phenomena, such as a notion of self, a feeling of pride, listening to music, and seeing a color (referred to as qualia). The problem is described by two leading neuroscientists, V S Ramachandran and Colin Blakemore

> The riddle of qualia is best illustrated with a thought experiment. Imagine a neuroscientist in some future century, who has complete knowledge of the workings of the brain—including the mechanisms of color vision—but who happens to be color blind and cannot herself distinguish between red and green. She uses the latest scanning techniques to generate a total description of all the electrical and chemical events in the brain of a normal human

as he looks at a red object. The functional account may seem complete, but how could it be so without an explanation of the nature of the unique experience of red, which the scientist herself has never had? There is a deep epistemological gulf between descriptions of physical events in the brain and the personal, subjective experiences that we presume to be associated with those events. [*][41]

Even if it were possible to upload an artificial version of a human's working brain onto a computer—and I have argued above that this is extremely unlikely—all of these predictions wrongly assume that the person's mind has also been uploaded.

Reliability of previous predictions

Predictions from 1965 to 1993 by leaders in the field about the development of AI, and in particular the point at which AI surpasses human intelligence—described either as the Singularity or the achievement of an ultraintelligent machine—are given above. [†] They have proved spectacularly wrong.

In 1996 Eliezer S Yudkowsky predicted that the Singularity would be achieved by 2021. [‡]

Ray Kurzweil, however, claims a high degree of accuracy for his predictions. For example, he says that in 1990 he made 147 predictions for 2009 of which only three were wrong. [42] This is a somewhat generous view of his own predictions. For instance, in 1999 he predicted (and I quote him word for word) that by 2019

- computers are largely invisible: they are embedded everywhere—in walls, tables, chairs, desks, clothing, jewelry, and bodies
- people routinely use three-dimensional displays built into their glasses or contact lenses
- blind persons routinely use eyeglass-mounted reading-navigation systems, which incorporate the new, digitally controlled, high-resolution optical sensors
- the computational capacity of a $4,000 computer is approximately equal to the computational capacity of the human brain (20 million billion calculations per second)
- automated driving systems have been found to be highly reliable and have now been installed in nearly all roads. While humans are still

---

[*] For further consideration of subjective experiences, see Hands (2017,) pp. 577–578
[†] See page 169
[‡] See page 169

allowed to drive on local roads (although not on highways), the automated driving systems are always engaged and ready to take control when necessary to prevent accidents
- household robots for performing cleaning and other chores are now ubiquitous and reliable.[43]

In 2005, he predicted that

- By the end of this decade, computers will disappear as distinct physical objects, with displays built in our eyeglasses, and electronics woven in our clothing providing full-immersion visual virtual reality. Thus, 'going to a Web site' will mean entering a virtual-reality environment—at least for the visual and auditory senses—where we can directly interact with products and people, both real and simulated.[44]
- Computers arriving at the beginning of the next decade [i.e. 2010] will become essentially invisible... Displays will be built into our eyeglasses and contact lenses and images projected directly onto our retinas.[45]
- These resources will provide high-resolution, full-immersion visual-auditory virtual reality at any time.[46]
- Virtual personalities that overlay the real world will help us with information retrieval and our chores and transactions. These virtual assistants won't always wait for questions and directives but will step forward if they see us struggling to find a piece of information.[47]
- In the early part of the second decade of this century [i.e. 2010–2015] visual–auditory virtual-reality environments will be full immersion, very high resolution, and very convincing... Virtual environments will provide high-quality virtual laboratories where experiments can be conducted in chemistry, nuclear physics, or any other scientific field. Students will be able to interact with a virtual Thomas Jefferson or Thomas Edison or even to *become* a virtual Thomas Jefferson... The devices needed to enter these high-quality, high-resolution virtual classrooms will be ubiquitous and affordable even in third world countries. Students at any age, from toddlers to adults, will be able to access the best education in the world at any time and from any place.[48]

None of these predictions has proved correct, and so they provide little confidence that Kurzweil's prediction for the Singularity to occur in 2045 will be any more accurate than earlier failed predictions of this event.

Conclusions

1. The more we learn about the functioning of the human brain, the more we realize how much we do not know.

2. All the previous predictions of when AI will overtake human intelligence—referred to as the Singularity or the emergence of superintelligent machines—have been significantly wrong.

3. All the current predictions of when AI will be harnessed by humans to transform themselves into new, immortal posthumans will almost certainly prove equally unrealistic.

4. Most predictions for such an evolutionary transformation describe the process as one of uploading a human mind onto a superfast computer or other synthetic substrate like a robot, or else enabling that mind to roam freely through the material universe. They are based on unfounded if not fallacious claims, namely

   (a) the functioning of an individual's 1.5kg of jelly-like biological brain containing approximately 85 billion non-neuronal cells (which include glia and other cells, like endothelial cells) plus 86 billion neurons of basically three different types dynamically passing signals to each other via some 500 trillion synaptic connections, with the capacity to change these connections in response to new information and sensory stimulation as well as in response to damage or dysfunction, can all be emulated as computer software;

   (b) an individual's brain is the same thing as his or her mind, and that brain emulation reproduces intact that particular individual's consciousness, self-reflection, memories, intentions, imaginings, beliefs, feelings, personality, and subjective experiences.

5. Such an evolutionary transformation of the human species has a vanishingly small probability of ever being achieved.

Part 4

A DIFFERENT FUTURE

12

The nature of scientific predictions

The more important fundamental laws and facts of physical science have all been discovered, and these are now so firmly established that the possibility of their ever being supplanted in consequence of new discoveries is exceedingly remote.

Albert Michelson, 1894

In Part 4 I will offer a radically different forecast for the future of humankind.

First I will consider the nature of scientific predictions in general, discuss what the predictions in Parts 1, 2, and 3—however different they are—have in common, and say how my forecast is different from these. The following two chapters will set out this radically different forecast.

Scientific predictions

Predicting the development of science and technology in general is hazardous. Even our best minds have made some spectacularly wrong predictions.

For instance, mathematician, physicist, and engineer Lord Kelvin, President of the Royal Society, said in 1883 that "X-rays will prove to be a hoax."[1] He concluded that "[h]eavier-than-air flying machines are impossible"[2] in 1895, eight years before Orville and Wilbur Wright made the first manned flight. In 1900 he echoed the words of the Nobel Prize-winning physicist who established the speed of light as a fundamental constant, Albert Michelson, quoted beneath this chapter's heading, when he said "[t]here is nothing new to be discovered in physics now. All that remains is more and more precise measurement."[3]

As for spaceflight, Richard van der Riet Woolley, who was later appointed Britain's Astronomer Royal, commented in 1936 "The whole procedure [of shooting rockets into space]…presents difficulties of so fundamental a nature, that we are forced to dismiss the notion as essentially impracticable."[4] Woolley's predecessor as Astronomer Royal, Sir Harold Spencer Jones, shared the same view and was reported as saying "Space travel is bunk" in 1957, two weeks before Sputnik orbited the Earth.[5]

Technology plays a key role in many predictions of humankind's future, but as far as computers are concerned some of those best placed to know have erred significantly when envisaging developments. Chairman of IBM Thomas Watson said in 1943 "I think there is a world market for maybe five computers."[6] Addressing a World Future Society meeting in Boston in 1977, founder of Digital Equipment Corporation Ken Olsen opined "There is no reason anyone would want a computer in their home."[7] When launching MSX in 1989 Bill Gates announced "We will never make a 32-bit operating system." Four years later he launched Microsoft's 32-bit operating system, Windows NT 3.1.[8]

Discoverer of the atomic nucleus Ernest Rutherford said in 1930 "The energy produced by the breaking down of the atom is a very poor kind of thing. Anyone who expects a source of power from the transformations of these atoms is talking moonshine."[9] Albert Einstein came to the same conclusion in 1932: "There is not the slightest indication that nuclear energy will ever be obtainable. It would mean that the atom would have to be shattered at will."[10]

Predictions of humankind's future

Evaluating the very different predictions for the future of humankind in Parts 1, 2, and 3 led me to conclude that all had a negligible probability of being realized.

In those cases where specific predictions can be checked against outcomes, all have been disproven.

In Part 1's consideration of extinction predictions, Chapter 4 gives three examples of Paul Ehrlich's many predictions of a population explosion and its consequences. In 1968 he predicted that the battle to feed all of humanity was over: "In the 1970s hundreds of millions of people will starve to death in spite of any crash programs embarked upon now. At this late date nothing can prevent a substantial increase in the world death rate." In 1972 he predicted that by the year 2000 the UK will be simply a small group of impoverished islands inhabited by some 70 million hungry people of little or no concern to the other 5–7 billion inhabitants of a sick world. In the same year he said he would take even money that England will not exist in the year 2000.*

The *Limits to Growth* authors' predictions of world population growth rates have also been disproven.†

As far as climate change is concerned, specific predictions have been made by leading specialists about the melting of the Arctic ice cap and the consequences of disastrous sea-level rises. On June 20, 2008 David Barber,

* See page 41
† See page 40

Canada's Research Chair in Arctic System Science, said "We're actually projecting this year that the North Pole may be free of ice for the first time."[11] On August 10, 2008 Professor Wieslaw Maslowski of the Naval Postgraduate School in Monterey, California forecast that by 2013 the Arctic would be ice-free between mid-July and mid-September.[12] Peter Wadhams, Professor of Ocean Physics and Head of the Polar Ocean Physics Group at the University of Cambridge, was a review editor for the IPCC report AR5 Climate Change 2013: The Physical Science Basis. In 2012 he predicted that the final collapse of the Arctic sea ice "would occur in 2015–16 at which time the summer Arctic (August to September) would become ice-free."[13]

The summer Arctic ice cap has indeed shown an overall retreat since 1979, and the 12 lowest extents have occurred in the years 2007–2018 inclusive. However, all the predictions of the summer ice cap disappearing were wrong (see Table 12.1).

Table 12.1 Minimum arctic ice extent, 2007–2018

Rank	Year	Minimum Ice Extent millions of km^2
1	2012	3.39
2	2007, 2016	4.16
4	2011	4.34
5	2015	4.43
6	2008, 2010, 2018	4.59
9	2017	4.67
10	2013, 2014	5.03
12	2009	5.15

Source: National Snow and Ice Data Center,
http://nsidc.org/arcticseaicenews/2018/09/ 27 September 2018

In 2008, the year Barber predicted an ice-free North Pole, the minimum Arctic ice was 4.59 million km^2, ranking it joint 6th in in terms of minimum Arctic ice extent.

In 2013, the year Maslowski's computer model predicted a 2-month ice-free North Pole, the minimum was 5.03 million km^2, the second largest coverage in those 12 years.

In the summer of 2015, the year Wadhams predicted a summer ice-free North Pole, the minimum was 4.43 million km^2, a 30 percent increase on the figure for 2012, the year of his prediction.

Chapter 5 lists a series of predictions about artificial intelligence that have all been wrong. Pioneer Herbert Simon predicted in 1965 that machines would be capable, within 20 years, of doing any work a human can do.[*] British mathematician I J Good predicted in 1965 that it was more probable than not that, within the 20th Century, an ultraintelligent machine would be built.[†] Marvin Minsky, cofounder of MIT's Computer Science and Artificial Intelligence Laboratory, predicted in 1970 that within about 10 years an ultraintelligent machine would have incalculable intellectual powers that a human mind may not be able to control.[‡] Eric Drexler predicted in 1986 that, within a few decades, thinking machines would likely surpass us in terms of intelligence.[§] Mathematician Vernor Vinge predicted in 1993 that within 30 years we would have the technological means to create a superhuman intelligence, and shortly thereafter the human era would be ended.[¶]

In Part 2's predictions of human survival, Chapter 7 examines survival by colonizing space. Princeton physicist Gerard K O'Neill developed in the 1970s a series of proposals for thousands of space colonies, initially for populations of 10,000 each, in near-Earth orbit that could be built using then-current technology and which would not only be self-financing but also wealth-generating by supplying low-cost energy to the Earth. These would lead to space colonies of several million people. He predicted that the first such colony would be established between 1990 and 2005. Others predicted that this would be achieved even earlier.[**]

In 1978 space science and astronomy author Iain Nicolson predicted the establishment of a lunar base by the early 1990s and manned expeditions to the nearer planets about the end of 20th Century.[††]

Chapter 8 assesses predictions of survival by extending the healthspan of humans. The futurist organization 2045 Initiative claimed that by 2020 there would be widespread use of affordable human-looking robots controlled by brain–computer interfaces.[‡‡]

Part 3's evaluation of the predictions that individuals will be transformed, principally by uploading their minds onto a computer or hologram, included predictions by futurist Ray Kurzweil of the steps on this path. In 1990 he made five such predictions for developments by or before the early 21st Century that were not realized. In 1999 he predicted another five developments that

[*] See page 77
[†] See page 77
[‡] See page 78
[§] See page 78
[¶] See page 78
[**] See page 105
[††] See page 110
[‡‡] See page 119

would take place before 2019 that likewise failed to materialize, and in 2005 he made another five predicted developments that would occur before 2020 that also did not happen.[*]

Common features
However different these predictions are, they have three things in common

(1) They start from the then-current level of science and technology.
(2) They assume that technological development will increase exponentially.
(3) They assume that the future of humankind is determined by the future of individual humans.

A different forecast
By contrast, the forecast I make in the next chapter is based on extrapolating into the future the pattern of scientific evidence shown in human evolution from the origin of the universe. As such it is an empirically based hypothesis rather than a speculative prediction.

I will show, moreover, that what has increased exponentially is not technological development but human reflective consciousness. Thus humans, for instance, eventually took the collective decision—however disputatious the process—to halt and then reverse the technological development of nuclear weapons with increased destructive power.[†] We are currently in the process of collectively deciding to restrict technological developments that result in increasing greenhouse gases in the atmosphere.

---

[*] See page 177 et seq.
[†] See pages 24, 27 et seq., and 32 et seq.

13

The pattern of human evolution

A new type of thinking is essential if mankind is to survive and move to higher levels.

Albert Einstein, 1946

In this chapter I shall summarize what we know of human evolution to see if there is a pattern that can be projected to show how humankind will most probably evolve in the future.

In *COSMOSAPIENS Human Evolution from the Origin of the Universe*[1] I examined all the available scientific evidence and, where such evidence was absent, the most reasonable scientific conjectures about how we evolved from the origin of the universe. This showed that our evolution comprised three distinct stages:

(1) The evolution of matter (inanimate)
(2) The evolution of life (conscious)
(3) The evolution of modern humans (reflectively conscious)

The evolution of matter

evolution   A process of change occurring in something, espe-
                 cially from a simple to a more complex state.

Evolution thus defined makes clears that it is not limited to biological evolution but is a phenomenon we observe throughout the universe.

Physically, we consist of matter and energy, and this can be traced back to primordial energy at the beginning of the universe. The word "universe" has come to mean different things. To avoid misunderstandings, I give here the definition that I use together with other terms used by cosmologists.

universe   All the matter and energy that exists in the one dimen-
                 sion of time and the three dimensions of space.

observable universe	That part of the universe containing matter capable of being detected by astronomical observation. According to current orthodox cosmology it is circumscribed by the speed of light and the time since matter and radiation decoupled some 380,000 years after the universe came into existence in a Big Bang.
megaverse	A speculated higher-dimensional universe in which our universe of three spatial dimensions is embedded. Some speculations posit many megaverses comprising the cosmos.
cosmos	All that exists, which includes various speculations of dimensions other than the three dimensions of space and one of time that we perceive and also other universes with which we have no physical contact and about which we cannot obtain observable or experimental information.
multiverse	A speculated cosmos that contains our universe plus multiple if not infinite other universes with which we have no physical contact and about which we cannot obtain observable or experimental information. Several different kinds of multiverse, each having different properties, have been proposed.

Why and how the universe came into existence are metaphysical questions or, for most people on the planet, religious questions. Religion is outside the scope of this chapter.

Because evidence of the start of the universe is not obtainable, we have no choice but to rely on metaphysical conjecture. The conjecture adopted by most cosmologists is that the universe, including space and time together with a single force of nature, erupted into existence from nothing as a point-like fireball of radiation in a Hot Big Bang.

As the universe rapidly expanded and cooled, the gravitational force separated out from the single universal force of nature to leave a grand unified force. At the same time the radiation produced fundamental particles and antiparticles that initially annihilated each other and converted back into radiation before developing into a seething soup of radiation energy in the form of massless photons together with a much smaller proportion of electrons, quarks, gluons, and other fundamental particles plus their corresponding antiparticles.

Why and how this primordial energy evolved into the universe we observe today has been the subject of very many cosmological conjectures. Most employ mathematical models that incorporate arbitrary constants like Lambda, the cosmological constant, whose value is adjusted to try and reconcile each particular model with our observations. These models have invoked such things as inflation: the idea that the universe underwent a huge and near-instantaneous expansion, inflating by trillions of times in what may have been less than a trillion trillionth of a second either immediately before or immediately after the Hot Big Bang. The latest models propose that the universe consists of 4.9 percent observable matter, 26.8 percent unknown dark matter, and 68.3 percent unknown dark energy.

Whenever these cosmological conjectures have been subject to observational or experimental testing, they have been disproven. Although dark matter has been inferred from its gravitational effects, 40 years of investigations have failed to identify its nature or experimentally confirm the existence of some of the particles postulated to comprise dark matter. 20 years investigation have similarly failed to identify the nature of the mysterious dark energy invoked to explain how the universe has expanded.

The only empirical conclusion we can reach is that from an initial disordered, seething soup of photons and simple fundamental particles, primordial matter evolved to what we observe today.

Large scale

On a large scale we see a complex hierarchy of dynamic structures: stars, many of which are orbited by planets, orbiting a center to form a galaxy; rotating galaxies forming a local group; rotating local groups forming a cluster; and massive sheet-like superclusters separated by large bubble-like voids.

Each structure, such as a galaxy, is not identical to another such structure at the same level (in the way, say, that the units of silicon crystals are identical to each other); each higher level of the hierarchy, like a local group, is not a repeat of the lower level (in this case, a galaxy) on a larger scale. The universe is a complex whole.

The evolutionary pattern here is one of combination and complexification (increasing complexity).

Small scale

To reach this scale and structure from the conjectured Hot Big Bang, the current scientific orthodoxy is that the point-like universe expanded and cooled to the stage at which quark triplets combined inside a range of particles called hadrons, of which the stable protons and neutrons constitute the basic building blocks of all the matter we observe today. The proton has an electrical charge equal in strength to that of an electron, but it is positive compared with the electron's negative charge; it has a mass 1,836 times greater than that of an electron. A proton is also called a hydrogen ion.[*]

Initially, the numbers of protons and neutrons were equal; however, the mass of a neutron is very slightly greater than the mass of a proton, and hence it requires more energy to create a neutron. When the universe was about 1 second old, fewer neutrons were produced because their greater mass required greater energy. Protons and neutrons separated out in the ratio of 7:1.

Some 100 to 200 seconds later, colliding neutrons and protons combine by fusion, bound by the strong interaction,[†] with the release of a photon of energy. A proton-neutron pair is called a nucleus of deuterium, which is an isotope[‡] of hydrogen. Deuterium nuclei combine with each other and with other combination products to form nuclei of helium-3, helium-4, tritium, and rare amounts of lithium-7. This extremely rapid, multistage process of nuclear combination is called nucleosynthesis and its principal product is the stable helium-4 (see Figure 13.1).

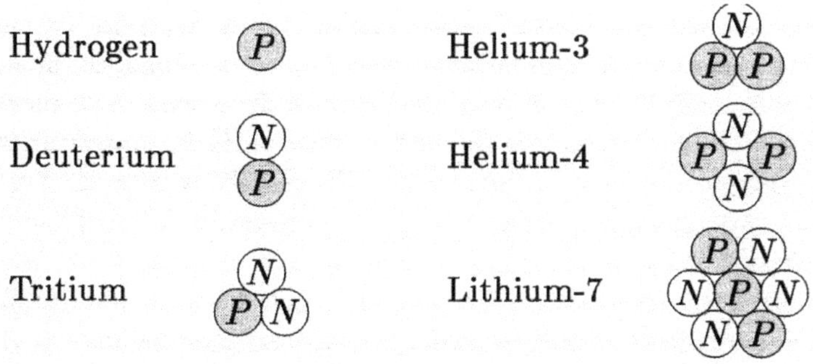

Figure 13.1 Products of the Big Bang nucleosynthesis
The isotopes of hydrogen are given special names: hydrogen-2 is called deuterium and hydrogen-3 is called tritium.

When the universe expands and cools below a hundred million degrees (10^8K), the temperature is not hot enough to cause fusion and so nucleosynthesis

[*] Atoms are electrically neutral; ions are atoms that have either lost or gained one or more electrons and so have either a positive or a negative electrical charge,. A hydrogen atom consists of one proton and one electron, and so a proton is the same as a positively charged hydrogen ion.

[†] A fundamental interaction that confines quarks into proton, neutron, and other hadron particles.

[‡] One element is distinguished from another by having a different number of protons in the nuclei of its atoms; this determines its chemical activity. The most commonly occurring form of an element is the one with the most stable nucleus, which consists of protons and neutrons. In this case the most stable form of hydrogen has no neutrons in its nucleus. Other forms of an element that have the same number of protons but a different number of neutrons are called isotopes of the element. Hence deuterium is an isotope of hydrogen. See Glossary for *atom, element, isotope,* and *atomic number.*

shuts down, leaving about 95 percent of the nuclei by number as stable protons (hydrogen-1) and about 5 percent by number as stable helium-4 nuclei, with just traces of deuterium, helium-3, and lithium-7 nuclei. At this time the average density of matter is the same as the density of water.

After about 380,000 years the universe cools to the point at which negatively charged electrons combine with positively charged nuclei to form electrically neutral, stable diatomic molecules* of hydrogen (H_2) plus trace amounts of deuterium (D_2 and HD) together with atoms of helium (He) and traces of lithium (Li). Electromagnetic radiation decouples from matter and spreads through the expanding and cooling universe to form the cosmic microwave background that we detect today.

Density differences in the expanding cloud of molecules—mainly hydrogen gas—create gravitational fields that slow down the denser regions until they separate out into different clouds light-years across that continue to contract under their own gravity. Their centers heat up as they do so by the conversion of gravitational potential energy of the infalling molecules to kinetic energy, thus increasing the temperature at the center or core; meanwhile, the space between the clouds continues to expand.

About 200–500 million years after the Big Bang some of these clouds have contracted so much, and their cores have become so hot—15 million Kelvin—that they ignite due to hydrogen atoms combining through fusion, emitting hot, bright radiation from their cores that counteracts further gravitational collapse. Thus the first generation of stars form. Cosmologists conjecture that the gravitational force of unknown dark matter causes galaxies to take shape. The only elements in the universe at this point are hydrogen, helium, and traces of lithium.

As the universe continues to expand, the first generation of larger stars consume their hydrogen and undergo gravitational collapse to the point at which their increasing temperature causes helium atoms to combine through fusion to produce carbon.

The naturally occurring elements up to iron in the periodic table are produced by the expansion and collapse of differently sized stars in a process of nuclear fusion with the release of energy. Iron-56 is stable and cannot combine with a proton to produce the next heaviest element, cobalt. However, iron-56 captures three neutrons over a period of thousands of years, whereupon one neutron decays into a proton and an electron to create the more stable cobalt. This process of slow neutron capture inside stars produces many of the stable elements heavier than iron.

---

* A molecule is the smallest physical unit of a substance that can exist independently, consisting of one atom or several atoms bonded by sharing electrons. See Glossary for the distinction between *molecule*, *atom*, *ion*, and *element*.

Other postulated processes such as clouds of interstellar gas and dust produced by supernovae and stellar winds undergo gravitational collapse to produce second- and third-generation stars.

These different processes generate successively larger and more complex nuclei, leading to the nuclei of some 94 naturally occurring elements in the universe.

The evolutionary pattern underlying all these various processes beginning with the simple nuclei of hydrogen is combination and complexification.

At the high temperatures, and hence high energies, in a star its material consists of plasma: a chaotic gas of positively charged nuclei of elements, negatively charged electrons, plus neutral neutrons and photons of electromagnetic energy. After a star has burned up its nuclear fuel and undergoes gravitational collapse, the resulting supernova flings most of this plasma into the cold of interstellar space. When the temperature of the plasma falls to 3,000K the nuclei of elements capture electrons to form stable neutral atoms and molecules in accordance with the Principle of Conservation of Energy, the Principle of Conservation of Charge, and the Law of Electromagnetic Interaction.

While these conservation principles and this law are necessary, they are not sufficient to explain why the negatively charged electrons are not attracted into the positively charged nuclei. This is where quantum theory revolutionized our understanding of matter at the small scale. The laws of quantum mechanics and the Pauli Exclusion Principle provide science's current explanation of how cooled stellar plasma formed the building blocks of life.

Laws of quantum mechanics

According to quantum theory, something as small as an electron behaves as though it were both a particle and a wave. A negatively charged electron can interact with a positively charged nucleus only by surrounding it in a shell-like orbit, called an orbital, that has a discrete energy, say E_2. The electron can lose a quantum of energy, E, by dropping to a lower-energy orbital, say E_1, represented by

$$E = E_2 - E_1 = h\nu$$

where h is Planck's constant and ν is the frequency of the energy lost as electromagnetic radiation.

Conversely, an electron can gain energy by absorbing a quantum of energy and jumping from a lower- to a higher-energy orbital.

Expressed in the International System of Units, the value of h is $6.62607015 \times 10^{-34}$ Joule seconds. No theory explains why this should be so.

Without these discrete energy values of orbiting electrons, every atom would be different and none would be stable.

Pauli Exclusion Principle

The Pauli Exclusion Principle states that no two electrons in an atom or molecule can have the same four quantum numbers.[*] Again, no theory explains why this should be so other than that Pauli's insight enabled the developing field of quantum theory to accord with observation and experiment.

The Pauli Exclusion Principle is different from other physical laws because it is nondynamic—it has no function of distance or time—and it has nothing to say about the behavior of an individual electron but only applies to a system of two or more electrons. This universal law selects a small set of energy states of matter from an otherwise inconceivably vast array of possibilities; it makes every atom of the same element identical; and it dictates how an atom can bond with other atoms, either of the same element or of other elements.

The evolutionary pattern here is convergence. Constrained by the laws of quantum mechanics and the Pauli Exclusion Principle, the vast array of possibilities converges to just 94 elements that occur in nature. Several more elements have been synthesized in the laboratory. All elements discovered to date are shown in the periodic table, in which elements are grouped according to their physico-chemical properties (see Figure 13.2).

These elements are ordered along horizontal rows in the periodic table according to atomic number, the number of protons in the nucleus of the atom. The rows are arranged so that elements with nearly the same chemical properties occur in the same column (group), and each row ends with a noble gas element, which has its outer—or valence—orbital filled with the maximum number of electrons permitted by the Pauli Exclusion Principle and is highly stable and generally inert. The position of an element in the periodic table provides chemists with a powerful guide to the expected properties of molecules made from atoms of the element and explains how simple atoms evolve into the more complex molecules of which living things consist.

---

[*] This principle has since been extended to state that no two types of fermion (a class of particles that includes electrons, protons, and neutrons) in a given system can be in states characterized by the same quantum numbers at the same time.

Periodic Table

The Royal Society of Chemistry's interactive periodic table features history, alchemy, podcasts, videos, and data trends across the periodic table. Click the tabs at the top to explore each section. Use the buttons above to change your view of the periodic table and view Murray Robertson's stunning Visual Elements artwork. Click each element to read detailed information.

H 1																	He 2
Li 3	Be 4											B 5	C 6	N 7	O 8	F 9	Ne 10
Na 11	Mg 12											Al 13	Si 14	P 15	S 16	Cl 17	Ar 18
K 19	Ca 20	Sc 21	Ti 22	V 23	Cr 24	Mn 25	Fe 26	Co 27	Ni 28	Cu 29	Zn 30	Ga 31	Ge 32	As 33	Se 34	Br 35	Kr 36
Rb 37	Sr 38	Y 39	Zr 40	Nb 41	Mo 42	Tc 43	Ru 44	Rh 45	Pd 46	Ag 47	Cd 48	In 49	Sn 50	Sb 51	Te 52	I 53	Xe 54
Cs 55	Ba 56	La 57	Hf 72	Ta 73	W 74	Re 75	Os 76	Ir 77	Pt 78	Au 79	Hg 80	Tl 81	Pb 82	Bi 83	Po 84	At 85	Rn 86
Fr 87	Ra 88	Ac 89	Rf 104	Db 105	Sg 106	Bh 107	Hs 108	Mt 109	Ds 110	Rg 111	Cn 112	Nh 113	Fl 114	Mc 115	Lv 116	Ts 117	Og 118

Ce 58	Pr 59	Nd 60	Pm 61	Sm 62	Eu 63	Gd 64	Tb 65	Dy 66	Ho 67	Er 68	Tm 69	Yb 70	Lu 71
Th 90	Pa 91	U 92	Np 93	Pu 94	Am 95	Cm 96	Bk 97	Cf 98	Es 99	Fm 100	Md 101	No 102	Lr 103

Figure 13.2 Periodic Table of the elements as recognized by the Royal Society of Chemistry in 2022

Evolution of atoms

The atoms formed by the cooled plasma of nuclei and electrons ejected into interstellar space evolve into more complex forms by bonding. What drives this process is attaining the most stable and lowest-energy state possible. In practice this means the nearest electronic configuration to the one in which the valence orbital shell contains the maximum number of electrons permitted by the Pauli Exclusion Principle.

Atoms of the noble gas elements have this configuration naturally and are stable. Other atoms attain stability by bonding, either with one or more identical or different atoms, in one of four different ways.

Ionic bonding (exchange of electrons)

In ionic bonding an atom gives one or more of its valence electrons to an atom of an element that lacks a complement of electrons in its valence shell. For example, stable common (or table) salt is represented Na^+Cl^-. The donor positive ion and the recipient negative ion attract each other by the electric force.

Covalent bonding (sharing of electrons)

Instead of receiving an electron from an atom of a different element, atoms of one element can share one or more electrons with atoms of another element to form a compound molecule* through covalent bonding. For example,

---

* A molecule is the smallest physical unit of a substance that can exist independently, consisting of one atom or several atoms bonded by sharing electrons. See Glossary for the distinction between *molecule*, *atom*, *ion*, and *element*.

a chlorine atom can share an electron with another chlorine atom to form a diatomic chlorine molecule, Cl_2. Two atoms of hydrogen can share their electrons with the six in one oxygen atom's valence shell to produce the stable water molecule H_2O.

Metallic bonding

Metallic bonding occurs when atoms of the same element each lose an electron to form a lattice of positively charged ions held together by a pool of free electrons. Unlike in covalent bonding, the electrons in metallic bonding are free to move, and so a metallically bonded substance conducts electricity.

Van der Waals bonding

Van der Waals bonding is electrostatic bonding between electrically neutral molecules that arises because, due to the shape of the molecules, the distribution of electrical charge is not symmetrical. The microscopic separation of the positive and negative charge centers leads the positive end of one molecule to attract the negative end of an identical molecule, and so on. At normal atmospheric pressure, between a temperature of 0°C and 100°C van der Waals bonding keeps water molecules bound to each other in a fluid state, water. At a higher temperature, the higher energies break these bonds and water molecules exist as separate entities in a gaseous state, steam. At a lower temperature, with less thermal agitation, these bonds are sufficient to hold the molecules in a solid, crystalline state, ice (see Figure 13.3).

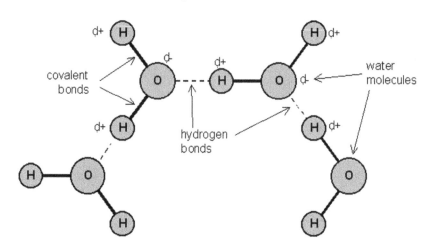

Figure 13.3 Van der Waals bonds, or hydrogen bonds, in liquid water
d+ and d– represent dipolar electrical charges

Crystalline structures

With the exception of helium, at appropriate temperatures all atoms, molecules, and ions exist in a solid state, usually crystalline, in which the atoms, molecules, or ions are bonded not just to one other but also to very many others in a lattice structure: a regularly ordered, repeating pattern extending in all three spatial dimensions. All four types of bonding form crystalline structures, and the particular structure and bonding method determine the solid's physical properties. Ionically bonded sodium and chlorine ions, for example, form crystals of common (or table) salt, while covalently bonded carbon atoms exist as soft graphite and as hard diamond.

Uniqueness of carbon

Carbon, the fourth most abundant element in the universe, has unique bonding properties. These derive in part because carbon has a high value of electronegativity, the relative ability of an atom to attract valence electrons. A carbon atom has four electrons in its outer or valence shell, when eight are permitted by the Pauli Exclusion Principle; as such, it is capable of bonding to four other atoms at once. It possesses the greatest tendency to form covalent bonds and, in particular, has a remarkable tendency to bond with itself; it is capable of forming not only a single bond, with one pair of shared valence electrons, but also a double bond (two pairs) or even a triple bond (three pairs). Another special property of carbon is its ability to bond in sheets, ring structures, and long chains that constitute strings of carbon atoms and other atoms.

These properties generate a uniquely vast range of large and complex molecules—called organic molecules—many of which are found in all forms of life identified thus far. Consequently, carbon is essential for life as we know it; without carbon we would not exist.

Molecules in space

Spectroscopic analysis indicates that interstellar space provides limited conditions for the evolution of complex molecules from the nuclei and electrons ejected by supernovae. The molecules that have been detected include simple diatomic ones like hydrogen, H_2, and carbon monoxide, CO, through organic molecules containing up to 13 atoms like acetone, $(CH_3)_2CO$, trans-ethyl methyl ether, $CH_3OC_2H_5$, and cyanodecapentayne, $HC_{10}CN$, but so far no more complex molecules have been discovered. Depending on the temperature of the region of space these interstellar atoms and molecules are found in the gaseous or solid ("interstellar dust") state.

Molecules of similar complexity have been found in our solar system in a class of meteorites known as carbonaceous chondrites. According to radio-carbon dating, these are typically about 4.5 billion to 4.6 billion years old and are thought to consist of material from the asteroid belt. These rocks, which comprise mainly silicates, contain a variety of organic molecules including simple amino acids, the building blocks of proteins.

The most complex molecules we have discovered have been found on our planet. Conditions on the surface of the Earth have provided the environment for the next stage of our evolution, the evolution of life, that I will consider in the next section.

Conclusions

The underlying pattern for the evolution of matter from the fundamental particles arising from a conjectured Hot Big Bang is combination leading to complexification plus convergence from the near-infinite possibilities thereby produced to organic molecules containing no more than 13 atoms.

This pattern of combination, complexification, and convergence was only possible because matter evolved in accordance with a series of physical and chemical laws together with specific values for six cosmological parameters and two dimensionless constants. Science cannot explain what caused these laws, parameters, and constants to exist.

The evolution of life

After examining many definitions of life, I define life as follows:

life	The ability of an enclosed entity to respond to changes within itself and in its environment, to extract energy and matter from its environment, and to convert that energy and matter into internally directed activity that includes maintaining its own existence.

This definition rejects the argument that there is no distinction between what is alive and what is not alive: nonliving things are not necessarily enclosed and do not possess the characteristic functions and internally directed activity of living things.

Just because the living/nonliving boundary is indistinct, as with a virus, this does not mean that there is no boundary. The change from nonliving to living represents not simply a difference in degree but a difference in kind. It marks a new stage in our evolution.

Conclusive fossil evidence of life—complex branched microorganisms—has been identified in rocks dated to 2 billion years ago, some 2.5 billion years after the Earth formed. Assuming that these microorganisms evolved from simpler lifeforms, life must have existed before then.

Precisely when and how living things emerged on Earth is impossible to establish because of the paucity of the fossil record in general and because nearly all sedimentary rock from the first two 2 billion years has been subducted or metamorphosed. The current best estimate is that life arose probably 3.5 billion years ago.

The simplest, and presumably the earliest, form of life is an independent prokaryote, a single cell in which its genetic information encoded in DNA is not enclosed in a nucleus within the cell.

In order to function independently—a virus is not independent—the simplest prokaryote needs a chromosome in the form of a folded loop of double-helical strands of DNA consisting of at least 36 million atoms configured in a specific structure. These strands unwind in order to act as templates to synthesize identical DNA strands needed for the cell to replicate itself and also to synthesize the proteins needed to repair and maintain itself (see Figure 13.4).

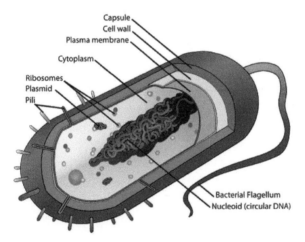

Figure 13.4 Structure of a bacterium, a simple independent prokaryote

Neither science nor any persuasive hypothesis is able to explain when and how such a size of cell with such a complexity of components, functions, and changing configurations emerged from the interactions of atoms and simple molecules consisting of up to 13 atoms on the surface of the newly formed Earth.

As with the emergence of matter, it is most probably beyond the ability of science to explain the emergence of life.

Once life had emerged, it evolved. The pattern of the fossil record over time is from simple to more complex species: prokaryotes appear before eukaryotes, unicellular eukaryotes before multicellular, radially symmetrical before bilateral and cephalized,* invertebrates before vertebrates, fishes before amphibians, reptiles before birds, mammals before primates, and apes before humans.

This is not a linear progression but a networking, fusing, and branching evolution from a universal common ancestor into very many lineages that, for the vast majority, end in extinction.

Lineages reach stasis, in which the last species in the lineage shows little change either before extinction or, less commonly, for some tens or even hundreds of millions of years to the present day.

While competition and rapid environmental change cause the extinction of species, collaboration causes the evolution of species. It enables the survival and propagation of life from prokaryotes collaborating in colonies to sustain and replicate themselves, organelles collaborating within a unicellular eukaryote to sustain and replicate the cell, specialized cell groups collaborating within multicellular organisms, and animals collaborating in societies like colonies of insects, shoals of fishes, flocks of birds, and families, clans, troops, and the other social groups of many mammals. Collaboration also takes place between members of different species. It can be instinctive, conditioned, or coercive.

For unicellular and animal species, collaboration principally takes the form of a group within a species communicating and working together to construct a communal shelter, produce and rear offspring, forage, defend themselves, attack prey, and, where necessary, migrate to a supportive habitat for their survival and reproduction. Such a habitat must provide adequate sources of food plus protection from anything that threatens their lives, including other species preying on them. In some cases several groups within a species, and even within related species, also collaborate for mutual benefit, particularly for migration.

Migration illustrates another characteristic that distinguishes living things from inanimate matter: only living things can move of their own volition.

The evolution of life, however, is more than biological evolution. The pattern of the evolution of life is one of increasing consciousness.

consciousness	Awareness of the environment, other organisms, and self that can lead to action; a property shared by all organisms in differing degrees, from rudimentary levels in very simple organisms to more sophisticated levels in organisms with complex cerebral systems.

Consciousness thus defined may be mapped by its consequent actions, namely

---

* An evolutionary trend in which, over many generations, the mouth, sense organs, and nerve cells become concentrated at the front end of an animal, producing a head region.

by an organism's behavior. It emerges in rudimentary form in prokaryotes, the most primitive and ancient lifeforms on Earth, evidenced by the actions they take to survive.

Consciousness rises along animal lineages, demonstrated by the evolution of more complex and varied actions, notably the addition of innate, learned, social, and innovative behaviors. As progressively more complex species evolved along the human lineage, learned, social, and innovative behaviors increased in significance.

The physical correlate of this rise in consciousness is the evolution in animals of an electrochemical nervous system enabling progressively more rapid, varied, and flexible responses to external stimuli. It is characterized by three inter-related trends.

Growth
With growth, net increases in the number of neurons, or nerve cells, and their connections develop.

Complexification
The nervous system complexifies by increasing the number of neurons and their modifiable connections until the human brain emerges as the most complex thing in the known universe. It also complexifies through the growth in number and size of specialized interconnected groups of neurons processing and controlling responses to an increasing range of external and internal stimuli. The neocortex—the most recently evolved and most complex part of the brain—shows the greatest growth from early mammals to humans, correlating with an increase in innovative behavior—a mark of intelligence—from mammals to primates, followed by a vastly greater increase in innovative behavior and intelligence in humans.

Convergence
Growth and complexification are accompanied by a progressive convergence, from a diffuse network of neurons in simple primitive animals to a centralized nervous system in vertebrates in which most neuron groups become concentrated in the head, with the rest present in the spinal column.

Conclusions
Mobility differentiates living things from inanimate matter.

The underlying pattern of combination in the evolution of matter has developed for the evolution of life into collectivization.

| **collectivization** | Working together involuntarily, whether by instinct or conditioned learning or coercion. |

Like the evolution of matter, the evolution of life also shows an underlying pattern of complexification together with convergence that, in the human lineage, produces a rise in consciousness.

The evolution of modern humans

After examining the various definitions of modern humans, *Homo sapiens*, proposed by specialists in different disciplines, I concluded that none was satisfactory. What makes humans unique is not bipedalism, type of teeth, cranial capacity, skeletal structure, hairlessness, genes, or neural activity in areas of the brain. Such characteristics are either exhibited by other organisms or else the human variant differs only by a small degree from that of some other organisms.

We do possess, however, one characteristic that is unique.

The evolution of life was characterized by a rise in consciousness. With increasing complexity, convergence and, in the case of humans, optimization of the nervous system, consciousness rises along the human lineage to the point *where it becomes conscious of itself.* Like water heated to 100°C, a phase change occurs: consciousness reflects on itself.

| **reflective consciousness** | The property of an organism by which it is conscious of its own consciousness; that is, not only does it know but also it knows that it knows. |

Humans may thus be defined as

| **Homo sapiens** | The only species known to possess reflective consciousness. |

This faculty enables humans to think about themselves and their relationship with the rest of the universe of which they know they are a part.

The most compelling evidence for this faculty is humans asking, and attempting to answer, such questions as: What are we? Where did we come from? What is the universe in which we exist? and so on: the stuff of religion, of philosophy, and subsequently also of science.

This is the full flowering of reflective consciousness. It did not, however, spring suddenly into existence fully formed, just as a mass of heated water does not suddenly all turn into steam when the temperature reaches 100°C.

We detect the first glimmerings of reflective consciousness in prehistoric times through the evidence of new faculties that it generates and of faculties possessed by prehumans that it transforms.

Chief among the faculties that reflective consciousness radically transforms are comprehension, memory, foresight, cognition, learning, invention, intention, and communication. The new faculties it generates include thought, reasoning, insight, imagination, creativity, abstraction, will, language, belief, and morality. Its possession demarcates cooperation (rational, voluntary collaboration) from collectivism (instinctive, conditioned, or coercive collaboration).

These faculties tend to act synergistically, and the results of such actions leave evidence. For example, comprehension combined with invention, foresight, and imagination produces specialized composite tools; cognition combined with imagination produces beliefs in supernatural powers that result in religious rituals; cognition combined with communication produces representational art that results in paintings and sculptures; add imagination and such art extends to images that are not observed in life; add abstraction and the art extends to symbols.

Evidence for the use of composite tools (as distinct from, say, a stone used by a chimpanzee to crack open a nut) is claimed at several sites from 72,000 years ago and even from one site dating as far back as 164,000 years ago. The earliest evidence for the use of symbols and the capacity for artistic expression appears at different levels of the Blombos Cave on South Africa's southern Cape coast dating from at least 100,000 to 75,000 years ago in the form of pieces of ochre engraved with abstract designs plus perforated seashells, some of which are daubed with ochre. These are assumed to have been used as personal ornaments, and similar ones have been discovered in Israel, Algeria, and Morocco tentatively dated from 80,000 to over 100,000 years ago. More sophisticated cave paintings in southern France date from 35,000 years ago.

A ceremonial burial has been claimed to date from 115,000 years ago in Israel, while the world's oldest ritual use of ochre in burials and the first recorded cremations appear some 40,000 ± 2,000 years ago at Lake Mungo in Australia's western New South Wales.

Members of many species with high levels of consciousness use sounds and gestures to communicate fear, warning, threat, pleasure, and other emotions both to other members and to other species. Reflective consciousness, however, transforms communication into language, which I define as

language The communication of feelings, narratives, explanations, or ideas by a complex structure of learned spoken or written or signed symbols that convey meaning in the culture within which they are employed.

Language's unique ability to transmit experiences and ideas not only to other living members of the human species but also to succeeding generations, who thereby benefit from accumulated wisdom, enabled the increasingly rapid flowering of reflective consciousness.

The only unambiguous evidence of language is written records. The earliest writing systems were cuneiform engraved on clay tablets from around 5,000 years ago in Sumer, Mesopotamia, and Egyptian hieroglyphs engraved on stone from roughly the same period. But clearly these evolved from earlier proto-writing that in turn had developed from pictorial symbols, the origin of which probably lies in the painted artworks and symbols together with symbols carved in ochre mentioned previously.

The first glimmerings of reflective consciousness thus appear as different manifestations of new or radically transformed faculties at various places and periods, like bubbles of steam bursting out at different times from different areas on the surface of boiling water. At the surface some bubbles may condense back to liquid. But above this transitional surface, while water molecules may have the same 100°C temperature as those forming the liquid below, they are indisputably gas: a phase change has occurred. Likewise, consciousness has entered a new, reflective phase that signals the presence of *Homo sapiens*.

A combination of the available evidence indicates that the emergence of self-reflective humans took place during the Later Stone Age in Africa and the Upper Paleolithic on different continents, spanning roughly 40,000 to 10,000 years ago, although incomplete or questionable evidence suggests that reflective consciousness may well have emerged earlier.

Like the emergence of matter and the emergence of life, because of the absence or paucity of evidence it is almost certain that science will never be able to identify precisely when humans emerged.

The evolution of self-reflective humans may be divided into three overlapping phases: primeval thinking, philosophical thinking, and scientific thinking.

Primeval thinking

I define this phase as

primeval thinking	The first phase of reflective consciousness when reflection on self and its relationship with the rest of the universe is rooted principally in survival and superstition.

This phase was the only kind of reflective thinking for some 90 percent of modern human existence. It produced six things that had profound consequences for human evolution:

(1) the transition from humans adapting to the environment to adapting the environment to their needs;
(2) the transition from a nomadic hunter–gatherer existence to settled communities;
(3) the invention and dissemination of technologies that drove the growth of agricultural villages into city-states and then empires, each with a social hierarchy based on specialized functions;
(4) the invention and development of writing;
(5) the foundations of astronomy and mathematics; and
(6) the development of belief systems and religions.

Cooperation made these developments possible, but it struggled against the instinct for competition ingrained in humans over millions of years of prehuman ancestry that produced battles for the control of human settlements.

As human societies became more centered and grew in size, they developed the complexity of a social hierarchy that reflected the inherited skills and functions of its members, typically a ruler, priests, warriors, merchants and craftsmen, farmers, and slaves. The overall pattern across the globe was an increase in size, complexity, and convergence of human societies.

Figure 13.5 gives a simplified representation of the evolution of some of the main strands of primeval thinking following the emergence of reflective consciousness. It is not a conventional tree diagram, like a genealogical tree with fixed relationships, but a two-dimensional snapshot of a four-dimensional dynamic process in which its branches and sub-branches not only changed over time—developing, ramifying still further, or withering, becoming moribund, or dying—but also interacted with other branches to hybridize or mutate or generate a new branch.

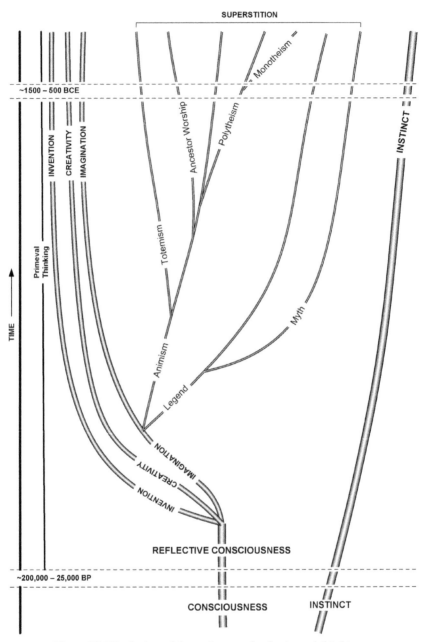

Figure 13.5 Evolution of the main strands of primeval thinking
Unlike a conventional tree diagram with fixed relationships, this is a simplified snapshot of
a four-dimensional dynamic and interactive process. It is not drawn to scale and the dates
are best estimates. BP = before present.

For example, imagination—the ability of the mind to form images, sensations, and ideas not seen or otherwise experienced at the time—not only gave rise to superstitious beliefs, such as a spirit with the body of a man and the head of a lion, but it also interacted with creativity to produce new, practical things, such as the wheel, while creativity also gave rise to non-practical things, like abstract art.

Invention—the ability to make new things—may have resulted from the interaction of creativity and imagination, but it could also have resulted from experimentation, such as trial and error when mixing liquid copper and tin in different quantities to produce an alloy, bronze, with properties superior to either for use as tools and weapons.

Figure 13.5 also shows instinct, which was ingrained for several million years in our hominid ancestors.

instinct   An innate, impulsive response to stimuli, usually determined by biological necessities such as survival and reproduction.

Instinct did not vanish when reflective consciousness emerged from consciousness to distinguish *Homo sapiens* from other species. To the contrary, even today instinct remains a powerful force and must be taken into account when trying to understand human behavior.

Philosophical thinking
The second phase of human evolution began when reflection on the self and its relationship with the rest of the universe branched off from superstition into philosophy.

philosophy   Love of wisdom; thinking about ultimate reality, the essence and causes of things, the natural world, human behavior, and thinking itself.

Philosophy emerged roughly 3,000 years ago at different places across the globe and was characterized by a desire to seek explanations that did not invoke imagined spirits or anthropomorphic gods or God, which had been believed for more than 20,000 years.

Philosophers employed insight, often resulting from disciplined meditation, and reasoning, based on prior assumptions or interpretations of evidence.

The insights of seers—whether Indian, Chinese, Greek, or Roman—tended to share common features, in particular the underlying unity of all things. In most cases this underlying unity or ultimate reality was experienced as something ineffable, best described as a transcendent cosmic consciousness or intelligence existing formlessly outside of space and time but also immanent in that it gives rise to all the phenomena perceived by our physical senses and our mind; arising from this underlying unity the essence of each of us is identical to the whole. Moreover, this ultimate reality is manifest in, or regulates, how the cosmos functions, and we should harmonize our lives with it in order to achieve fulfillment.

Reasoning was employed in teaching insights and also as a method of inquiry.

Where thinking focused on ethics—how we should behave—virtually all ancient philosophers, whether using insight or reasoning, taught that we will only achieve happiness or tranquility by acting unselfishly and doing to all others as we would have them do to us. This ran counter to the prevailing inherited instinctive drive in their societies for aggression, warfare, and conquest. At root it is a prescription for cooperation not competition in order to achieve progress for humankind.

A fundamental divergence between insight and reasoning occurred from late in the 12th Century CE when the West adopted reasoning as virtually the only method of philosophical thinking, although the evidence does not support the superiority of one method over the other.

Scientific thinking

The third phase of human evolution is characterized by scientific thinking, through which knowledge and understanding are obtained empirically rather than by philosophical speculation or belief based on claimed supernatural revelation.

The meaning of science has changed over the centuries. The contemporary definition I use here is the one I formulated in Chapter 6:

science	The attempt to understand and explain natural phenomena by using systematic—preferably measurable—observation or experiment and to apply reason to the knowledge thereby obtained in order to infer testable laws and make predictions or retrodictions.

Although science overlaps with technology, I think it useful to make a distinction between them.

technology	The invention, making, and use of tools or machines to solve a problem.

Science is inseparable from its method. This, too, has changed over time.

The current understanding is that the scientific method consists of five steps summarized in the following definition.

scientific **method** **(notional)**	1. Data is collected by systematic observation of, or experiment on, the phenomenon being studied. 2. A provisional conclusion, or hypothesis, is inferred from this data. 3. Predictions deduced from this hypothesis are tested by further observations or experiments. 4. If these tests confirm the predictions, and independent testers reproduce the confirmations, then the hypothesis is accepted as a scientific theory until such time as new data conflict with the theory. 5. If new data conflict with the theory, then the theory is either modified or discarded in favor of a new hypothesis that is consistent with all the data.

In practice these steps are not always followed. Insight, rather than Step 2, has usually been responsible for major scientific advances.

Scientific thinking emerged at different times in three overlapping groups: physical sciences, life sciences, and medical sciences.

physical **sciences**	The branches of science that study inanimate phenomena; they include astronomy, physics, chemistry, and the Earth sciences.
life **sciences**	The branches of science that study features of living organisms, such as plants, animals, and humans, and also the relationships between such things.
medical **sciences**	The branches of science that are applied to maintain health, prevent and treat disease, and treat injuries.

The medical sciences have their roots in the healing practices of ancient times, which were entangled with superstition, and they emerged as part of modern science in the 17th Century, as did the life sciences. The oldest physical science, astronomy, dates from prehistoric times, when it developed to serve superstitious beliefs, before it emerged as a modern science in the 16th Century. Physics, the fundamental physical science, emerged from natural philosophy in the 16th and 17th Centuries. During this period, commonly referred to as the Scientific Revolution, many of the ancient ideas of medicine, astronomy, and natural philosophy were disproved and new, empirically based theories proposed. Most of its practitioners nonetheless retained superstitious beliefs.

By the 19th Century the study of humans and their social relationships led to the social sciences branching from the life sciences.

Once it had emerged, scientific thinking evolved with increasing speed mainly due to five synergistic factors:

(1) cooperation among scientists through scientific societies dedicated to sharing knowledge and thinking and also through teamwork in specific scientific investigations that developed from the local through the national to the international levels;

(2) aids to calculation that developed from mechanical calculating machines to personal computers and supercomputers;

(3) the dissemination of knowledge, which stimulates new thinking, that developed from hand-operated moveable metal typeface printing machines to the Internet, followed by the World Wide Web that not only provides virtually instantaneous communication of new knowledge but also globalization of that knowledge;

(4) the development of new technologies designed for specific scientific investigations;

(5) the widening access to education that resulted in the training of more scientists.

Figure 13.6 gives an overview of the evolution of scientific thinking from natural philosophy—the branch of reasoning that attempts to understand the natural world perceived by our senses and how it operates—to the present day, with its ramification into specialized branches.

This simplified two-dimensional snapshot does not show the psychological sciences or the other social sciences such as archeology, anthropology, and sociology that branched from the life sciences during the late 19th Century, nor the profusion of specialist sub-branches. It serves to illustrate the divergent, ramifying pattern of scientific thinking since the late 16th Century.

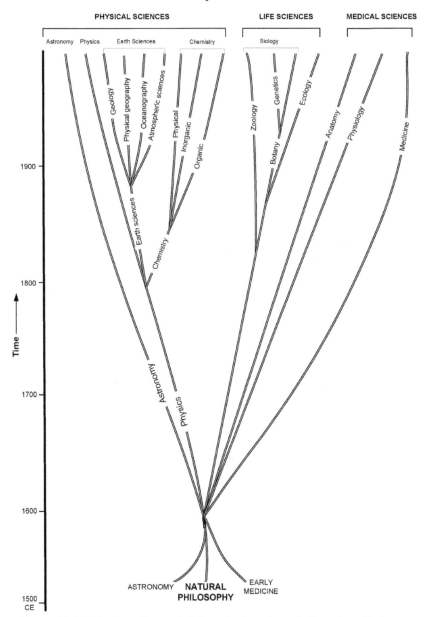

Figure 13.6 Evolution of natural philosophy into the main branches of science
A simplified, two-dimensional snapshot of a four-dimensional dynamic and interactive
process. For the sake of clarity, not all branches and sub-branches are shown. Superstition's
interaction with natural philosophy and with physics, for example, played a significant
role. Exactly when a new shoot emerges as a distinct sub-branch is difficult to determine;
accordingly, the timescale shown is simply the best estimate.

Counter to this diverging trend, however, is one of convergence led by the fundamental science of physics as illustrated in Figure 13.7

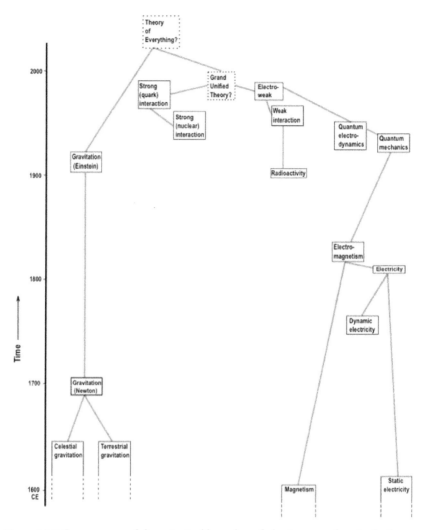

Figure 13.7 Convergence of the principal branches of physics towards a single theory that describes all the interactions between all forms of matter

In the late 17th Century Newton recognized that the force that causes objects to accelerate to the ground is the same force that causes planets to orbit the Sun and moons to orbit their planets. Electrical current was discovered in the middle of the 18th Century and was realized to be a manifestation of the power of static electricity, which had been known since ancient times, while from the first quarter of the 19th Century physicists showed that the electrical force and the magnetic force are different aspects of an underlying electromagnetic force.

The realization that underlying apparently different physical phenomena was the same cause increased rapidly in the 20th Century. Physicists theorized that the electromagnetic force itself and the weak nuclear force were particular manifestations of the same force, which they called the electroweak interaction. The theory predicted the existence of new particles, which experimentalists found.

Theoretical physicists subsequently produced several mathematical models for a Grand Unified Theory (GUT) that unites the electroweak force and the strong nuclear force, the strongest of all known force that acts only over very small distances within an atomic nucleus and binds together particles within the nucleus, although no experimental data have been produced so far that validate any of these models.

The holy grail of physics, however, is to unite these theories, which seek to explain interactions of phenomena on the scale of the very tiny—the size of an atom or smaller—with relativity theory, which explains interactions on the scale of the very large—the size of a star and above—in a Theory of Everything. Theoretical physicists have advanced candidates for such a theory, like the many versions of the string conjecture and loop quantum gravity. While currently there is no known way to subject these hypotheses to empirical testing, the thrust of theoretical physics, especially over the last 30 years, has been to try and show that all physical phenomena in the universe are lower energy manifestations of one fundamental energy at the beginning of the universe.

Prominent theoretical physicists, such as Erwin Schrödinger, Max Planck, and Fritjof Capra, have pointed out that this convergent trend in Western physics has much in common with Eastern mystical insights that see all material phenomena as a manifestation of the cosmic consciousness that is the source and ground of reality.

Conclusions

The underlying pattern of human evolution since reflective consciousness marked its full emergence some 40,000 to 10,000 years ago up to the present day shows several characteristic features.

The collectivization that marked the evolution of life developed for self-reflective humans into cooperation.

Struggling against our instinctive urge to compete inherited over millions of years of prehuman ancestry, cooperation developed from agricultural villages through to global organizations like the United Nations Children's Fund (UNICEF). Progress in science, for instance, was achieved primarily through cooperation. Individuals certainly made significant conceptual breakthroughs, but these were achieved through cooperation facilitated by the founding of scientific societies, the publishing of their findings, and the development of international teams to investigate phenomena, exemplified by the construction and operation of the Large Hadron Collider, the world's largest and most powerful particle accelerator designed to investigate how fundamental particles react.

Life's underlying pattern of complexification continued for human evolution, not in terms of physical change, but in terms of ideas and inventions, and also in terms of our social interactions. An individual member of the most highly conscious nonhuman species, like chimpanzees, belongs to only one social group at a time. The purposes of that mainly kin-related group are survival and reproduction. By contrast, humans belong simultaneously to very many social groups whose purposes range far beyond survival and reproduction and that operate at family, local, regional, national, supranational, and global levels.

The evolution of life's underlying pattern of convergence developed into a similar pattern for humans. Despite extending their habitat to encompass the whole globe, humans didn't diverge into different species.

The convergent trend is also evident in the intercommunicating, interacting, and cooperating social networks that function at family, local, regional, national, supranational, and global levels. These are producing a shared human consciousness that reflects on such things as the survival of our species, our planetary habitat, other species on the planet, and our future evolution and relationship with the rest of the cosmos, of which we know we are a part.

This convergence of thinking only began about 65 years ago and illustrates another striking pattern: human evolution has been accelerating at an ever-increasing rate. Humans fully emerged as a self-reflective species at least 40,000 and up to 10,000 years ago. If we take the mean of that range, 25,000 years ago, as the starting point, then for 88 percent of that time human societies were exclusively primeval, when reflections on the self and its relationship with the rest of the universe were based on superstition and concerned solely with survival. Only in the last 12 percent of that time did human reflection include the pursuit of knowledge and understanding for its own sake through philosophical insight and reasoning, while the scientific age employing systematic observation and testing of evidence occupies less than 2 percent of human existence.

To use the 24-hour clock analogy, if humans emerged at time zero then philosophical thinking emerged at 2 hours 53 minutes before midnight, while scientific thinking emerged only at 28 minutes before midnight, and convergent thinking at 3 minutes before midnight, illustrated in Figure 13.8.

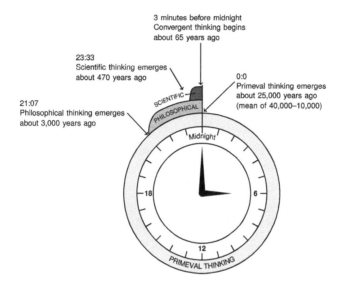

3 minutes before midnight
Convergent thinking begins
about 65 years ago

23:33
Scientific thinking emerges
about 470 years ago

21:07
Philosophical thinking emerges
about 3,000 years ago

0:0
Primeval thinking emerges
about 25,000 years ago
(mean of 40,000–10,000)

SCIENTIFIC

PHILOSOPHICAL

Midnight

18

6

12

PRIMEVAL THINKING

Figure 13.8 The phases of human evolution represented by a 24-hour clock

The changing duality of human nature

A basic duality in human nature has been evident from the emergence of humans, manifested in such things as cooperation versus competition, selflessness versus selfishness, and altruism versus aggression.

But this conflict is not static. Because reflective consciousness has been evolving at a rapidly increasing rate from its emergence, it is changing the balance of this duality. While the aggressive, competitive instinct remains a more powerful but decreasing force shaping human evolution, it has been countered by an increasing comprehension that peaceful cooperation is the only way for the human species to survive and continue to evolve.

In the not-too-distant future, this rapidly increasing reflective consciousness that generates cooperation, altruism, complexification, and convergence will prove more powerful than the instinct that generates competition, aggression, hierarchism, and divergence.

Integrating these dynamic patterns in the evidence for the evolution of modern humans may be represented schematically as in Figure 13.9.

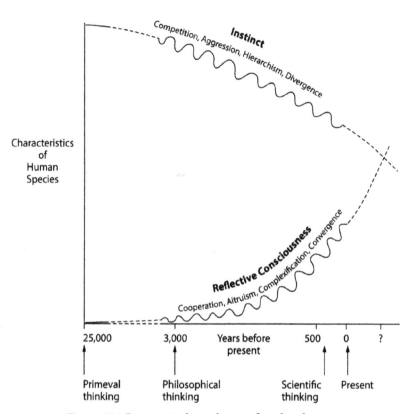

Characteristics
of
Human
Species

Instinct

Competition, Aggression, Hierarchism, Divergence

Reflective Consciousness

Cooperation, Altruism, Complexification, Convergence

| 25,000 | 3,000 | Years before present | 500 | 0 | ? |

Primeval
thinking

Philosophical
thinking

Scientific
thinking

Present

Figure 13.9 Patterns in the evolution of modern humans
The wavy lines indicate groping progression, a series of advances overcoming setbacks.

In the next chapter I shall project this pattern into the future to identify where this cosmic evolutionary process most probably will lead.

14

The fourth stage of human evolution

If the co-operation of some thousands of millions of cells in our brain can produce our consciousness, the idea becomes vastly more plausible that the co-operation of humanity, or some sections of it, may determine what Comte called a Great Being.

J B S Haldane, 1932

It is wise to acknowledge that all things are one.

Heraclitus, 6th Century BCE

Continuing the pattern of cooperation, complexification, and convergence strongly suggests a radical break for the next, fourth stage of human evolution. It will not be an evolution of individual humans but an evolution of humans as a whole.

Through cooperation the reflective consciousness of individuals has been groping towards a shared human consciousness that reflects on itself, its future, and the cosmos of which it knows it is a part.

Just as the cooperation of some thousands of millions of cells in one human brain generates a complex reflective consciousness for that individual human, so too the cooperation of thousands of millions of human minds will generate a complex reflective consciousness for all those participating humans.

That consciousness will not be anchored in individual human minds.

In Stage 2 of our evolution, individual lifeforms escaped the immobility of their inanimate roots to evolve in a supportive habitat. In Stage 3 individual humans cooperated to escape the supportive habitat in which they had emerged and to spread throughout the planet. In Stage 4 the collective mind that emerges will most likely evolve to escape its biological roots and spread throughout the universe as a cosmic consciousness.

Elsewhere in the universe?

One question to ask is: Has this process taken place elsewhere in the universe? The answer will illuminate the nature of such a cosmic consciousness.

In 1961 radio astronomer Frank Drake devised an equation that multiplied 7 different parameters based on the evolution of intelligent life on Earth to predict that 10 other civilizations in our galaxy would be detectable by their emitting radio and television signals as we do. This generated great excitement and prompted a NASA project to detect extraterrestrial intelligence. It led in 1984 to the incorporation of a nonprofit research organization, the SETI (Search for Extraterrestrial Intelligence) Institute. The search thus far has produced no evidence of any other intelligent life.

Absence of evidence is not evidence of absence, but other searches have failed so far to find evidence of any forms of life, however primitive, in our solar system or elsewhere.

However, the ongoing discovery of stars in our galaxy possessing orbiting planets has prompted a widespread belief that the Earth isn't special, and in a galaxy of some hundred billion stars there must be very many planets on which intelligent life evolved.

That belief is without foundation. Six conditions are necessary for the organic molecules of up to 13 atoms found in interstellar space and on asteroids to evolve into things as complex as humans:

1. a planet with essential elements and molecules;
2. sources of energy;
3. a minimum and probably a maximum mass;
4. protection from hazardous radiation and asteroid and cometary impacts;
5. a narrow temperature range just below, at, and just above the planet's surface;
6. the stability of this biosphere over billions of years.

A concurrence of galactic, stellar, and planetary factors provides these six conditions on Earth.

(1) It formed as a rocky planet comprising or subsequently acquiring the elements and molecules essential for life.
(2) Its mass lies within the narrow range that supports a biosphere.
(3) Its location within a narrow circumstellar habitable zone has been atypically shielded over 4.5 billion years from life-destroying cometary bombardment by the gravitational effect of an outer gas giant, Jupiter.

(4) As the planet was forming it was impacted by a planetesimal with sufficient mass at just the right relative velocity and angle to produce several
features favorable for the evolution of complex life: an abnormally
large iron core that generates a powerful protective magnetosphere; an
abnormally thin crust that enables the movement of tectonic plates;
and an abnormally large moon that produces an optimal rotation, a
relatively stable axial tilt, and tidal flows in its oceans.

(5) The planet has feedback mechanisms that maintain a surface temperature range that is favorable for biochemical reactions and has enabled
liquid water to remain on its surface for some 4 billion years despite
the large increase in energy radiated by its evolving parent star.

(6) Its parent star is single, it has a mass within the narrow range required
for stability over 4.5 billion years, and it is located in the relatively
small and changing galactic habitable zone over such a period.

Together these factors produce a changing flow of energy through a physico-
chemical system that has remained stable but far from thermodynamic equi-
librium over some 4 billion years, enabling it to generate the complexification
necessary for the emergence and evolution of varieties of lifeforms.

These factors contradict the view that the Earth is just an ordinary planet
orbiting an ordinary star in an ordinary galaxy of some hundred billion stars
forming part of the observable universe of an estimated hundred billion galaxies.
The Earth, if not unique, is a rare location in the galaxy, if not the universe,
in possessing the conditions necessary for the emergence and evolution of
lifeforms as complex of humans.

The limitations of science

Thus far I have attempted to use a scientific approach by analyzing the pattern
in the available evidence, but science has limitations in what it can tell us.

As we saw previously, it can show that we evolved from a conjectured Hot
Big Bang according to certain physical and chemical laws. In addition, it can
show that the values of two dimensionless constants need to be fine-tuned
to permit the evolution of any atoms or molecules. Moreover, the values of
six cosmological parameters need to be fine-tuned to produce a universe
that enables matter to evolve to the complexity of the atoms and molecules
of which we consist. Furthermore, the values of three parameters in stellar
nucleosynthesis need to be fine-tuned to enable the production of sufficient
carbon for the evolution of those organic molecules essential for the existence
of humans and all known lifeforms.

Science, however, cannot tell us what caused this conjectured Hot Big Bang or what caused all the physical and chemical laws plus the values of all these essential fine-tuned parameters to exist.

Nature of the human cosmic consciousness

To explore the nature of the human cosmic consciousness we must move beyond science and into metaphysics.

I think there is a higher reality that humans now, in their third stage of evolution, are incapable of understanding, just as rocks cannot understand that the Sun provides light and warmth, and chimpanzees cannot understand the existence of black holes.

Finally, I speculate that, in its fourth stage of evolution, the human cosmic consciousness will be able to comprehend such a higher reality. Furthermore, the human cosmic consciousness may well constitute that higher reality and be the cause of all the physical and chemical laws and parameters that enable it to evolve in an eternal, continuous cycle of self-creation. That is, it forms a cosmic consciousness that underlies everything and from which everything unfolds.

The existence of such an eternal, continuous cycle of self-creation seems a more reasonable explanation than the proposition that the universe exploded into existence from nothing together with uncaused laws and parameters. Some may even call it God.

Notes

Chapter 2: Natural disasters

1 Sandberg (2018) pp. 5–6, Beech (2011)

2 Alvarez, et al. (1980)

3 Alvarez (1997)

4 Schulte, et al. (2010)

5 Courtillot and Fluteau (2010)

6 Keller, et al. (2010)

7 Archibald, et al. (2010)

8 Elliott (2000)

9 Schoene, et al. (2019)

10 Morrison (2019,) p. 29

11 https://www.space.com/35008-comet-strike-danger-to-earth.html December 13, 2016

12 Vereš (2019, p. 90)

13 Vereš and Schmidt (2019, p. 66)

14 https://www.space.com/35008-comet-strike-danger-to-earth.html, December 13, 2016

15 Zhang, et al. (2019)

16 Ibid.

17 Sandberg (2018), p. 7

18 Lanphere, et al. (2002), Matthews, et al. (2015)

19 Whiteside, et al. (2010)

20 Jessica Whiteside, personal communication October 17, 2019

21 Jessica Whiteside, personal communication November 4, 2019

22 Wignall (2011)

23 Ibid., Sobolev, et al. (2011)

24 David Pyle, personal communication November 5, 2019

25 Jessica Whiteside, personal communication November 6, 2019

26 Mike Poland, personal communication October 29, 2019

27 https://www.usgs.gov/faqs/what-a-supervolcano?qt-news_science_products=0#qt-news_science_products, accessed September 23, 2019

28 https://www.history.com/topics/world-war-i/1918-flu-pandemic#section_4, accessed May 3, 2020

29 Erkoreka (2009)

30 David Morens, personal communication October 25, 2019

31 David Morens, personal communication November 1, 2019

32 Anton Ercoreka, personal communication November 5, 2019

33 https://www.niaid.nih.gov/news-events/1918-influenza-pandemic-video, accessed October 29, 2019

34 Madhav, et al. (2017), Morens, et al. (2010), https://www.cdc.gov/flu/pandemic-resources/1918-pandemic-h1n1.html accessed September 24, 2019, Erkoreka (2009), Erkoreka (2010), Johnson (2002)

35 http://www.euro.who.int/en/health-topics/communicable-diseases/influenza/pandemic-influenza, accessed September 24, 2019

36 https://www.worldometers.info/world-population/world-population-by-year/ accessed 25 September 2019

37 Madhav, et al. (2017)

38 Morens, et al. (2010)

39 https://www.who.int/news-room/fact-sheets/detail/hiv-aids, accessed September 25, 2019

40 Madhav, et al. (2017)

41 https://www.who.int/news-room/fact-sheets/detail/hiv-aids accessed September 25, 2019

42 https://www.who.int/gho/hiv/epidemic_status/deaths/en/, accessed September 4, 2019

43 MacPhee and Greenwood (2013), Sandberg (2018) p. 10

44 https://www.history.com/topics/middle-ages/black-death updated June 6, 2019, https://www.census.gov/data/tables/time-series/demo/international-programs/historical-est-worldpop.html accessed September 4, 2019

45 https://www.who.int/en/news-room/fact-sheets/detail/plague accessed September 4, 2019

46 https://www.mayoclinic.org/diseases-conditions/plague/symptoms-causes/syc-20351291 accessed September 25, 2019

47 https://www.who.int/en/news-room/fact-sheets/detail/plague accessed September 4, 2019

48 https://www.who.int/dg/speeches/detail/who-director-general-s-opening-remarks-at-the-media-briefing-on-covid-19---11-march-2020, March 11, 2020, https://www.who.int/emergencies/diseases/novel-coronavirus-2019/events-as-they-happen April 2, 2020, https://www.who.int/emergencies/diseases/novel-coronavirus-2019/technical-guidance/naming-the-coronavirus-disease-(covid-2019)-and-the-virus-that-causes-it accessed April 5, 2020

49 https://www.who.int/news-room/q-a-detail/q-a-coronaviruses March 9, 2020, https://www.ijidonline.com/article/S1201-9712(20)30011-4/fulltext accessed April 6, 2020

50 https://news.un.org/en/story/2020/03/1060702 March 31, 2020

51 https://www.weforum.org/agenda/2020/04/pandemics-coronavirus-covid19-economics-finance-stock-market-crisis/ April 3, 2020

52 https://www.weforum.org/agenda/2020/03/stock-market-volatility-coronavirus/ March 23, 2020

53 *Nature Reviews Drug Discovery*19, 305–306 (2020), https://www.nature.com/articles/d41573-020-00073-5

54 *South China Morning Post* September 25, 2020, https://www.scmp.com/news/china/society/article/3103121/coronavirus-who-backed-chinas-emergency-use-experimental

55 *New York Times* August 11, 2020, https://www.nytimes.com/2020/08/11/world/europe/russia-coronavirus-vaccine-approval.html

56 https://www.gov.uk/government/publications/regula-tory-approval-of-pfizer-biontech-vaccine-for-covid-19/information-for-healthcare-professionals-on-pfizerbiontech-covid-19-vaccine

57 *New York Times* December 2, 2020 https://www.nytimes.com/2020/12/02/world/europe/pfizer-coronavirus-vaccine-approved-uk.html

58 "Covid-19 Vaccine Tracker," *Regulatory Focus* May 21, 2021, https://www.raps.org/news-and-articles/news-articles/2020/3/covid-19-vaccine-tracker

59 "Comparing the COVID-19 Vaccines: How Are They Different?" Kathy Katella *Yale Medicine*, May 13, 2021 https://www.yalemedicine.org/news/covid-19-vaccine-comparison

60 "Sputnik V COVID-19 vaccine candidate appears safe and effective" Ian Jones and Polly Roy *The Lancet*, 397, Issue 10275, pp. 642–643, February 20, 2021 https://www.thelancet.com/journals/lancet/article/PIIS0140-6736(21)00191-4/fulltext

61 "Covid-19: Chinese vaccines may need changes to improve efficacy, admits official" Owen Dyer British *Medical Journal*, 373, n969, April 13, 2021, https://www.bmj.com/content/373/bmj.n969

62 https://www.bbc.co.uk/news/world-latin-america-59051105, https://www.euronews.com/2021/10/26/jair-bolsonaro-sanctioned-by-social-media-companies-for-covid-vaccine-misinformation

63 World Health Organization https://www.who.int/initiatives/act-accelerator/covax

64 https://healthpolicy-watch.org/can-covax-finally-deliver-on-its-delayed-vaccine-promises/

65 https://www.nature.com/articles/d41586-021-02532-4#ref-CR2, September 17, 2021

66 https://covid19.who.int, October 20, 2021

67 https://www.worldometers.info/world-population/, May 28, 2021

Chapter 3: Warfare and accident

1 https://www.timeshighereducation.com/news/populism-and-polarisation-threaten-science-nobel-laureates-say August 31, 2017, accessed September 11, 2018

2 Section 7.5.7 of Sublette (to be published), which evaluates the differing estimates made at the time and subsequently, Carey Sublette, personal communications November 6–21, 2018

Notes

3   http://www.nuclearweaponarchive.org/Russia/TsarBomba.html, September 3, 2017, accessed September 2, 2018; https://www.pbs.org/wnet/secrets/the-world's-biggest-bomb-about-this-episode/846/, May 16, 2011, accessed September 2, 2018

4   http://www.nuclearweaponarchive.org/Israel/index.html accessed September 2, 2018

5   http://www.atomicarchive.com/History/coldwar/page22.shtml, http://www.atomicarchive.com/Treaties/Treaty15.shtml, accessed September 11, 2018

6   https://www.armscontrol.org/print/2556 June 1, 2017, accessed September 11, 2018; "Renewed US-Russia nuke pact won't fix emerging arms threats," *Associated Press* January 27, 2021; "Russia welcomes US proposal to extend nuclear treaty," *AP NEWS* January 22, 2021; "Russia ratify extension of the New START nuclear arms control treaty," *Reuters* January 27, 2021; "United States extends nuclear treaty with Russia for five years" *Washington Post* February 3, 2021

7   SIPRI Yearbook 2020 (2020)

8   Ibid.

9   https://edition.cnn.com/2019/08/01/politics/us-missile-test-inf-treaty/index.html

10 *The Sunday Times* November 29, 2017, p. 12

11 Stockholm (2018)

12 https://www.newyorker.com/news/news-desk/world-war-three-by-mistake, December 23, 2016

13 Stockholm (2018)

14 https://fas.org/pir-pubs/nuclear-war-nuclear-winter-and-human-extinction/ October 14, 2015, accessed September 2, 2018

15 http://science.sciencemag.org/content/222/4630/1283 accessed November 27, 2018

16 Ehrlich, et al. (1984)

17 https://adamant.typepad.com/seitz/2006/12/preherein_honor.html December 20, 2006, accessed November 21, 2018; Seitz (2011)

18 https://www.foreignaffairs.com/articles/1986-06-01/nuclear-winter-reappraised,accessed November 28, 2018

19 https://adamant.typepad.com/seitz/2006/12/preherein_honor.html December 20, 2006, accessed November 21, 2018; Seitz (2011)

20 Emanuel (1986)

21 http://www.icnnd.org/Documents/Starr_Nuclear_Winter_Oct_09.pdf accessed November 21, 2018

22 Ibid.

23 Kerry Emanuel, personal communication November 29, 2018

24 http://worldpopulationreview.com/world-cities/hiroshima-population/ accessed September 2, 2018

25 Kerry Emanuel, personal communication December 19, 2018

26 https://pugwash.org/1955/07/09/statement-manifesto/ accessed September 12, 2018

27 http://disarmament.un.org/treaties/t/tpnw accessed December 15, 2020

Notes

28 Alexandra Levy, Vice President, Atomic Heritage Foundation, USA, personal communication December 3, 2018

29 Tannenwald (1999), Tannenwald (2007)

30 Pinker (2012) p. 327

31 https://www.wsj.com/articles/SB120036422673589947 January 15, 2008, accessed December 5, 2018

32 https://www.globalzero.org accessed December 15, 2020

33 http://www.icanw.org/campaign-news/ican-receives-2017-nobel-peace-prize/ accessed December 12, 2018

34 https://www.nytimes.com/2018/04/08/world/middleeast/syria-chemical-attacks-assad.html accessed December 12, 2018

35 Taubenberger and Morens (2006)

36 http://disarmament.un.org/treaties/t/bwc accessed December 16, 2020

37 https://www.nti.org/learn/biological/ accessed December 16, 2020

38 Riedel (2004)

39 https://www.telegraph.co.uk/news/2017/02/17/biological-terrorism-could-kill-people-nuclear-attacks-bill/ accessed October 22, 2018

40 Riedel (2004)

41 https://www.nti.org/learn/biological/ accessed October 22, 2018; http://edition.cnn.com/2008/CRIME/08/06/anthrax.case/index.html accessed October 22, 2018; https://www.nytimes.com/2011/10/10/science/10anthrax.html accessed October 22, 2018

42 National Academies of Sciences and Medicine (2018)

43 Hatch, et al. (1990)

44 http://www.who.int/ionizing_radiation/chernobyl/20110423_FAQs_Chernobyl.pdf accessed October 22, 2018

45 https://www.iaea.org/sites/default/files/chernobyl.pdf accessed October 22, 2018

46 https://www.britannica.com/event/Fukushima-accident accessed October 22, 2018

47 http://www.world-nuclear.org/information-library/safety-and-security/safety-of-plants/fukushima-accident.aspx accessed October 23, 2018

48 https://www.ft.com/content/000f864e-22ba-11e8-add1-0e8958b189ea accessed October 22, 2018

49 Drexler (1992, p. 146)

50 https://foresight.org/nano/Ecophagy.php April 2000, accessed December 23, 2018

51 Kurzweil (2006,) p. 400

52 Phoenix and Drexler (2004)

53 Dowling, et al. (2004)

54 Kassem, et al. (2017); https://www.manchester.ac.uk/discover/news/scientists-create-worlds-first-molecular-robot-capable-of-building-molecules/ September 20 2017 accessed September 28, 2018

Chapter 4: Population explosion and climate change

1   Ehrlich (1968), p. xi
2   Ibid. (pp. 24–25)
3   Dixon (1971)
4   Meadows, et al. (1972)
5   Cole (1973)
6   https://www.thesolutionsjournal.com/article/the-history-of-the-limits-to-growth/ March 2010, accessed September 13, 2018
7   Meadows, et al. (2004)
8   Office for National Statistics, https://www.ons.gov.uk/peoplepopulationandcommunity/populationandmigration/populationestimates/datasets/populationestimatesforukenglandandwalesscotlandandnorthernireland, Mid-2000 download
9   https://www.bbc.co.uk/news/science-environment-46398057 December 3, 2018, accessed December 28, 2018
10 https://www.theaustralian.com.au/higher-education/frank-fenner-sees-no-hope-for-humans/news-story/8d77f0806a8a3591d47013f7d75699b9 June 16, 2010, accessed December 28, 2018
11 http://www.dailymail.co.uk/news/article-419258/Controversial-scientist-predicts-planetary-wipeout.html November 29, 2006, accessed January 30, 2018
12 https://www.vice.com/en_us/article/wd4egq/near-term-extinctionists-believe-the-world-is-going-to-end-very-soon August 21, 2013
13 Wallace-Wells (2019), p. 204
14 http://guymcpherson.com
15 Wallace-Wells (2019)
16 Ibid. (pp. 3–4)
17 Sahney and Benton (2008)
18 Ogden and Sleep (2012)
19 http://news.mit.edu/2014/ancient-whodunit-may-be-solved-microbes-did-it March 31, 2014, accessed June 14, 2019
20 https://www.britannica.com/science/Permian-extinction updated August 9, 2018
21 https://unfccc.int/process-and-meetings/the-paris-agreement/the-paris-agreement
22 Wallace-Wells (2019), p. 13
23 Ibid. (p. 20)
24 Ibid. (p. 29)
25 See comments by scientists on his 2017 article https://climatefeedback.org/evaluation/scientists-explain-what-new-york-magazine-article-on-the-uninhabitable-earth-gets-wrong-david-wallace-wells/
26 Shiva (2019), p. 5
27 "The Plot to Forge a Climate Warrior" Dominic Green *The Sunday Times* August 18, 2019, p. 25

28 https://www.theguardian.com/environment/2018/dec/04/
leaders-like-children-school-strike-founder-greta-thunberg-tells-un-climate-summit

29 https://www.theguardian.com/environment/2019/apr/16/
greta-thunberg-urges-eu-leaders-wake-up-climate-change-school-strike-movement

30 https://www.bbc.co.uk/news/world-europe-47568227 March 14, 2019

31 https://www.bbc.co.uk/newsround/48039003 April 26, 2019, accessed May 5, 2019

32 https://www.theguardian.com/environment/2019/sep/21/
across-the-globe-millions-join-biggest-climate-protest-ever

33 Thunberg pp. 48 and 46

34 https://www.visionlearning.com/en/library/Earth-Science/6/Composition-of-Earths-
Atmosphere/107 accessed January 16, 2019, http://www.theweatherprediction.com/haby-
hints/155/, accessed April 12, 2019

35 http://www.environment.gov.au/climate-change/climate-science-data/climate-science/
greenhouse-effect accessed December 30, 2018, Hands (2017) pp. 286–288

36 https://www.bgs.ac.uk/discoveringGeology/climateChange/general/causes.html accessed
April 12, 2019

37 http://news.bbc.co.uk/1/hi/sci/tech/3869753.stm July 6, 2004, accessed January 3, 2018,
https://www.swissinfo.ch/eng/sunspot-activity-hits-1-000-year-high/3990930 July 12,
2004, accessed January 3, 2019, Sami Solanki, personal communications February 21 and
24, 2019

38 https://www.bgs.ac.uk/discoveringGeology/climateChange/general/causes.html accessed
April 12, 2019

39 https://www.bgs.ac.uk/discoveringGeology/climateChange/general/causes.html, https://
en.wikipedia.org/wiki/Milankovitch_cycles#Axial_tilt_(obliquity) accessed April 12, 2019

40 http://www.theweatherprediction.com/habyhints/155/ accessed April 12, 2019

41 https://www.bgs.ac.uk/discoveringGeology/climateChange/general/causes.html accessed
April 12, 2019

42 https://www.esrl.noaa.gov/csd/assessments/ozone/1998/faq9.html

43 https://volcanoes.usgs.gov/vhp/gas_climate.html January 2018, Gerlach (2011)

44 http://oceanmotion.org/html/impact/conveyor.htm, https://oceanservice.noaa.gov/facts/
conveyor.html, https://science.nasa.gov/science-news/science-at-nasa/2004/05mar_arctic/,
https://pubs.geoscienceworld.org/gsa/geology/article/38/4/383/130267/what-caused-the-
younger-dryas-cold-event accessed April 15, 2019, Golledge, et al. (2019)

45 https://www.bgs.ac.uk/discoveringGeology/climateChange/general/causes.html accessed
April 12, 2019

46 https://www.britannica.com/science/Quaternary November 8, 2017

47 Hands (2017) Chapter 26 The Emergence of Humans

48 Kukla (2002)

49 Dutton and Lambeck (2012)

50 Shakun, et al. (2012)

51 https://www.britannica.com/science/Quaternary updated November 2017, https://www.giss.nasa.gov/research/briefs/gornitz_09/ accessed April 9, 2019

52 https://www.britannica.com/science/global-warming updated April 1, 2019

53 Shakun, et al. (2012), Marcott, et al. (2013)

54 http://www.atmo.arizona.edu/students/courselinks/fall12/atmo336/lectures/sec5/holocene.html 2012

55 http://whc.unesco.org/en/list/179

56 http://www.atmo.arizona.edu/students/courselinks/fall12/atmo336/lectures/sec5/holocene.html, 2012, Hands (2017), pp. 465–470

57 https://www.ipcc.ch/about/history/ accessed December 30, 2018

58 https://unfccc.int/files/essential_background/background_publications_htmlpdf/application/pdf/conveng.pdf

59 Solomon (2007), pp. 749–750

60 https://www.ipcc.ch/site/assets/uploads/2018/02/WG1AR5_SPM_FINAL.pdf

61 https://www.metoffice.gov.uk/hadobs/hadcrut4/data/current/time_series/HadCRUT.4.6.0.0.annual_ns_avg.txt accessed November 17, 2020

62 IPCC, 2013: *Climate Change 2013: The Physical Science Basis. Contribution of Working Group I to the Fifth Assessment Report of the Intergovernmental Panel on Climate Change* Summary for Policy Makers, p. SPM-5

63 https://www.bbc.co.uk/news/science-environment-24292615 September 27, 2013, accessed December 15, 2013

64 http://ane4bf-datap1.s3-eu-west-1.amazonaws.com/wmocms/s3fs-public/ckeditor/files/Draft_Statement_7_February.pdf?5.6rzIGwBm5lwDSTPbgprB2_EgrjzRVY accessed March 8, 2019

65 https://public.wmo.int/en/media/press-release/wmo-climate-statement-past-4-years-warmest-record November 29, 2018

66 https://www.ipcc.ch/report/ar6/wg1/, https://www.ipcc.ch/report/ar6/wg1/downloads/report/IPCC_AR6_WGI_SPM.pdf, https://www.ipcc.ch/site/assets/uploads/2021/08/IPCC_WGI-AR6-Press-Release_en.pdf

67 https://www.bbc.co.uk/news/science-environment-58130705

68 https://origin.cpc.ncep.noaa.gov/products/analysis_monitoring/ensostuff/ONI_v5.php

69 http://ane4bf-datap1.s3-eu-west-1.amazonaws.com/wmocms/s3fs-public/ckeditor/files/Draft_Statement_7_February.pdf?5.6rzIGwBm5lwDSTPbgprB2_EgrjzRVY accessed March 8, 2019

70 https://www.ametsoc.org/ams/index.cfm/publications/bulletin-of-the-american-meteorological-society-bams/explaining-extreme-events-from-a-climate-perspective/ December 12, 2018

71 Andela, N et al. "A human-driven decline in global burned area" *Science* Vol 356 Issue 6345, pp. 1356-1362 (30 June 2017) https://www.science.org/doi/10.1126/science.aal4108

72 https://www.iii.org/fact-statistic/facts-statistics-wildfires#Annual%20Number%20 of%20Acres%20Burned%20in%20Wildland%20Fires,%201980-2019

73 https://www.nps.gov/articles/wildfire-causes-and-evaluation.htm

74 https://journals.ametsoc.org/mwr/article/108/11/1915/62099/ An-Analysis-of-Super-Typhoon-Tip-October-1979

75 https://wmo.asu.edu/mortality_records; https://www.aoml.noaa.gov/hrd/tcfaq/E9.html

76 Cited in Koonin (2021), p. 117

77 https://www.epw.senate.gov/public/_cache/files/0/7/07472bb4-3eeb-42da-a49d-964165860275/01AFD79733D77F24A71FEF9DAFCCB056.11614hearingwitnesstesti monycurry.pdf

78 https://www.spectator.com.au/2015/11/i-was-tossed-out-of-the-tribe-climate-scientist-judith-curry-interviewed, November 28, 2015, accessed April 28, 2019

79 https://judithcurry.com/2017/01/03/jc-in-transition/, January 3, 2017, accessed April 29, 2019

80 http://www.eas.gatech.edu/news/judith-curry-named-one-top-50-women-stem, April 18, 2018, accessed April 30, 2019

81 https://www.thegwpf.org/images/stories/gwpf-reports/mckitrick-ipcc_reforms.pdf, 2011, accessed January 9, 2019

82 https://www.thetimes.co.uk/article/un-must-investigate-warming-bias-says-former-climate-chief-lgplj89s8dz February 15, 2010, accessed December 30, 2018

83 https://www.theguardian.com/environment/2016/sep/30/james-lovelock-interview-by-end-of-century-robots-will-have-taken-over, September 30, 2016, accessed December 28

84 https://www.nytimes.com/2014/07/16/us/skeptic-of-climate-change-john-christy-finds-himself-a-target-of-suspicion.html?_r=1, *New York Times*, July 15, 2014

85 https://www.rossmckitrick.com/temperature-data-quality.html, updated 2014

86 Richard Black, personal communications, August 27 and 29, 2019

87 Black (2018) p.102

88 Wickham, et al. (2013)

89 https://journals.ametsoc.org/doi/abs/10.1175/JAMC-D-19-0002.1

90 Testimony of John R Christy to US House Committee on Science, Space & Technology, March 29, 2017, https://www.nsstc.uah.edu/aosc/testimonials/ChristyJR_Written_170329. pdf, supporting peer-reviewed papers: (a) Christy, J R,2017: Lower tropospheric temperature [Global climate; Temperature; Lower Tropospheric Temperature [in "State of the Climate in 2016"],*Bull. Amer. Meteor. Soc.* 98, (8), S16–S17; (b) McKitrick, R and J R Christy 2018: A test of the tropical 200–300 hPa warming rate in climate models. *Earth and Space Science*, American Geophys; (c) Christy, J R and R T McNider 2017: Satellite bulk tropospheric temperatures as a metric for climate sensitivity. *A-P J. Atmos. Sci.*, 53(4), 1–8

91 Mills, T C "Skinning a cat": alternative models of representing tempera-ture trends. *Climatic Change* 101, 415–426 (2010) https://doi.org/10.1007/ s10584-010-9801-1

Notes

92 Robertson, Simon "Transparency, trust, and integrated assessment models: An ethical consideration for the Intergovernmental Panel on Climate Change" *WIREs Climate Change* 2021;12:e679 https://wires.onlinelibrary.wiley.com/doi/10.1002/wcc.679

93 Skea, J, Shukla, P, Al Khourdajie, A, & McCollum, Det al. (2021) "Intergovernmental Panel on Climate Change: Transparency and integrated assessment modeling" *WIREs Climate Change, e727* https://wires.onlinelibrary.wiley.com/doi/10.1002/wcc.679

94 Koonin (2021) p. 249

95 Ibid. p. 4

96 "Climate Science Is Not Settled" *Wall Street Journal* September 19, 2014 https://www.wsj.com/article/climate-science-is-not-settled-1411143565

97 Koonin (2021)

98 Ibid, p. 2

99 Ibid, p. 171

100 Ibid, (pp. 177–183)

101 Ibid, (pp. 249–255)

102 Global mean temperatures from https://www.metoffice.gov.uk/hadobs/hadcrut4/data/current/time_series/HadCRUT.4.6.0.0.annual_ns_avg.txt accessed November 17, 2020, Globally averaged Mauna Loa annual mean CO_2 in parts per million from Dr Pieter Tans, NOAA/GML (www.esrl.noaa.gov/gmd/ccgg/trends/) and Dr Ralph Keeling, Scripps Institution of Oceanography (scrippsco2.ucsd.edu/), ftp://aftp.cmdl.noaa.gov/products/trends/co2/co2_annmean_mlo.txt, accessed November 17, 2020

103 https://origin.cpc.ncep.noaa.gov/products/analysis_monitoring/ensostuff/ONI_v5.php accessed 8 July 2019

104 https://www.ipcc.ch/site/assets/uploads/2018/05/ipcc_90_92_assessments_far_wg_I_spm.pdf

105 Essex, et al. (2007)

106 Field and Barros (2014) p. 300

107 Ibid. p. 275

108 "Behind science's mask, XR is a doomsday cult," *The Sunday Times* October 13, 2019

109 Ulmschneider (2006) Heidelberg pp. 245–246

Chapter 5: Artificial intelligence

1 https://www.bbc.co.uk/news/technology-30290540 December 2, 2014, accessed September 18, 2018

2 https://www.bbc.co.uk/news/technology-30333671 December 5, 2015, accessed October 24, 2018

3 Hawking (2018) p. 186

4 https://www.bbc.co.uk/news/31047780 January 29, 2015, accessed September 18, 2018

5 https://globalchallenges.org/global-risks/ accessed December 22, 2020

6 Campbell, et al. (2002)

7 https://www.nytimes.com/2011/02/17/science/17jeopardy-watson.html accessed October 31, 2018

8 https://www.wired.com/2017/05/win-china-alphagos-designers-explore-new-ai/ May 27, 2017

9 https://waymo.com/ontheroad/ accessed September 21, 2018, personal communication from Waymo November 9, 2018

10 https://ifr.org/ifr-press-releases/news/robots-double-worldwide-by-2020 accessed September 21, 2018

11 https://ifr.org/ifr-press-releases/news/robot-sales-rise-again October 28, 2021

12 https://www.ifr.org/service-robots accessed September 21, 2018

13 *The Sunday Times* October 22, 2017

14 https://www.straitstimes.com/asia/east-asia/japan-classrooms-to-use-ai-robots-to-help-teach-english, August 21, 2018

15 Fry (2018) p.8

16 Ibid. pp. 10-11

17 https://www.rdm.ox.ac.uk/news/artificial-intelligence-added-to-cardiologists-toolbox January 5, 2018, accessed October 2, 2018

18 Quoted in Crevier (1993) p. 109

19 Good (1965) p. 33

20 Ibid. p. 78

21 *Life* November 20, 1970, p. 58

22 Drexler (1992) p. 145

23 Vinge (1993)

24 Bostrom (2014)

25 https://www.stonetemple.com/digital-personal-assistants-study/#which_smartest, https://www.forbes.com/sites/kevinmurnane/2018/05/03/dumb-and-dumber-comparing-alexa-siri-cortana-and-the-google-assistant/#6c17cbdb36e7 accessed September 20, 2018

26 Liu, et al. (2017)

27 Fry (2018) pp. 166-167

28 Harari (2016) p. 312

29 Ibid.

30 https://www.wired.com/2016/02/googles-self-driving-car-may-caused-first-crash/ accessed September 21, 2018

31 https://www.ntsb.gov/investigations/AccidentReports/Reports/HWY18MH010-prelim.pdf accessed October 9, 2018

32 https://qz.com/783009/the-scary-similarities-between-teslas-tsla-deadly-autopilot-crashes/ September 20, 2018

33 *The Sunday Times* Business & Money, p. 4, August 22, 2021

34 Harari (2016) p. 319

35   See, for example, https://www.vox.com/2017/2/28/14745596/yuval-harari-sapiens-inter-
      view-meditation-ezra-klein accessed October 9, 2018
36   Fry (2018) p. 13
37   Hands (2017) p. 403

Chapter 6: Reflections and conclusions

1   Ibid. pp. 573–574
2   The Consensus Project, https://skepticalscience.com/tcp.php?t=home, is a page of the
     website Skeptical Science: Getting Skeptical About Global Warming Skepticism founded
     and maintained by John Cook, then a research student in cognitive psychology at the
     University of Western Australia and research fellow in climate communication at the
     Global Change Institute, University of Queensland.

     The Consensus Project page refers to "Our peer-reviewed paper Quantifying the
     Consensus on Anthropogenic Global Warming in the Scientific Literature." This is a
     seven-page letter published on May 15, 2013 in *Environmental Research Letters*, an online
     open access website. Its lead author is Cook, together with eight supporters of The
     Consensus Project. With the letter is a 3½-minute video by Cook summarizing its conclu-
     sions, in which he emphasizes that 97% of climate scientists endorse the consensus that
     humans are the cause of global warming.

     To arrive at this conclusion Cook says he and his team analyzed the evolution of the
     scientific consensus on anthropogenic global warming (AGW) [the theory that climate
     change is caused by human industry and agriculture] in the peer-reviewed scientific litera-
     ture. They examined 11,944 climate paper abstracts from 1991 to 2011, matching the
     topics "global climate change" or "global warming". They found that 66.4% of abstracts
     expressed no position on AGW, 32.6% endorsed AGW, 0.7% rejected AGW, and 0.3%
     were uncertain about the cause of global warming. Among the abstracts expressing a posi-
     tion on AGW, 97.1% endorsed the consensus position that humans are causing global
     warming.

     In a second phase of their study, they invited 8,547 authors to rate their own papers.
     Only 1,200 scientists (i.e. 14%) responded. Of these, 35.5% expressed no position on
     AGW. Of the 64.5% who did so, Cook claimed that 97.2% endorsed the consensus and
     this showed a striking consistency.

     Two observations on this paper and its claims are evident.

     Firstly, hardly anyone doubts that humans are causing global warming. The issue is
     whether humans are the principal if not sole cause of global warming.

     Secondly, 66% of abstracts expressed no position on AGW. To conclude that since
     33% of the remaining 34% expressed the view that humans are causing global warming
     and 33/34 = 97, then 97% of scientists constitute a consensus that humans cause global
     warming demonstrates, at best, an unfamiliarity with statistics.

     The claim is usually interpreted to mean that the sole cause of global warming is human activity, most particularly the emission of CO_2. Very many people, including many climate scientists, now believe that 97% of climate scientists have an identical view on the cause of and remedies for climate change.

John Cook campaigning for what he believes to be the case is fair enough, but we shouldn't be misled by claims that are without foundation.

3   Tol (2016)

Chapter 7: Space colonization

1   http://www.telegraph.co.uk/news/uknews/1359562/Colonies-in-space-may-be-only-hope-says-Hawking.html, October 16, 2001

2   http://www.dailymail.co.uk/sciencetech/article-419573/Mankind-colonise-planets-survive-says-Hawking.html#ixzz55fHLEcEe, December 1, 2006

3   https://aeon.co/essays/elon-musk-puts-his-case-for-a-multi-planet-civilisation, September 30, 2014

4   http://www.bbc.co.uk/news/science-environment-42969020, February 7, 2018

5   https://aeon.co/essays/elon-musk-puts-his-case-for-a-multi-planet-civilisation, September 30, 2014

6   http://fortune.com/2017/12/07/boeing-dennis-muilenburg-elon-musk-mars/; https://www.nasa.gov/centers/marshall/news/releases/2015/nasa-s-space-launch-system-is-the-rocket-for-the-ride-to-mars.html

7   https://www.nasa.gov/content/journey-to-mars-overview, accessed June 8, 2018, https://www.lockheedmartin.com/en-us/products/mars-base-camp.html, accessed June 8, 2018; https://www.scientificamerican.com/article/lockheed-martin-reveals-plans-for-sending-humans-to-mars/, September 29, 2017

8   https://oig.nasa.gov/audits/reports/FY16/IG-16-003.pdf, published October 29, 2015

9   *Nature Scientific Reports* 7, Article number: 1832 (2017)

10   https://science.nasa.gov/science-news/science-at-nasa/2001/ast01oct_1, October 1, 2001

11   http://www.spaceref.com/news/viewpr.html?pid=19543, April 12, 2006

12   https://www.nasa.gov/mission_pages/station/research/experiments/1038.html, May 2, 2018

13   Smith (2014)

14   http://www.history.com/topics/space-race, accessed February 1, 2018

15   https://www.space.com/16773-first-space-station-salyut-1.html, accessed June 12, 2018

16   Berry (1976)

17   Heppenheimer (1978)

18   Johnson, et al. (1977)

19   Brand (1977)

20   Nicolson (1978)

21   Martin (1978)

22   Wolfe and Wysack (1979)

23   O'Neill, et al. (1979)

24   O'Neill (1974b)

25   O'Neill (1974a)

26   O'Neill (1977)

27   Ibid. pp. 123–148

28   Heppenheimer (1978) p. 69

29   Ibid. pp. 71–74

30   Nicolson (1978) p. 93

31   Ibid. p. 96

32   Ibid. pp. 127–140

33   Martin (1978)

Chapter 8: Extending healthspan

1   Vanderwerker Jr (1976)

2   Finch (2011)

3   Pliny and Healy (1991) p. 91

4   Snyder (1963)

5   https://www.blatchford.co.uk/about-blatchford/our-heritage/ accessed July 13, 2018

6   Crawford, et al. (2013)

7   http://broughttolife.sciencemuseum.org.uk/broughttolife/people/louiswashkansky accessed July 16, 2018

8   http://broughttolife.sciencemuseum.org.uk/broughttolife/people/christiaanbarnard accessed July 16, 2018

9   https://www.nhlbi.nih.gov/health-topics/total-artificial-heart accessed July 17, 2018

10   https://www.jarvikheart.com/history/robert-jarvik-on-the-jarvik-7/ and https://www.nytimes.com/1983/03/24/obituaries/barney-clark-dies-on-112th-day-with-permanent-artificial-heart.html accessed August 23, 2018

11   Cohrs, et al. (2017) https://futurism.com/this-3d-printed-human-heart-can-do-every-thing-a-real-one-can/, https://edition.cnn.com/2017/07/20/health/3-d-printed-heart-silicone-study/index.html

12   Pandarinath, et al. (2017)

13   George, Jacob et al "Restoring Touch Generates Sense of Ownership Over Prosthetic Hands" Abstract 642.04 Summary in Neuroscience 2017 (Soc for Neuroscience).pdf

14   Sakellarridi, Sofia, et al "Why learning can be difficult? A brain-machine interface study with a tetraplegic human" Abstract 777.06 Summary in Neuroscience 2017 (Soc for Neuroscience).pdf

15   http://2045.com/about/ accessed August 28, 2018

16   http://2045.com/ideology/ and http://gf2045.com/read/265/ accessed August 28, 2018

17 Alimardani, et al. (2016a), Alimardani, et al. (2016b)

18 Quoted in Doudna and Sternberg (2018) p. 189

19 Blaese, et al. (1995), Lyon and Corner (1995) pp. 216–240.

20 McCabe and McCabe (2008) p. 243

21 Wilson (2009)

22 Sibbald (2001), McCabe and McCabe (2008) pp. 244-250

23 Hacein-Bey-Abina, et al. (2002)

24 Hacein-Bey-Abina, et al. (2008), https://www.sciencedaily.com/
releases/2008/08/080807175438.htm accessed August 8, 2018, and http://blogs.plos.org/
dnascience/2014/10/09/good-guy-virus-scid-x1-gene-therapy-take-2/, accessed August 8,
2018

25 Wilson (2009)

26 https://www.jax.org/news-and-insights/jax-blog/2014/march/pros-and-cons-of-
znfs-talens-and-crispr-cas accessed September 6, 2018

27 Cong, et al. (2013)

28 Doudna and Sternberg (2018) p. xv

29 Ibid. p. 181

30 https://www.broadinstitute.org/what-broad/areas-focus/project-spotlight/questions-and-
answers-about-crispr accessed July 18, 2018

31 Jinek, et al. (2012)

32 https://science.sciencemag.org/content/339/6121/819

33 Doudna and Sternberg (2018) p. xv

34 Ibid. (pp. 112–113)

35 Jinek, et al. (2012)

36 Gasiunas, et al. (2012)

37 https://www.sciencemag.org/news/2020/09/
latest-round-crispr-patent-battle-has-apparent-victor-fight-continues

38 https://www.nobelprize.org/prizes/chemistry/2020/press-release/

39 https://www.wired.com/story/wired-guide-to-crispr/ April 27, 2018

40 Doudna and Sternberg (2018) p. 117 plus Doudna personal communication September
26, 2018

41 Cong, et al. (2013)

42 Mali, et al. (2013)

43 Wu, et al. (2013)

44 Doudna and Sternberg (2018) p. 157

45 https://clinicaltrials.gov/ct2/show/NCT03450369?term=CRISPR&cntry=US&draw=2&
rank=17 accessed December 29, 2020

46 https://clinicaltrials.gov/ct2/results?cond=&term=CRISPR&cntry=US&state=&city=&di
st=&Search=Search accessed December 29, 2020

47 https://clinicaltrials.gov/ct2/show/NCT03081715?term=CRISPR&cntry=CN&draw=3

&rank=12 https://clinicaltrials.gov/ct2/show/NCT02793856?term=CRISPR&cntry=CN &draw=3&rank=14 accessed December 29, 2020

48 https://clinicaltrials.gov/ct2/results?cond=&term=CRISPR&cntry=CN&state=&city=&d ist=&Search=Search accessed December 29, 2020

49 Doudna and Sternberg (2018) pp. 155–156 and http://www.sciencemag.org/ news/2017/02/how-battle-lines-over-crispr-were-drawn

50 http://www.crisprtx.com/index.php accessed July 25, 2018

51 http://ir.crisprtx.com/news-releases/news-release-details/crispr-therapeutics-and-vertex-provide-update-fda-review accessed August 15, 2018

52 Kosicki, et al. (2018)

53 https://www.newscientist.com/article/2174149-crispr-gene-editing-is-not-quite-as-precise-and-as-safe-as-thought/ accessed August 15, 2018

54 Haapaniemi, et al. (2018), Ihry, et al. (2018), https://www.cam.ac.uk/research/news/ genome-editing-tool-could-increase-cancer-risk-in-cells-say-researchers accessed August 19, 2018

55 See, for example, https://ipscell.com/2018/06/could-cancer-risk-claw-crisprs-potential/ accessed August 19, 2018 plus Doudna personal communication October 18, 2018

56 Church (2017)

57 Doudna and Sternberg (2018) p. 231

58 Schmidt, et al. (2017)

59 Glass, et al. (2006)

60 http://diyhpl.us/wiki/transcripts/human-genome-editing-summit/2018-hong-kong/ jiankui-he-human-genome-editing/ November 28, 2018

61 https://www.theverge.com/2018/11/29/18116830/crispr-baby-he-jiankui-genetics-ethics-science-health-mutation accessed January 9, 2019; https://www.theatlantic.com/science/ archive/2018/12/15-worrying-things-about-crispr-babies-scandal/577234/ December 4, 2018

62 https://www.apnews.com/0be63430c5914f09a124b968c844d994 November 29, 2018

63 Doudna and Sternberg (2018) pp. 230–231

Chapter 9: Immortality

1 https://www.smithsonianmag.com/smart-news/2000-year-old-texts-reveal-first-emperor-chinas-quest-eternal-life-180967671/ accessed February 21, 2018; Wright (2001)p. 49

2 Ibid. pp. 316–339

3 https://www.newyorker.com/magazine/2017/04/03/silicon-valleys-quest-to-live-forever accessed March 9, 2018

4 https://unitybiotechnology.com/pipeline/, https://clinicaltrials.gov/ct2/show/ NCT05275205 accessed July 10, 2022

5 https://www.calicolabs.com

6   https://elifesciences.org/articles/31157

7   https://journals.plos.org/plosbiology/article?id=10.1371/journal.pbio.3000528

8   https://www.g3journal.org/content/9/9/2863

9   https://doi.org/10.7554/eLife.72664

10 de Grey, et al. (2002)

11 Warner, et al. (2005)

12 de Grey (2005)

13 http://www2.technologyreview.com/sens/ for all the submissions and rebuttals

14 http://www.lifeextension.com/magazine/2013/7/Interview-with-Aubrey-de-Grey-PhD/
    Page-01 accessed January 4, 2018

15 de Grey personal communication March 23, 2018

16 de Grey and Rae (2008) p. 325

17 Personal communications November 30–December 18, 2017

18 https://singularityhub.com/2017/11/10/3-dangerous-ideas-from-ray-
    kurzweil/#sm.0000mzzlhxz10ct6zmm1gvtnc3k37 accessed March 2, 2018

19 See, for example, Arte German & French TV, *Aux frontières de l'immortalité*, November
    16, 2008; http://www.billionaire.com/people/peter-thiel/2875/could-human-beings-live-
    for-1000-years accessed January 5, 2018; Lain and de Grey p. 14; https://www.youtube.
    com/watch?v=CaK25IWXKpQ November 28, 2017

20 http://www.billionaire.com/people/peter-thiel/2875/could-human-beings-live-for-1000-
    years accessed March 13, 2018

21 Draghici, et al. (2015)

22 Boominathan, et al. (2016)

23 Personal communication December 18, 2017

24 Reply to my question at a meeting on November 28, 2017, see https://www.youtube.com/
    watch?v=CaK25IWXKpQ

25 Personal communication 11 March 11, 2018

26 Lopez-Otin, et al. (2013)

27 https://www.smithsonianmag.com/innovation/human-mortality-hacked-life-exten-
    sion-180963241 accessed January 5, 2018

28 Fossel (2015), Fossel (1996)

29 Fossel (2015) p. 55

30 Funk, et al. (2000)

31 Jucker (2010)

32 https://www.washingtonpost.com/news/wonk/wp/2018/01/12/why-coming-up-with-a-
    drug-for-alzheimers-is-so-devilishly-hard/?utm_term=.35d598876f09 accessed January
    18, 2018

33 Fossel (2015) p. 131

34 Fossel, personal communication 30 April 2018

35 Fossel (2015) p. 70

36   Jaskelioff, et al. (2010)

37   Bernardes de Jesus, et al. (2012)

38   https://www.aging-us.com/article/102430/text#fulltext

39   https://www.nature.com/news/lawsuit-challenges-anti-aging-claims-1.11090 July 31, 2012

40   Harley, et al. (2011)

41   Harley, et al. (2013)

42   Fossel (2015) pp. 183–185

43   https://www.telocyte.com accessed January 3, 2021; Telocyte Newsletter January 4, 2021; plus personal communications July 1, 2017–January 4, 2018, November 18, 2019, January 1 2021, January 4, 2021, and September 6, 2022

44   Fossel (2015) p. 191

45   Fossel (1996) p.1

46   Hands (2017)

47   Dong, et al. (2016)

48   Vijg and Le Bourg (2017) https://www.the-scientist.com/?articles.view/articleNo/49758/title/Evidence-for-Human-Lifespan-Limit-Contested/ June 28, 2017

49   https://edition.cnn.com/2017/05/11/health/humans-old-age-partner/index.html May 11, 2017

50   https://www.newyorker.com/magazine/2017/04/03/silicon-valleys-quest-to-live-forever accessed January 24, 2018

51   Alberts (2002) p. 1170

52   Bianconi, et al. (2013)

53   le Bourg (2017)

54   Calado and Dumitriu (2013)

55   de Grey and Rae (2008) pp. 150–155

56   Salloway, et al. (2014)

57   Ettinger (1965)

58   https://www.alcor.org/about/ accessed January 1, 2021

59   *Wired* November 18, 2002 https://www.wired.com/2002/11/ray-kurzweils-plan-never-die

60   http://www.cryonics.org accessed March 28, 2018

61   https://www.technologyreview.com/s/541311/the-false-science-of-cryonics/ September 15, 2015

62   *The Guardian* November 18, 2016 https://www.theguardian.com/science/2016/nov/18/the-cryonics-dilemma-will-deep-frozen-bodies-be-fit-for-new-life

63   See, for example, Hands (2017) pp. 172–174, 388, 409, 573–576

Chapter 11: Transforming humans

1   Bostrom (2009)

Notes

2 http://rebrain.2045.com/expert/16.html accessed March 1, 2019

3 http://2045.com/articles/30869.html accessed February 27, 2019

4 http://2045.com/tech2/ accessed March 1, 2019

5 Kurzweil (2006)

6 Kurzweil (1990)

7 Kurzweil (1999)

8 Kurzweil (2006) p. 143

9 Ibid. p. 145

10 Ibid. p. 197

11 Ibid. p. 25

12 http://www.singularity.com/qanda.html accessed April 1, 2019

13 Kurzweil (2006) p. 30

14 Ibid. p. 389

15 Kurzweil (2013)

16 https://www.newyorker.com/books/page-turner/ray-kurzweils-dubious-new-theory-of-mind November 15, 2012

17 Sandberg and Bostrom (2008)

18 Bostrom (2009)

19 All from "What is uploading?" https://humanityplus.org/philosophy/transhumanist-faq/ accessed January 4, 2021

20 "What is the Singularity?" https://humanityplus.org/philosophy/transhumanist-faq/ accessed January 4, 2021

21 "What is a posthuman?" https://humanityplus.org/philosophy/transhumanist-faq/ accessed January 4, 2021

22 Harari (2016)

23 https://www.theguardian.com/culture/2017/mar/19/yuval-harari-sapiens-readers-questions-lucy-prebble-arianna-huffington-future-of-humanity accessed January 4, 2021

24 Ullam (1958) p.5

25 http://yudkowsky.net/obsolete/singularity.html

26 https://www.yudkowsky.net/singularity accessed January 4, 2021

27 Kurzweil (2013,) p. 4

28 Kurzweil (2006) p. 491

29 https://www.reuters.com/article/us-china-space-idUSKBN17U0GG April 28, 2017, accessed March 29, 2019; https://www.space.com/11048-china-space-station-plans-details.html March 7, 2011, accessed March 29, 2019

30 Kurzweil (2006) p. 147

31 Hands (2017) p. 317

32 von Bartheld, et al. (2016)

33 Hands (2017) p. 403

34 Allen and Greaves (2011)

35 Sarma (2018)

36 Iibid. and http://openworm.org accessed June 4, 2019

37 https://www.newyorker.com/books/page-turner/ray-kurzweils-dubious-new-theory-of-mind November 15, 2012

38 http://www.nybooks.com/articles/archives/2013/mar/21/homunculism

39 Kurzweil (2013) p. 213

40 See, for example, https://www.britannica.com/topic/personality accessed June 2, 2019

41 Ramachandran and Blakemore (2001)

42 https://www.kurzweilai.net/images/How-My-Predictions-Are-Faring.pdf

43 Kurzweil (1999) pp. 202–206

44 Kurzweil (2006) p. 105

45 Ibid. p. 312

46 Ibid. p. 313

47 Ibid.

48 Ibid. p. 337

Chapter 12: The nature of scientific predictions

1 https://www.technologynetworks.com/tn/lists/10-failed-scientific-predictions-276945 accessed December 10, 2019

2 http://scienceworld.wolfram.com/biography/Kelvin.html accessed December 10, 2019

3 https://www.nbcnews.com/id/wbna52111904 accessed December 10, 2019

4 https://documents.pub/document/astronomers-royal.html p. 43

5 William Reville, Associate Professor of Biochemistry and Public Awareness of Science Officer, University College Cork, https://www.irishtimes.com/news/science/future-imperfect-1.1239449 January 7, 2010

6 https://list25.com/25-famous-predictions-that-were-proven-to-be-horribly-wrong/2/ accessed January 8, 2021

7 https://list25.com/25-famous-predictions-that-were-proven-to-be-horribly-wrong/3/ accessed January 8, 2021

8 https://www.zdnet.com/article/in-his-own-words-bill-gates-best-quotes/ accessed January 8, 2021

9 https://quoteinvestigator.com/2018/11/26/moonshine/ accessed January 8, 2021

10 https://www.technologynetworks.com/tn/lists/10-failed-scientific-predictions-276945 accessed January 8, 2021

11 http://www.washingtonwildlife.net/ht/display/ArticleDetails/i/11116 June 20, 2008, accessed April 24, 2019

12 https://www.theguardian.com/environment/2008/aug/10/climatechange.arctic accessed May 1, 2019

13   https://www.theguardian.com/environment/2012/sep/17/arctic-collapse-sea-ice accessed
     May 1, 2019

Chapter 13: The Pattern of Human Evolution

1   Hands (2017)

Bibliography

The dates in parentheses are the dates of the editions consulted. If the date of the first edition of the work is different, this date is given at the end of its title.

Alberts, Bruce et al. (2002) (4th ed.) *Molecular Biology of the Cell* New York: Garland Science

Alimardani, Maryam, et al. (2016a) "The Importance of Visual Feedback Design in BCIs; from Embodiment to Motor Imagery Learning" *PLOS ONE* 11: 9, e0161945

—(2016b) "Removal of Proprioception by BCI Raises a Stronger Body Ownership Illusion in Control of a Humanlike Robot" *Scientific Reports* 6: 33514

Allen, Paul G and Mark Greaves (2011) "The Singularity Isn't Near" *MIT Technology Review* https://www.technologyreview.com/s/425733/paul-allen-the-singularity-isnt-near/ 12 October

Alvarez, L W, et al. (1980) "Extraterrestrial Cause for the Cretaceous–Tertiary Extinction" *Science* 208: 1095–1108

Alvarez, Walter (1997) *T Rex and the Crater of Doom* Princeton, NJ: Princeton University Press

Andela, N, et al. (2017) "A Human-Driven Decline in Global Burned Area" *Science* 356: 1356–1362

Archibald, J David, et al. (2010) "Cretaceous Extinctions: Multiple Causes" *Science* 328: 5981, 973-a

Beech, Martin (2011) "The Past, Present and Future Supernova Threat to Earth's Biosphere" *Astrophysics and Space Science: An International Journal of Astronomy, Astrophysics and Space Science* 336: 287–302

Bernardes de Jesus, B, et al. (2012) "Telomerase Gene Therapy in Adult and Old Mice Delays Aging and Increases Longevity without Increasing Cancer" *EMBO Mol Med* 4: 691–704

Berry, Adrian (1976) *The Next Ten Thousand Years: A Vision of Man's Future in the Universe* London: Coronet

Bianconi, E, et al. (2013) "An Estimation of the Number of Cells in the Human Body" *Annals of Human Biology* 40: 463–471

Black, Richard (2018) *Denied: The Rise and Fall of Climate Contarianism* The Real Press

Blaese, R M, et al. (1995) "T Lymphocyte-Directed Gene Therapy for ADA-SCID: Initial Trial Results after 4 Years" *Science* 270: 475–480

Boominathan, A, et al. (2016) "Stable Nuclear Expression of *ATP8* and *ATP6* Genes Rescues a mtDNA Complex V Null Mutant" *Nucleic Acids Res* 44: 9342–9357

Bostrom, Nick (2009) "The Future of Humanity" *Geopolitics, History, and International Relations* 2, 41–78

—(2014) *Superintelligence: Paths, Dangers, Strategies* Oxford: Oxford University Press

Brand, Stewart (editor) (1977) *Space Colonies* Harmondsworth: Penguin

Calado, Rodrigo T and Bogdan Dumitriu (2013) "Telomere Dynamics in Mice and Humans" *Seminars in Hematology* 50: 165–174

Campbell, Murray, et al. (2002) "Deep Blue" *Artificial Intelligence* 134: 57–83

Church, George (2017) "Compelling Reasons for Repairing Human Germlines" *New England Journal of Medicine* 377: 1909–1911

Cohrs, Nicholas H, et al. (2017) "A Soft Total Artificial Heart—First Concept Evaluation on a Hybrid Mock Circulation" *Artificial Organs* 41: 948–958

Cole, H S D and Christopher Freeman (1973) *Models of Doom: A Critique of the Limits to Growth* New York: Universe Publishing

Cong, Le, et al. (2013) "Multiplex Genome Engineering Using CRISPR/Cas Systems" *Science* 339: 819–823

Courtillot, Vincent and Frederic Fluteau (2010) "Cretaceous Extinctions: The Volcanic Hypothesis" *Science* 328: 973–974

Crawford, Alexandra Z, et al. (2013) "A Brief History of Corneal Transplantation: From Ancient to Modern" *Oman Journal of Ophthalmology* 6: Suppl 1 S12–S17

Crevier, Daniel (1993) *AI: The Tumultuous History of the Search for Artificial Intelligence* New York: Basic Books

de Grey, Aubrey D N J (2005) "Like It or Not, Life-Extension Research Extends Beyond Biogerontology" *EMBO Reports* 6: 11, 1000

de Grey, Aubrey and Michael Rae (2008) (Paperback, with a New Afterword) *Ending Aging: The Rejuvenation Breakthroughs That Could Reverse Human Aging in Our Lifetime* 2007 New York: St. Martin's Griffin

de Grey, Aubrey D, et al. (2002) "Time to Talk SENS: Critiquing the

Immutability of Human Aging" *Annals of the New York Academy of Sciences* 959: 452–462; discussion 463–455

Dixon, Bernard (1971) "In Praise of Prophets" *New Scientist and Science Journal* 51: 769, 606

Dong, Xiao, et al. (2016) "Evidence for a Limit to Human Lifespan" *Nature* 538 257

Doudna, Jennifer A and Samuel H Sternberg (2018) *A Crack in Creation: The New Power to Control Evolution* 2017 London: Vintage

Dowling, Ann, et al. (2004) "Nanoscience and Nanotechnologies: Opportunities and Uncertainties" London: *The Royal Society & The Royal Academy of Engineering Report*, i–xii, 1–116

Draghici, C, et al. (2015) "Concise Total Synthesis of Glucosepane" *Science* 350: 294–298

Drexler, K Eric (1992) *Engines of Creation: The Coming Era of Nanotechnology* 1986 Oxford: Oxford University Press

Dutton, A and K Lambeck (2012) "Ice Volume and Sea Level During the Last Interglacial" *Science* 337: 216–219

Ehrlich, Paul R (1968) *The Population Bomb* New York: Ballantine Books

Ehrlich, Paul R, et al. (1984) *The Cold and the Dark: The World after Nuclear War* New York; London: Norton

Elliott, David K (2000) "Extinctions and Mass Extinctions" in *Oxford Companion to the Earth* edited by Paul L Hancock and Brian J Skinner, Oxford; New York: Oxford University Press

Emanuel, K A (1986) "Towards a Scientific Exercise" *Nature* 319: 6051, 23

Erkoreka, Anton (2009) "Origins of the Spanish Influenza Pandemic (1918–1920) and Its Relation to the First World War" *Journal of Molecular and Genetic Medicine* 3: 190–194

—(2010) "The Spanish Influenza Pandemic in Occidental Europe (1918–1920) and Victim Age" *Influenza Other Respir Viruses* 4: 81–89

Essex, Christopher, et al. (2007) "Does a Global Temperature Exist?" *Journal of Non-Equilibrium Thermodynamics* 32: 1, 1

Ettinger, Robert Chester Wilson (1965) *The Prospect of Immortality* 1962 London: Sidgwick & Jackson

Field, Christopher B and Vicente R Barros (2014) *Climate Change 2014: Impacts, Adaptation, and Vulnerability. Part A, Global and Sectoral Aspects: Working Group II Contribution to the Fifth Assessment Report of the Intergovernmental Panel on Climate Change* Cambridge, UK; New York: Cambridge University Press

Finch, Jacqueline (2011) "The Ancient Origins of Prosthetic Medicine" *Lancet* 377: 548–549

Fossel, Michael (1996) *Reversing Human Aging* New York: William Morrow
—(2004) *Cells, Aging, and Human Disease* Oxford; New York: Oxford University Press
—(2015) *The Telomerase Revolution: The Enzyme That Holds the Key to Human Aging…And Will Soon Lead to Longer, Healthier Lives* Dallas, Texas, USA: BenBella Books

Fry, Hannah (2018) *Hello World: How to Be Human in the Age of the Machine* New York: Doubleday

Funk, W D, et al. (2000) "Telomerase Expression Restores Dermal Integrity to *In Vitro*-Aged Fibroblasts in a Reconstituted Skin Model" *Experimental Cell Research* 258: 270–278

Gasiunas, Giedrius, et al. (2012) "Cas9-crRNA Ribonucleoprotein Complex Mediates Specific DNA Cleavage for Adaptive Immunity in Bacteria" *Proceedings of the National Academy of Sciences of the United States of America* 109: E2579–E2586

Gerlach, Terry (2011) "Volcanic versus Anthropogenic Carbon Dioxide" *Eos, Transactions American Geophysical Union* 92: 24, 201–202

Glass, William G, et al. (2006) "CCR5 Deficiency Increases Risk of Symptomatic West Nile Virus Infection" *Journal of Experimental Medicine* 203: 35–40

Golledge, Nicholas R, et al. (2019) "Global Environmental Consequences of Twenty-First-Century Ice-Sheet Melt" *Nature* 566: 7742, 65–72

Good, Irving John (1965) "Speculations Concerning the First Intelligent Machine" 31-88 in *Advances in Computing* vol. 6 edited by F Alt and M Rubinoff. New York: Academic Press

Gordon, Michael (2001) "U.S. Nuclear Plan Sees New Weapons and New Targets" *The New York Times* https://archive.nytimes.com/www.nytimes.com/learning/teachers/featured_articles/20020311monday.html

Haapaniemi, Emma, et al. (2018) "CRISPR-Cas9 Genome Editing Induces a p53-Mediated DNA Damage Response" *Nature Medicine* 24: 7, 927–930

Hacein-Bey-Abina, Salima, et al. (2002) "Sustained Correction of X-Linked Severe Combined Immunodeficiency by *Ex Vivo* Gene Therapy" *New England Journal of Medicine* 346: 1185–1193

Hacein-Bey-Abina, Salima, et al. (2008) "Insertional Oncogenesis in 4 Patients after Retrovirus-Mediated Gene Therapy of SCID-X1" *Journal of Clinical Investigation* 118: 9, 3132–3142

Hands, John (2017) *COSMOSAPIENS: Human Evolution from the Origin of the Universe* 2015 New York: Overlook Duckworth

Harari, Yuval Noah (2016) *Homo Deus: A Brief History of Tomorrow* London: Harvill Secker

Harley, Calvin, et al. (2011) "A Natural Product Telomerase Activator as Part of a Health Maintenance Program" *Rejuvenation Research* 14: 1, 45–56

Harley, Calvin, et al. (2013) "A Natural Product Telomerase Activator as Part of a Health Maintenance Program: Metabolic and Cardiovascular Response" *Rejuvenation Research* 16: 5, 386–395

Hatch, M C, et al. (1990) "Cancer Near the Three Mile Island Nuclear Plant: Radiation Emissions" *American Journal of Epidemiology* 132: 3, 397–412; discussion 413–397

Hawking, Stephen (2018) *Brief Answers to the Big Questions* New York: Bantam

Heppenheimer, T A (1978) *Colonies in Space* 1977 New York: Warner Books

Ihry, Robert J, et al. (2018) "p53 Inhibits CRISPR-Cas9 Engineering in Human Pluripotent Stem Cells" *Nature Medicne* 24: 7, 939–946

Jaskelioff, Mariela, et al. (2010) "Telomerase Reactivation Reverses Tissue Degeneration in Aged Telomerase-Deficient Mice" *Nature* 469, 102

Jinek, Martin, et al. (2012) "A Programmable Dual-RNA-guided DNA Endonuclease in Adaptive Bacterial Immunity" *Science* 337: 6096, 816–821

Johnson, Niall P A S and Juergen Mueller (2002) "Updating the Accounts: Global Mortality of the 1918–1920 'Spanish' Influenza Pandemic" *Bulletin of the History of Medicine* 76: (1), 105–115

Johnson, Richard D, et al. (1977) *Space Settlements: A Design Study* Washington, DC: Scientific and Technical Information Office, National Aeronautics and Space Administration

Jucker, Mathias, Konrad Beyreuther, Christian Haass, Roger M Nitsch, and Ives Christen (editors) (2010) *Alzheimer: 100 Years and Beyond* 2006 Berlin: Springer

Kassem, Salma, et al. (2017) "Stereodivergent Synthesis with a Programmable Molecular Machine" *Nature* 549: 7672, 374–378

Keller, Gerta, et al. (2010) "Cretaceous Extinctions: Evidence Overlooked" *Science* 328: 5981, 974–975

Koonin, Steven E (2021) *Unsettled: What Climate Science Tells Us, What It Doesn't, and Why It Matters* Dallas, TX: BenBella Books

Kosicki, Michael, et al. (2018) "Repair of Double-Strand Breaks Induced by CRISPR–Cas9 Leads to Large Deletions and Complex Rearrangements" *Nature Biotechnology* 36: 765–771

Kristensen, Hans M and Robert S Norris (2014) "Worldwide Deployments of Nuclear Weapons" *Bulletin of the Atomic Scientists* 70: 96–108

Kukla, George J et al. (2002) "Last Interglacial Climates" *Quaternary Research* 58: 1, 2–13

Kurzweil, Ray (1990) *The Age of Intelligent Machines* Cambridge, Mass; London: MIT Press

—(1999) *The Age of Spiritual Machines: When Computers Exceed Human Intelligence* 1995 New York: Viking

—(2006) *The Singularity Is Near: When Humans Transcend Biology* 2005 London: Penguin

—(2013) *How to Create a Mind: The Secret of Human Thought Revealed* London: Duckworth

Lain, Douglas & Aubrey de Grey (2016) *Advancing Conversations: Aubrey de Grey—Advocate for an Indefinite Human Lifespan* London: Zero Books

Lanphere, Marvin A, et al. (2002) "Revised Ages for Tuffs of the Yellowstone Plateau Volcanic Field: Assignment of the Huckleberry Ridge Tuff to a New Geomagnetic Polarity Event" *GSA Bulletin* 114: 5, 559–568

le Bourg, Éric (2017) "The Search for the 'Anti-Aging Pill': A Critical Viewpoint" in *Anti-Aging Drugs: From Basic Research to Clinical Practice* edited by Alexander Vaiserman. London: Royal Society of Chemistry

Liu, Feng, et al. (2017) "Intelligence Quotient and Intelligence Grade of Artificial Intelligence" *Annals of Data Science* 4: 2, 179–191

Lopez-Otin, C, et al. (2013) "The Hallmarks of Aging" *Cell* 153: 6, 1194–1217

Lyon, Jeff and Peter Corner (1995) *Altered Fates: Gene Therapy and the Retooling of Human Life* London: W W Norton

MacPhee, Ross D E and Alex D Greenwood (2013) "Infectious Disease, Endangerment, and Extinction" *International Journal of Evolutionary Biology* 2013, 571939

Madhav, Nita, et al. (2017) "Pandemics: Risks, Impacts, and Mitigation" in *Disease Control Priorities: Improving Health and Reducing Poverty. 3rd Edition*. Washington, DC: The International Bank for Reconstruction and Development/The World Bank

Mali, Prashant, et al. (2013) "RNA-guided Human Genome Engineering via Cas9" *Science* 339: 6121, 823–826

Marcott, Shaun A, et al. (2013) "A Reconstruction of Regional and Global Temperature for the Past 11,300 Years" *Science* 339: 6124, 1198

Martin, A R (editor) (1978) *Project Daedalus: The Final Report on the BIS Starship Study* London: British Interplanetary Society

Matthews, Naomi E, et al. (2015) "Age of the Lava Creek Supereruption and Magma Chamber Assembly at Yellowstone Based on 40Ar/93Ar and U–Pb Dating of Sanidine and Zircon Crystals" *Geochemistry, Geophysics, Geosystems* 16: 8, 2508–2528

McCabe, Linda L and Edward R B McCabe (2008) *DNA: Promise and Peril* Berkeley, CA; London: University of California Press

Meadows, Donella H, et al. (1972) *The Limits to Growth: A Report for the*

Club of Rome's Project on the Predicament of Mankind New York: Potomac Associates

Meadows, Donella H, et al. (2004) (3rd revised, expanded and updated edition) *Limits to Growth: The 30-Year Update* London: Chelsea Green Publishing

Morens, David M, et al. (2010) "Pandemic Influenza's 500th Anniversary" *Clinical Infectious Diseases* 51: 12, 1442–1444

Morrison, David (2019) "The Cosmic Impact Hazard" in *Planetary Defense: Global Collaboration for Defending Earth from Asteroids and Comets* edited by Nikola Schmidt. Berlin: Springer

National Academies of Sciences, Engineering and Medicine (2018) *Biodefense in the Age of Synthetic Biology* Washington, DC: The National Academies Press

Nicolson, Iain (1978) *The Road to the Stars* Newton Abbot, Devon: Westbridge Books

O'Neill, Gerard K (1974a) "The Colonisation of Space" *Physics Today* 27: 32

—(1974b) "A Lagrangian Community?" *Nature* 250, 636

—(1977) *The High Frontier: Human Colonies in Space* London: Cape

O'Neill, Gerard K, et al. (1979) *Space Resources and Space Settlements: Technical Papers Derived from the 1977 Summer Study at NASA Ames Research Center, Moffett Field, California* Washington, DC: National Aeronautics and Space Administration, Scientific and Technical Information Branch

Ogden, Darcy E and Norman H Sleep (2012) "Explosive Eruption of Coal and Basalt and the End-Permian Mass Extinction" *Proceedings of the National Academy of Sciences of the United States of America* 109: 1, 2012, 59–62

Pandarinath, Chethan, et al. (2017) "High Performance Communication by People with Paralysis Using an Intracortical Brain–Computer Interface" *eLife* 6: e18554 https://elifesciences.org/articles/18554 21 Feb

Phoenix, Chris and Eric Drexler (2004) "Safe Exponential Manufacturing" *Nanotechnology* 15: 8, 869

Pinker, Steven (2012) *The Better Angels of Our Nature: A History of Violence and Humanity* 2011 London: Penguin

Pliny the Elder (1991) *Natural History* translated with an Introduction by John F Healy, London: Penguin Books

Ramachandran, V S and Colin Blakemore (2001) "Consciousness" in *The Oxford Companion to the Body* edited by Colin Blakemore and Sheila Jennett. Oxford: Oxford University Press

Riedel, Stefan (2004) "Biological Warfare and Bioterrorism: A Historical Review" *Baylor University Medical Center Proceedings* 17: 4, 400–406

Robertson, Simon (2021) "Transparency, Trust, and Integrated Assessment Models: An Ethical Consideration for the Intergovernmental Panel on Climate Change" *WIREs Climate Change* 12: e679

Sahney, Sarda and Michael J Benton (2008) "Recovery from the Most Profound Mass Extinction of All Time" *Proceedings of the Royal Society B: Biological Sciences* 275: 1636, 764–765

Salloway, S, et al. (2014) "Two Phase 3 Trials of Bapineuzumab in Mild-to-Moderate Alzheimer's Disease" *New England Journal of Medicine* 370: 4, 322–333

Sandberg, Anders (2018) *Human Extinction from Natural Hazard Events* Oxford: Oxford University Press

Sandberg, Anders and Nick Bostrom (2008) "Whole Brain Emulation: A Roadmap" http://www.fhi.ox.ac.uk/brain-emulation-roadmap-report.pdf

Sarma, Gopal P, et al. (2018) "OpenWorm: Overview and Recent Advances in Integrative Biological Simulation of *Caenorhabditis elegans*" *Philosophical Transactions of the Royal Society B: Biological Sciences* 373: 20170382

Schlosser, Eric (2013) *Command and Control: Nuclear Weapons, the Damascus Accident, and the Illusion of Safety* London: Allen Lane

Schmidt, Amand F, et al. (2017) "*PCSK9* Genetic Variants and Risk of Type 2 Diabetes: A Mendelian Randomisation Study" *Lancet Diabetes & Endocrinology* 5: 2, 97–105

Schoene, Blair, et al. (2019) "U–Pb Constraints on Pulsed Eruption of the Deccan Traps across the End-Cretaceous Mass Extinction" *Science* 363: 6429, 862

Schulte, Peter, et al. (2010) "The Chicxulub Asteroid Impact and Mass Extinction at the Cretaceous–Paleogene Boundary" *Science* 327: 5970, 1214–1218

Seitz, Russell (2011) "Nuclear Winter Was and Is Debatable" *Nature* 475: 37

Shakun, Jeremy D, et al. (2012) "Global Warming Preceded by Increasing Carbon Dioxide Concentrations During the Last Deglaciation" *Nature* 484: 49–54

Shiva, Vandana (2019) *This Is Not A Drill: An Extinction Rebellion Handbook* London: Penguin

Sibbald, Barbara (2001) "Death but One Unintended Consequence of Gene-Therapy Trial" *CMAJ* 164: 11, 1612

Skea, J, P Shukla, A Al Khourdajie, & D McCollum (2021) "Intergovernmental Panel on Climate Change: Transparency and Integrated Assessment Modeling" *WIREs Climate Change* 12: e727

Smith, Cameron M (2014) "Estimation of a Genetically Viable Population for Multigenerational Interstellar Voyaging: Review and Data for Project Hyperion" *Acta Astronautica* 97: 16–29

Snyder, Charles (1963) "Ambroise Paré and Ocular Prosthesis" *Arch Ophthalmol* 70: 130–132

Sobolev, Stephan V, et al. (2011) "Linking Mantle Plumes, Large Igneous Provinces and Environmental Catastrophes" *Nature* 477: 312–316

Solomon, Susan (2007) *Climate Change 2007: The Physical Science Basis: Contribution of Working Group I to the Fourth Assessment Report of the Intergovernmental Panel on Climate Change* Cambridge: Cambridge University Press

Stockholm International Peace Research Institute (2018) *SIPRI Yearbook 2018* Oxford: Oxford University Press

Stockholm International Peace Research Institute (2020) *SIPRI Yearbook 2020* Oxford: Oxford University Press

Sublette, Carey (to be published) *Handbook of Nuclear Weapons* Lanham, MD: Rowman & Littlefield

Tannenwald, Nina (1999) "The Nuclear Taboo: The United States and the Normative Basis of Nuclear Non-Use" *International Organization* 53: 3, 433–468

—(2007) *The Nuclear Taboo: The United States and the Non-Use of Nuclear Weapons since 1945* Cambridge: Cambridge University Press

Taubenberger, J K and D M Morens (2006) "1918 Influenza: The Mother of All Pandemics" *Emerging Infectious Diseases* 12: 1, 15–22

Thunberg, Greta (2019) *No One Is Too Small To Make A Difference* London: Penguin

Tol, Richard S J (2016) "Comment on 'Quantifying the Consensus on Anthropogenic Global Warming in the Scientific Literature'" *Environmental Research Letters* 11: 4, 048001

Ullam, S (1958) "John Von Neumann (1903–1957)" *Bulletin of the American Mathematical Society* 64: 3, 1–49

Ulmschneider, Peter *Intelligent Life in the Universe: Principles and Requirements Behind Its Emergence* Berlin: Springer-Verlag

Vanderwerker, Earl E Jr. (1976) "A Brief Review of the History of Amputations and Prostheses" *ICIB* 15: 15–16

Vereš, Peter (2019) "Technical Architecture to Deepen Our Solar System Awareness" 71–94 in *Planetary Defense: Global Collaboration for Defending Earth from Asteroids and Comets* edited by Nikola Schmidt. Berlin: Springer

Vereš, Peter and Nikola Schmidt (2019) "Methods, Means and Governance of NEO Observation" in *Planetary Defense: Global Collaboration for Defending Earth from Asteroids and Comets* edited by Nikola Schmidt. Berlin: Springer

Vijg, J and E Le Bourg (2017) "Aging and the Inevitable Limit to Human Life Span" *Gerontology* 63: 5, 432–434

Vinge, Vernor (1993) "The Coming Technological Singularity: How to Survive in the Post-human Era" https://edoras.sdsu.edu/~vinge/misc/singularity.html

von Bartheld, Christopher S, et al. (2016) "The Search for True Numbers of Neurons and Glial Cells in the Human Brain: A Review of 150 Years of Cell Counting" *Journal of Comparative Neurology* 524: 18, 3865–3895

Wallace-Wells, David (2019) *The Uninhabitable Earth* London: Allen Lane

Warner, H, et al. (2005) "Science Fact and the SENS Agenda. What Can We Reasonably Expect from Ageing Research?" *EMBO Reports* 6: 11, 1006–1008

Whiteside, J H, et al. (2010) "Compound-Specific Carbon Isotopes from Earth's Largest Flood Basalt Eruptions Directly Linked to the End-Triassic Mass Extinction" *Proceedings of the National Academy of Sciences of the United States of America* 107: 15, 6721–6725

Wickham, C, et al. (2013) "Influence of Urban Heating on the Global Temperature Land Average Using Rural Sites Identifed from MODIS Classifications" *Geoinformatics & Geostatistics: An Overview* 1: 1–6

Wignall, Paul B (2011) "Lethal Volcanism" *Nature* 477, 285-–286

Wilson, James M (2009) "A History Lesson for Stem Cells" *Science* 324: 5928, 727–728

Wolfe, L Stephen and Roy L Wysack (1979) *Handbook for Space Pioneers: A Guide for Pioneers from Earth to the Eight Planets Now Available for Colonization* Newton Abbot: Westbridge Books

Wright, David Curtis (2001) *The History of China* Westport, CT; London: Greenwood Press

Wu, Yuxuan, et al. (2013) "Correction of a Genetic Disease in Mouse via Use of CRISPR-Cas9" *Cell Stem Cell* 13: 6, 659–662

Zhang, Qicheng, et al. (2019) "Orbital Deflection of Comets by Directed Energy" *The Astronomical Journal* 157: 5, 201

Glossary

The following definitions are not the only meanings of the words listed. They are the precise meanings used in this book and are given here in order to minimize misunderstanding of what I am saying. Words in italics are defined elsewhere in this Glossary.

algorithm

A step-by-step procedure for solving a problem or accomplishing an objective.

anthropogenic climate change

Climate change caused by human activities.

artificial intelligence (sometimes called machine intelligence)

Intelligence demonstrated by machines: the ability to acquire and successfully apply knowledge for a purpose such as learning, planning, solving problems, recognizing speech, and manipulating and moving objects.

asteroid

A rocky object smaller than a planet that orbits the Sun or another star; also known as a minor planet. The orbits of most of the asteroids in the solar system are between the orbits of Mars and Jupiter, while some are beyond Neptune.

atherosclerosis

A disease in which plaque builds up inside arteries, which are blood vessels that carry oxygen-rich blood to the heart and other parts of the body. Plaque is made up of fat, cholesterol, calcium, and other substances found in the blood. Over time, plaque hardens and narrows the arteries.

cancer   A group of diseases in which cells in a specific part of the body grow and reproduce uncontrollably. The cancerous cells can invade and destroy surrounding healthy tissue, including organs, or spread to other parts of the body.

chromosome   A structure that contains the genetic information of a cell. In a human cell, it consists of threadlike strands of DNA wrapped in a double helix around a core of proteins within the cell nucleus; in addition to this nuclear chromosome, the cell may contain other small chromosomes within, for example, a mitochondrion.

climate   The average over several decades of regular variations during the year of surface and air temperatures, air pressure, humidity, precipitation (such as rain, hail, or snow), sunshine, cloudiness, and winds for a specified region of the Earth.

climate change   A change in the climate measured over several decades.

collectivization   Working together involuntarily, whether by instinct or conditioned learning or coercion.

comet   A small body, usually a few kilometers across, consisting of water ice and frozen gases embedded with rock and dust that orbits the Sun and also other stars. Comets usually have eccentric orbits, typically with a much greater inclination to the plane of Earth's orbit around the Sun. When they pass close to the Sun they develop diffuse gaseous envelopes and sometimes long dust and ion tails.

consciousness Awareness of the environment, other organisms, and self that can lead to action; a property shared by all organisms in differing degrees, from rudimentary levels in very simple organisms to more sophisticated levels in organisms with complex cerebral systems.

cosmos All that exists, which includes various speculations of dimensions other than the three dimensions of space and one of time that we perceive and also other universes with which we have no physical contact and about which we cannot obtain observable or experimental information.

CRISPR Clustered Regularly Interspaced Short Palindromic Repeats, meaning repetitive sequences of DNA interspersed with fragments of viral DNA.

cryonics The freezing of a human body or severed head very soon after the person has been pronounced legally dead, with the speculative hope that it can be reanimated by some future technology and the person restored to life. Generally regarded as a pseudoscience.

cytoplasm Everything outside the cell nucleus and inside the cell membrane. It consists of a gelatinous, water-based fluid called a cytosol, which contains salts, organic molecules, and enzymes and in which are suspended organelles, the metabolic machinery of the cell.

diastereoisomer A molecule that has the same formula and structure as another but is arranged differently in space and is therefore not a mirror image of the other.

DNA

Deoxyribonucleic acid, located in cells, contains the genetic instructions used in the development and functioning of all known independent organisms and some viruses. Each DNA *molecule* normally consists of two long chains of four different nucleotides in a characteristic sequence; the chains (usually referred to as strands) are twisted into a double helix and joined by hydrogen bonds between the complementary bases adenine (A) and thymine (T) or cytosine (C) and guanine (G) so that its structure resembles a twisted ladder. When DNA is copied in a cell, the strands separate and each serves as a template for assembling a new complementary chain from molecules in the cell. DNA strands also act as templates for the synthesis of proteins in a cell through a mechanism that makes another nucleic acid, *RNA*, as an intermediary.

El Niño

An ocean–atmosphere event that occurs at irregular and unpredictable intervals every few years and is associated with a warming of sea temperatures across the equatorial Eastern Central Pacific Ocean by 0.5°C or more above the long-term average. It has extensive effects on weather and contributes to a warming of the global temperature. It is the complement of *La Niña*, which has cooling effects.

epimutation

A heritable change that does not affect the *DNA* sequence but results in a change in gene expression.

evolution

A process of change occurring in something, especially from a simple to a more complex state.

gamma ray burst

A brief, intense explosion of high-frequency electromagnetic radiation. Gamma ray bursts have been observed in distant galaxies and can last from 10 milliseconds to several hours. A typical burst releases as much energy in a few seconds as the Sun will in its entire 10-billion-year lifetime.

gene

The fundamental unit of inheritance, which normally comprises segments of *DNA*; the sequence of the bases in each gene determines individual hereditary characteristics, typically by encoding for protein synthesis.

genome

All the genetic material of an organism. It comprises *DNA* (or *RNA* in RNA viruses) and includes the genes, noncoding DNA, mitochondrial DNA, and chloroplast DNA.

genotype

The genetic makeup of an organism, as distinct from its physical characteristics.

germline cells (human)

Any cells whose *genome* can be inherited by subsequent generations. They include egg and sperm cells, and also the progenitors of these mature sex cells plus stem cells from the very early stages of the developing embryo.

glial cell

A supportive cell in the central nervous system. Unlike neurons, glial cells do not conduct electrical impulses; they surround neurons and provide support for, and insulation between, them.

global warming

A gradual increase in the overall temperature of the Earth's atmosphere and oceans, usually attributed to an increase in the greenhouse effect.

greenhouse effect

A natural process by which radiation from a planet's atmosphere warms the planet to a temperature above what it would be without its atmosphere.

Homo sapiens

The only species known to possess reflective consciousness.

human-level AI (sometimes called strong AI)

Artificial intelligence that is indistinguishable from human intelligence.

Glossary

human terminal extinction
Humans cease to exist without leaving any successors.

human transformational evolution
Humans evolve by being transformed into a new species.

insight
Seeing clearly the essence of a thing, usually suddenly after disciplined meditation or following an unsuccessful attempt to arrive at an understanding through reasoning.

instinct
An innate, impulsive response to stimuli, usually determined by biological necessities such as survival and reproduction.

intelligence
The ability to learn facts and skills and apply them for a purpose.

La Niña
An ocean–atmosphere event that occurs at irregular and unpredictable intervals every few years and is associated with a cooling of sea temperatures across the equatorial Eastern Central Pacific Ocean by 3–5°C. It has extensive effects on weather and contributes to a cooling of the global temperature. It is the complement of *El Niño*, which has warming effects.

language
The communication of feelings, narratives, explanations, or ideas through a complex structure of learned spoken, written, or signed symbols that convey meaning in the culture within which they are employed.

large igneous province (LIP)
An area of millions of square kilometers of lava formed by a series of eruptions over hundreds of thousands to millions of years of vast volumes of molten rock from deep cracks in the Earth that spread out from the cracks, cool, and solidify.

Law of Data
Interpretation
The degree to which scientists depart from an objective interpretation of the data in their investigation is a function of four factors: their determination to validate a hypothesis or confirm a theory; the length of time during which the investigation has occupied their life; the degree of their emotional investment in the project; and their career need to publish a significant paper or safeguard their reputation.

life
The ability of an enclosed entity to respond to changes within itself and in its environment, to extract energy and matter from its environment, and to convert that energy and matter into internally directed activity that includes maintaining its own existence.

life sciences
The branches of science that study features of living organisms, such as plants, animals, and humans, and also the relationships between such things.

macrophage
A large, white blood cell that is an integral part of the immune system. It detects, engulfs, and digests harmful microscopic bodies, including worn-out or dead cells and other debris.

medical sciences
The branches of science that are applied to maintain health, prevent and treat disease, and treat injuries.

mantle
The mostly solid bulk of the Earth's interior that lies between the Earth's dense, superheated core and its thin outer layer, the crust. The mantle is about 2,900 kilometers thick and makes up 84 percent of the Earth's total volume.

megaverse
A speculated higher-dimensional universe in which our universe of three spatial dimensions is embedded. Some speculations posit many megaverses comprising the cosmos.

microglia

A type of *glial cell* located throughout the brain and spinal cord (the central nervous system); they account for 10–15 percent of all cells within the brain. They provide an immune response in the central nervous system by acting as macrophages, removing cellular debris and dead neurons by engulfing and digesting them.

Milankovitch cycles

The collective effect of variations in the eccentricity of the Earth's orbit (over 100,000 years), the Earth's axial tilt (over 41,000 years), and the Earth's axial precession (over 23,000 years) resulting in cyclical variations of solar radiation reaching the Earth and strongly affecting climate patterns according to the hypothesis of Milutin Milankovitch.

mitochondrion

A membrane-bound organelle found in the cytoplasm of almost every eukaryotic cell (a cell with a clearly defined nucleus), the primary function of which is to generate useable energy in the form of adenosine triphosphate (ATP) for the cell

multiverse

A speculated *cosmos* that contains our *universe* plus multiple if not infinite other universes with which we have no physical contact and about which we cannot obtain observable or experimental information. Several different kinds of multiverse, each having different properties, have been proposed.

nanobot

A robot whose size is approximately one nanometer (10^{-9} meters). Such a small scale requires a robot constructed from single atoms or molecules. See *nanotechnology*.

Glossary

nanotechnology	The invention, manufacturing, and use of tools or machines constructed from single atoms or molecules. Compared with structures consisting of the same substances at a normal scale, nanostructures typically exhibit different properties such as chemical reactivity, mechanical strength, and optical, electrical, and mechanical behavior due to their larger surface-to-mass ratio and to quantum mechanical effects.
nucleotide	A subunit of *DNA* or *RNA* made up of three parts: a phosphate group, a 5-carbon sugar, and a nitrogenous base. The four nitrogenous bases in DNA are adenine, cytosine, guanine, and thymine. RNA contains uracil instead of thymine. Thousands of nucleotides are linked to form a DNA or an RNA molecule.
observable universe	That part of the universe containing matter capable of being detected by astronomical observation. According to current orthodox cosmology, the observable universe is circumscribed by the speed of light and the time since matter and radiation decoupled some 380,000 years after the universe came into existence in a Big Bang.
pandemic	A disease that spreads across several continents.
phenotype	The observable characteristics of an organism, such as shape, size, color, and behavior.
philosophy	Love of wisdom; thinking about ultimate reality, the essence and causes of things, the natural world, human behavior, and thinking itself.
physical sciences	The branches of science that study inanimate phenomena; they include astronomy, physics, chemistry, and the Earth sciences.

physicalism	The speculation or belief that only physical matter is real and that all other things, such as mind or consciousness or thoughts, will eventually be explained as physical things or their interactions.
posthuman	A member of an immortal species evolved from a human and distinguished from it by having its mind and personality uploaded from its body to a new substrate such as a robot, avatar, or a computer, or whose mind is able to roam freely through the universe.
primeval thinking	The first phase of *reflective consciousness* when reflection on the self and its relationship with the rest of the universe is rooted principally in survival and superstition.
reasoning	An attempt to understand the essence of a thing by a logical process based either on evidence or on assumptions taken as self-evident.
reflective consciousness	The property of an organism by which it is conscious of its own consciousness; that is, not only does it know but also it knows that it knows.
reverse engineering	Taking apart an object or system to see how is works in order to duplicate or enhance it.
RNA	Ribonucleic acid resembles *DNA* in that it consists of a chain of four nucleotides in a characteristic sequence, but uracil (U) replaces thymine (T) alongside adenine (A), cytosine (C), and guanine (G), and the strands are single, except in certain viruses.
science	The attempt to understand and explain natural phenomena by using systematic—preferably measurable—observation or experiment and to apply reason to the knowledge thereby obtained in order to infer testable laws and make predictions or retrodictions.

scientific method

(notional)

1. Data is collected by systematic observation of, or experiment on, the phenomenon being studied.

2. A provisional conclusion, or hypothesis, is inferred from this data.

3. Predictions deduced from this hypothesis are tested by further observations or experiments.

4. If these tests confirm the predictions, and the confirmations are reproduced by independent testers, then the hypothesis is accepted as a scientific theory until such time as new data conflict with the theory.

5. If new data conflict with the theory, then the theory is either modified or discarded in favor of a new hypothesis that is consistent with all the data.

Singularity
(technological)

The point at which the increase in artificial intelligence (AI) surpasses human intelligence; thereafter the exponential growth of such *superintelligence* achieved by technological self-improvement becomes incomprehensible to human biological intelligence.

somatic cells
(human)

Cells whose *DNA* cannot be transmitted to offspring. They are the majority of cells in a body and comprise organs and tissues such as the heart, brain, and skin.

supereruption

An eruption that produces at least 1,000 cubic kilometers of deposits.

superintelligence
(sometimes called
ultraintelligence)

Machine intelligence that vastly outperforms humans in every significant cognitive domain.

Glossary

supernova The collapse of a massive star into a neutron star or black hole when its nuclear fuel runs out (Type I) or else a white dwarf star is triggered into runaway nuclear fusion by acquiring matter, usually from a binary companion through accretion or merger (Type II). Either event generates a huge amount of electromagnetic radiation. Supernova remnants may be a source of cosmic rays.

supervolcano A volcano that has had an eruption with a Volcanic Explosivity Index (VEI) of 8, the largest value on the index, producing at least 1,000 cubic kilometers of deposits. These are often referred to as supereruptions.

technology The invention, making, and use of tools or machines to solve a problem.

telomerase The enzyme that re-lengthens shortened *telomeres*.

telomere A region of repetitive *DNA* structures that protects the end of a *chromosome* from deterioration or from fusion with neighboring chromosomes in a cell; it shortens with each cell division.

transhuman An individual in the process of evolving from a human to a posthuman and who possesses faculties far exceeding those of humans today.

universe All the matter and energy that exists in the one dimension of time and the three dimensions of space.

weather The current state of the atmosphere measured by temperature, pressure, humidity, precipitation (such as rain, hail, or snow), sunshine, cloudiness, and the direction of winds.

Illustration Credits

Figure 2.1	Public domain
Figure 3.1	© John Hands
Figure 4.1	Public domain
Figure 4.2	Dna–Dennis
Figure 4.3	NASA
Figure 4.4	By kind permission of Jeremy Shakun
Figure 4.5	By kind permission of John Korchok
Figure 5.1	Public domain
Figure 7.1	By kind permission of Iain Nicolson
Figure 7.2	NASA, painting by kind permission of Rick Guidice
Figure 7.3	NASA, painting by kind permission of Rick Guidice
Figure 7.4	NASA, painting by kind permission of Rick Guidice
Figure 7.5	NASA, painting by kind permission of Rick Guidice
Figure 8.1	US National Heart, Lung, and Blood Institute
Figure 8.2	By kind permission of Hiroshi Ishiguro
Figure 8.3	The National Human Genome Research Institute
Figure 9.1	By kind permission of TA Sciences
Figure 13.1	By kind permission of Alan Guth
Figure 13.2	By kind permission of the Royal Society of Chemistry
Figure 13.4	Mariana Ruiz Villarreal
Figure 13.5	© John Hands
Figure 13.6	© John Hands
Figure 13.7	© John Hands
Figure 13.8	© John Hands, digitally redrawn by Kevin Mansfield
Figure 13.9	© John Hands, digitally redrawn by Fakenham Prepress Solutions

Every effort has been made to trace all copyright holders, and the author and publisher will gladly rectify in future editions any errors or omissions brought to their attention.

Index

Index

Index

Index

Index

NASA (North American Space Agency)
    1970s proposals for space colonization
        105, 110
    health risk assessments 102
    Mars mission 102
    Moon missions 105
National Academy of Medicine Grand
    Challenge in Health Lonvevity 131
Near Earth Asteroids (NEAs). *see also*
    asteroid impacts
nervous systems, evolution of 201
Neumann, John von 169
neutrons, formation in early universe 190
New START treaty 27, 28
Newton, Sir Isaac 212
Nicolson, Iain 105, 111, 186
noble gas elements 194, 195
nuclear accidents 35
nuclear powered rockets 111
Nuclear Taboo hypothesis 32
nuclear weapons
    accidental deployment 28
    arms race 25, 26
    Big Ivan bomb (Soviet Union) 25, 170
    Global Zero (organization) 33
    Hiroshima and Nagasaki bombs (US) 24,
        32
    Minuteman III missiles (US) 28
    size and distribution 24, 25, 26, 29, 170
    treaties 27
    Trident II missiles (UK/US) 28
nuclear winter 29, 86
nucleosynthesis, in early universe 191, 219
nucleotides (defined) 140
Nunn, Sam 33

O

Obama, Barack 27, 89
ocean currents 52
O'Neill, Gerard K 105, 108, 109, 110, 186

OpenWorm project 83
organic molecules 197, 219
organs, growing from DNA 132
organ transplants 116
OTC deficiency 122
ozone 48, 51

P

pandemics
    Covid-19 17, 20, 22, 94
    defined 14
    HIV/AIDS 15, 22, 95
    influenza 14, 22, 94
    plague 16, 22, 94
Paré, Ambroise 116
Paris Agreement (on climate change) 44
Parkinson's disease 134, 143
Partridge, Linda 139
patents for gene editing technology 125
pathogen reservoirs 16
pattern recognition (human) 164
pattern recognition theory of mind (PRTM)
    165
Pauli Exclusion Principle 194, 195, 197
Pawelczyk, James 103
Pearce, David 166. *see also* Humanity+
    (organization)
Pepper (social robot) 75, 80
periodic table of elements 192, 194, 195
Permian-Triassic mass extinction 13, 43
Perry, William 33
personality (human) 175
Peter Vajik 110
Petrou, Anastasios 117
phenotype (defined) 120
philosophical thinking phase of human
    evolution 207, 215, 216
philosophy (defined) 207
physicalism 176
physical sciences (discipline) 209, 211, 212

Index

Index

Index

Lightning Source UK Ltd.
Milton Keynes UK
UKHW021400201222
414170UK00006B/176/J